When it comes t
it isn't just the
Three serious
got themselve
situations – a
be marriage!

Bestselling author Miranda Lee brings you
the best from Down Under in this exciting
collection. Three knee-tremblingly gorgeous,
heart-stoppingly rich and totally irresistible
bachelors are falling deeply in lust…and
irrevocably in love!

Don't miss out!

A KISS TO REMEMBER
A WEEKEND TO REMEMBER
A WOMAN TO REMEMBER

Red-hot
AUSTRALIANS

Red-hot

AUSTRALIANS

Sizzlingly sexy, seriously rich – these men are the best lovers in Sydney!

A KISS TO REMEMBER
A WEEKEND TO REMEMBER
A WOMAN TO REMEMBER

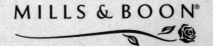

MILLS & BOON®

*MILLS & BOON and MILLS & BOON with the Rose Device
are registered trademarks of the publisher.
Harlequin Mills & Boon Limited,
Eton House, 18-24 Paradise Road, Richmond, Surrey, TW9 1SR*

RED-HOT AUSTRALIANS
© by Harlequin Enterprises II B.V., 2004

A Kiss to Remember, A Weekend to Remember and
A Woman to Remember were first published in Great Britain by
Harlequin Mills & Boon Limited in separate, single volumes.

A Kiss to Remember © Miranda Lee 1995
A Weekend to Remember © Miranda Lee 1996
A Woman to Remember © Miranda Lee 1996

ISBN 0 263 84109 X

62-0704

*Printed and bound in Spain
by Litografia Rosés S.A., Barcelona*

A KISS TO REMEMBER

by

Miranda Lee

A KISS TO REMEMBER

by

Miranda Lee

CHAPTER ONE

ANGIE looked over at the sulky-faced girl sitting on the other side of her desk and shook her head sadly. What was the world coming to when girls thought they were freaks just because they were still virgins at seventeen?

'Debbie, dear,' Angie said, with as much patience as she could muster at five to four on a Friday afternoon. 'It is not a crime *not* to be sexually active at your age. In fact, in view of the health hazards these days, I would say it was very sensible. Can't you at least wait till you leave school? This year is almost over, after all. You have less than twelve months to go before you graduate.'

Which could be part of the problem, Angie suspected. Next year—Debbie's final year—would be a very stressful one. A lot of Year Eleven students let their hair down at this time of the year. This year's exams were over, summer had arrived, and the end-of-year party scene had well and truly begun—with all the accompanying hazards of alcohol and drugs. A lot of girls lost their virginity at such times, but mostly this was an unpremeditated event. Debbie's decision to sleep with her boyfriend was hardly that.

'Look, I know you probably think you're madly in

5

love with this boy,' Angie went on. 'But love rarely lasts long at your age. Next year—or even next term—it will probably be another boy, then another. If you sleep with all of them, then…'

'I'm not at all in love with Warren,' Debbie denied, her defiant eyes shocking Angie. 'I just want to know what it's like, that's all. You read so much about it and everyone else is doing it.'

'Everyone else is *not* doing it!' Angie argued, her cheeks pinkening with what she hoped looked like indignation.

'That's all very well for you to say, Miss. I'll bet you know what it's like. I'll bet you've had loads of boyfriends!'

Angie could feel her face beginning to burn. 'Now, you look here, young lady,' she began firmly. 'My boyfriends are *my* business. What we are here to discuss is *your* sex-life, not mine! Besides, I happen to be twenty-four years old—not seventeen. Believe me when I tell you that when I was your age I definitely was a virgin.'

And you still are, a small dark voice pointed out drily in her head.

Angie scowled, both at the voice and at Debbie.

'As your school counsellor,' she continued, in her best lecturing tone, 'my advice to you is to wait till you are at least in a steady relationship before you take this step. Making love should not be an experiment—especially the first time. It should be a very special experience between two people who truly care about one another. It should be an experience to remember and look back on with good feelings, not regret.'

Even as she was saying the words Angie could see she was not getting through to the girl. Debbie confirmed this opinion by pouting and not meeting her eyes. 'Rebecca said you'd understand,' the girl grumbled. 'She said you'd help me like you did her.'

'Rebecca was an entirely different case,' Angie muttered, even as she knew she was defeated. Privately, she might be a romantic and an idealist. Professionally, she was a realist.

As Debbie's counsellor she had a responsibility to look after the girl's physical as well as her mental health. For they were intrinsically linked. Unhappily, she opened the bottom drawer and drew out a couple of condoms from the supply of samples she kept there, ready to be given out with discretion to any girl over the age of consent who came to her with a similar attitude to Debbie's.

'I am giving you these most reluctantly, Debbie, and only because you seem determined to do this. They are not my way of condoning your decision, or giving you permission, but I can't in all conscience see you without protection. Some young men aren't too caring about young women who give themselves to them without love,' she finished pointedly.

At last, Debbie had the good grace to blush. 'I didn't realise you were so old-fashioned,' she muttered. 'Rebecca said you were real cool.'

'You think it's cool to be promiscuous?' Angie asked sharply.

'No. But I think it's stupid to be ignorant about sex,' she flung back.

Angie stiffened.

Debbie stood up and went to leave, then stopped, glancing anxiously over her shoulder at Angie. 'You...you won't tell my parents, will you?'

'No. You're over the legal age of consent.'

The girl suddenly smiled at her. 'Thanks, Miss. And I promise to think about everything you said. See you next Monday!' And she fairly skipped out of the door.

Angie stayed sitting at her desk for a few minutes, gnawing away at her bottom lip and wondering if Debbie was right. Maybe she *was* impossibly old-fashioned. And impossibly romantic. And impossibly cautious.

Was it silly of her to wait for Mr Right to come along before she made love? Naïve of her to want to see stars when a man kissed her before she let him go further? Stupid of her to hope that it wouldn't end up a matter of making a conscious choice to go to bed with a man—to believe she would be so madly, blindly and irrevocably in love that it would just happen quite naturally!

'Yes, yes, yes!' her flatmate answered to all three questions, when Angie posed them to her as they drove home together that afternoon.

Angie remained unconvinced. Vanessa was thirty

years old and a terrible cynic about men and love. A maths and science teacher at the same girls' school where Angie was the school counsellor, she was a striking-looking though brittle brunette, who frightened most men off with her superior intelligence and incisive wit. Which was a shame because, basically, Vanessa liked men a lot.

They'd been colleagues at the same private girls' school for nearly a year, but had only been flatting together for a couple of months, Angie's previous flatmate having left to go overseas. This was the first time Angie had really opened up to the older woman about her personal life. And, to give Vanessa credit, she accepted the news of her inexperience without too much shock, though she was typically cutting in her advice.

'For pity's sake, go out and get yourself laid before it's too late. How can you possibly counsel all those randy little teenagers who come to you for advice if you don't have any first-hand knowledge of the subject? Good Lord, Angie, if you wait for Mr Right these days, you might go to your grave a virgin! Frankly, I can't understand how a girl who looks like you do made it through her teenage years without scores of horny boys jumping on your bones every five minutes!'

'I didn't say they didn't try…'

'And there wasn't one you fancied back?' Vanessa's tone was sheer scepticism.

An image swept into Angie's mind. Of brilliant

blue eyes and flashing white teeth, of windswept fair hair and golden-bronze skin, of a face like a Greek God and a body to match.

'There was one,' she admitted.

'Only *one*?' Vanessa squawked.

Angie smiled ruefully to herself. 'Believe me, after Lance, no other male has ever measured up.'

Which had always been the problem, hadn't it? Angie realised with sudden insight. Once you'd tasted ambrosia it was hard to settle for plain bread. She'd always told herself that her shrinking from casual sex had been because of that AIDS chap, who'd come to her high school and lectured them upon the dangers of such activities.

But it hadn't been that at all, Angie finally conceded. It was because subconsciously she'd compared every boy and then every man she met to Lance Sterling. And they'd all come up wanting.

'He sounds awfully intriguing,' Vanessa said.

'Intriguing,' Angie repeated thoughtfully. 'Yes, one could say that about him. Among other things.'

'Do tell. I'm dying of curiosity already.'

Angie frowned, aware that thoughts of Lance had been teasing her mind a lot this past week. Mostly because tonight was her brother's thirtieth birthday party, which she would be obliged to attend.

Anything to do with Bud always reminded her of Lance.

Not that her brother had anything much to do with Lance these days. Their once close friendship had waned after Lance married four years ago and moved to Melbourne to live. It had now come down to exchanging Christmas cards once a year.

Not that they'd ever had much in common, except for doing the same business degree at the same university in Sydney. Angie had never been able to work out exactly what Lance had seen in Bud—and vice versa. They had come from two entirely different worlds. They'd had two entirely different personalities.

Perhaps it had been the old case of an attraction of opposites. Or perhaps it had just amused Lance to have a simple country boy as a friend, whom he could impress with his sophistication and wealth. As it had amused him to impress his friend's simple country sister that fateful summer nine years ago...

CHAPTER TWO

ANGIE sat on the top step of the front veranda, waiting impatiently for her brother to arrive with his exciting-sounding friend. Bud had said in his last letter that they'd be leaving Sydney straight after breakfast. But it was a five-hour drive north up to Wilga, then another twenty minutes out to the farm. Since it was only ten to twelve, they probably wouldn't be here for at least another hour.

Still, Angie couldn't seem to settle to anything else. So she stayed where she was, anxiously watching the valley road and hoping against hope that they'd started out earlier than intended.

For the millionth time that morning she wondered what this Lance looked like.

Bud had said in his letters that his friend was very good-looking. But Bud's idea of good-looking and Angie's idea of good-looking were often poles apart. Their views on things differed as vastly as did their own looks.

Bud took after their mother, who was small and dark, with black wavy hair, chocolate-brown eyes and an inclination to put on weight easily. Angie, however, was a female version of their father—tall and athletically slim, with auburn hair and widely spaced green eyes.

Their natures were different as well. Bud was easily bored, and craved excitement and companionship all the time. Angie was far more placid and private. She was quite happy with her own company, liking nothing better than to go riding by herself, or to curl up all alone on her bed to write poetry or read a book. She liked to think rather than talk. Bud could talk underwater, like their mother.

A cloud of dust in the distance had Angie jumping to her feet, her hand hooding her eyes from the sunlight as she peered down the hill. A car was coming along the valley road, going as fast as her heart was suddenly beating.

It was Bud and his friend. She was sure of it.

Somewhere at the back of her mind Angie knew she was acting totally out of character, getting excited over a member of the opposite sex. Especially one she hadn't met yet.

She was not boy-mad, as were most other girls in her class. Her classmates actually thought her shy.

She let them think it.

Angie knew that she wasn't really shy. Just reserved. She liked her personal space and hated being harassed in any way. Unwanted male attention sometimes embarrassed and always annoyed her. Frankly, she found most boys at school exceedingly adolescent, noisy and irritating. She'd actually been relieved by her father's edict a couple of years back that she could not have a boyfriend till she was sixteen. It was the perfect excuse for her to turn down the invitations she received from her overeager admirers.

And there were many. For Angie was a very attractive girl. In the past few months some people had started using the word 'beautiful'.

Yet she never made any attempt to enhance her looks or look older, as some girls might have. She never used make-up, always wore her long straight hair up in a simple ponytail, and was happiest wearing jeans or shorts, plus one of her father's shirts.

Today was no different. Angie had too much common sense to try to attract someone like Bud's friend from Sydney. He was twenty-two, after all—one year older than Bud—and wouldn't look twice at a fifteen-year-old girl. On top of that he was very, very rich—the only son and heir of one of Sydney's wealthiest families.

Perhaps it was this last factor that Angie found so fascinating. She'd never met any really rich people before, and the things Bud had told her about Lance's home and lifestyle sounded very glamorous. Totally different from the simple country life the Browns led.

Angie had been amazed to hear that after finishing high school Lance had travelled the world for a whole year before starting uni. He and Bud had not become friends till this last year, and no doubt now that their degrees were finished their paths would soon diverge. Next year Bud would have to go out into the real world and find himself a job, whereas Lance would be automatically given a cushy executive position in one of the family's companies.

Sterling Industries had many fingers in many pies—from food and cleaning products to furniture, from plastics to various mining interests. Apparently, Lance had offered to find Bud a job, but Bud had refused, and Angie was proud of him for that. Not that she was worried about her brother going out on his own in search of a career. Bud had enough drive and energy to succeed in whatever he put his mind to.

The wire door creaked behind her, and Angie turned to see her mother coming out, wiping floury hands on the apron which was doing its best to circumnavigate her rotund middle. Though not yet forty, Nora Brown had long surrendered to her genes, plus her love of food.

Not that she worried about her weight. Nothing ever worried Nora Brown. She was easygoing, easy to please and easy to love. If she had a fault it was her tendency to be blunt with others at times. She was not rude, just a little tactless on occasion. Still, everyone loved her—especially her husband, Morris.

A very handsome man, Morris Brown could have had his pick of any number of local girls. He'd chosen Nora, who was short, plump, dark, and very ordinary-looking.

It was a tribute to Nora's totally natural self-esteem that she had never found this in any way amazing. She accepted Morris's love as her due, and loved him back with all the love in her ample bosom. Twenty-two years later, they still adored each other.

'Did I hear a car coming?' Nora asked hopefully.

'Flying, more like it,' Angie said.

Her mother stepped forward, dark eyes twinkling, a wide smile on her homely face. 'I'll bet that's my Buddy driving. Dear me, but he's a naughty boy when he gets behind the wheel of a car. I hope his father's still down on the river flats and can't see this.'

The car came into view, sending some gravel flying as it lurched around a corner on its way up the hill to the house. Red and gleaming, it had silver wheels and the top down.

The sounds of its manic approach sent the dogs shooting out from underneath the weatherboard house, barking in force. A motley lot, there was a brown kelpie named Betsie, a blue cattle-dog cross named Fang and a black Labrador who'd been a guide dog reject, suitably called Max, after the hero in *Get Smart*.

'Betsie! Fang! Max!' Nora called out. 'Stop that racket and get yourselves back under the house before you get run over.'

All three dived for cover just as the red Mercedes Sports came to a screeching halt at the bottom of the front steps. It wasn't her brother's Mercedes, Angie knew, since he didn't own a car, but it was Bud behind the wheel all right; she saw that straight away. He was grinning his head off as he glanced down at his watch.

'Made it before noon by a whole thirty seconds!' he exclaimed excitedly, then gave his passenger a smug look. 'You owe me twenty dollars.'

The sound of a rich laugh sent Angie's eyes swinging over to her brother's friend, and her heart just stopped. As she stared his head turned slowly towards them, his hand lifting lazily to comb back his thick blond hair. He tipped up his perfectly sculptured face and set dancing blue eyes upon them, his laughing mouth showing dazzling white teeth and a dimple in his right cheek.

'Hi,' he said. 'I'm Lance.'

'Hi there, Mum,' Bud called out. 'Hope we didn't scare the chooks too much.'

'Yes, sorry about the ruckus, Mrs Brown,' Bud's friend apologised, still smiling that overwhelmingly engaging smile of his. 'Your son here is insane when it comes to winning a bet.'

'That's all right, young man,' Nora returned. 'I already know my Buddy's weaknesses, as well as his strengths. One seems to be picking very nice friends.'

Bud groaned. 'For pity's sake, Mum, don't flatter him. He's already got a head as big as the Sydney Harbour Bridge.'

'I'll flatter whomever I like in my own house, you cheeky pup,' Nora pretended to reproach him. 'Now, get yourself out of that fancy car, come up here and give your old mother a hug. You too, young man. I'm partial to hugs.'

'Coming right up,' Lance chuckled, and with an

extraordinary amount of grace and athleticism, leapt
out of the car without opening the door, landing on
long legs which supported a body as perfect as his
face. Angie had an excellent view of it, standing
there, encased in hip-hugging jeans and a muscle-
moulding white T-shirt. When his legs moved to propel him up the three steps it looked even better.

Lance had been long hugged by the time Bud made
it out of the car and up the steps, by which time Lance
had turned his attention to Angie.

'Don't tell me *you're* Bud's little sister?' he
drawled, those brilliant blue eyes of his narrowing
upon her in a way which did incredible things to her
insides. Her previously stopped heart was suddenly
racing like a quarter horse in full gallop.

'Do I get a hug from you too?' he asked softly, not
waiting for permission but immediately taking her in
his arms and squeezing her tight.

After a moment's shock, Angie closed her eyes and
let the feel of his firm embrace wash through every
pore of her body. It was an experience alien to anything she had ever felt before, making her face flush
and her legs go to jelly.

Fear that she might slide down his body on to the
veranda in a melted heap forced her to hug him back.
But when she did so, he pulled her even more tightly
against him, making her fiercely aware of the physical
differences between males and females. Her breasts
were squashed flat against the hard expanse of his

broad chest, and there was a vague assortment of lumps and bumps pressing into her lower abdomen.

'You can let her go now,' Bud said, tapping Lance on the shoulder. 'And don't go getting any funny ideas about my sister. She's only fifteen, you know.'

Lance pulled back to hold her at arm's length, his hands still resting lightly on her hips as he looked her over a second time.

'She looks older,' he said, his voice once again having dropped to that low, lazy timbre which sent little shivers running down her spine.

'Who, Angie?' Bud sounded sceptical. 'Nah, she's just tall, the lucky devil.'

'Five foot ten in her bare feet,' her mother piped up proudly. 'Takes after her father. Buddy here takes after me,' she added, tousling her son's black curly head.

'Mum, stop that,' Bud objected. 'And stop calling me Buddy. You know I hate it.'

'You liked it well enough for your first eighteen years, me lad. Don't go letting life in the big city give you airs and graces. You haven't been giving him airs and graces, have you, Lance?'

Finally, Lance's hands slipped from Angie's hips and she gulped a steadying breath. She did her best to look composed but she just knew her cheeks were flaming.

'Not me, Mrs Brown,' he said, looking away from Angie's face at long last.

'Didn't think so. You seem a mighty fine boy—
even if you are from a filthy rich family.'

'Mum!' Bud groaned.

'Well, we all know money can spoil children,' his
mother stated quite ingenuously. 'But I can see Lance
here has grown up to be a credit to his mum and dad.
Where is it that your parents have gone to, Lance?'

'Europe, I think, Mrs Brown.'

Nora was taken aback. 'Don't you *know*?'

Lance's shrug was nonchalant. 'They don't like to
be tied down to a schedule. They just go with the
flow.'

'It seems a strange time to go away, just before
Christmas,' Nora muttered, frowning.

Angie had to agree with her. Christmas was for
families.

'Not to worry,' her mother went on, linking arms
with Lance and smiling broadly up at him. 'You're
spending Christmas with us. We'll look after you,
won't we, Angie?'

Vanessa gave a dry chortle. 'I'll bet your mother
wouldn't have made such an offer if she'd known
how her guest wanted the daughter of the house to
look after him. So what happened? How long before
he made a pass? And how did you possibly resist
him? He sounds gorgeous.'

Angie sighed, then slowed for a set of lights, stopping a little raggedly. 'He didn't make a pass. Not

once. And he stayed with us most of the summer, right till the end of January.'

'I don't believe it! He was obviously attracted to you.'

'Yes, I thought so too. And I was besotted with him. Followed him around like a puppy. Made every excuse to be wherever he was.'

'Didn't your brother mind that—his kid sister tagging along all the time?'

'No. Our family has always done things together. Bud and Dad spent a lot of time that summer showing Lance how to do country-style things. They taught him how to ride, how to plough, how to shoot. By the end of his stay he could drill a beer can at one hundred yards. It was only natural for me to help. And who else would be stupid enough to stand around putting empty beer cans on fence-posts for hours?'

The lights turned green and Angie eased ahead in the heavy city-going traffic.

'Did your family know you were ga-ga over him?' Vanessa asked.

'I don't think so. As I said before, I've always been a private person. I didn't wear my heart on my sleeve then any more than I do now. Certainly Dad and Bud never guessed. I think maybe Mum might have suspected something, though oddly enough she didn't say anything at the time—which wasn't like her at all. Maybe she was smart enough to see the passing nature of the situation and knew that any comment would have made my eventual agony worse.'

'But Lance knew, didn't he?'

'Oh, yes…Lance knew…'

'And how did he feel about you?'

Angie shrugged. 'Who knows? I thought he cared for me. He certainly liked me, and I think you're right in that he was attracted to me, but only in a superficial sense. I was only fifteen, after all. Of course I used to lie in bed every night fantasising that he was as secretly crazy about me as I was about him. I used to write the most sentimental poetry about him—reams of it. I also used to read something deep and mean-ingful into even the smallest attention he gave me. Every glance my way was a searing, passion-filled gaze in my adolescent mind. Every conversation we shared had hidden love messages behind it.'

Angie gave a soft, sad laugh. 'The family had a habit of sitting out on the front veranda every night, looking up at the stars and talking. On a few occa-sions the others went off to bed, leaving Lance and me alone. You've no idea how that set my teenage heart a-beating. Only a fifteen-year-old fool would wind romantic dreams around idle chit-chat.'

'What did you talk about?'

'Nothing important. Just general stuff. Movies. Mu-sic. Books. Poetry. Looking back, I think Lance was only humouring me by claiming to find my tastes and opinions incredibly sensible and mature.'

'Maybe not, Angie,' her flatmate argued. 'You're a deep thinker, and maybe too sensible for your own good, I'm beginning to think. Far too sensitive, too.

I can just picture you at fifteen. Very beautiful but very intense. Perhaps he didn't make a pass at you because that very intensity frightened him off.'

'Did I say he didn't make a pass at me? Yes, of course I did. Perfectly true, in fact. He didn't. He didn't have to. It was stupid me who made the pass. Eventually.'

Vanessa's head whipped round to stare over at her. 'You did? Good Lord! When? Where?'

'It was the night before he went back to Sydney. Out on the front veranda.'

'What on earth did you do? Do tell.'

CHAPTER THREE

GO TO bed, Angie willed desperately. Please go to bed. He's going home tomorrow. Don't you understand? I need to be alone with him!

Angie got the shock of her life when her mother immediately rose and announced her intention to retire for the night. When her father quickly followed, then Bud five minutes later, Angie thanked the Lord for His mercy. She swiftly moved from where she'd been perched up on the veranda railing to sit down next to Lance on the steps, her heart thudding at her boldness.

Lance was dressed in shorts and a singlet top, Angie in similar garb. The day had been hot and the night air was only just beginning to cool. Not that Angie felt cold. Sitting this close to Lance was a highly warming experience.

She stared down at her long brown legs, then over at his, tanned to a golden bronze by the long summer days. Her left thigh was barely an inch from his. If she moved it slightly, their skin would touch. She kept perfectly still, knowing her boldness did not extend that far.

'You don't get night skies like this down in Syd-

24

ney,' he mused, sighing and leaning back a little, the movement making his thigh brush against hers.

Angie jerked her feet up on to a higher step, her knees pressed together to stop them from trembling. So much for her boldness! 'I...I wouldn't know,' she said shakily.

'Your mum tells me you're going to come to Sydney to university when you finish school,' he said.

'I hope to. If Dad can afford it. Let's hope we don't have a drought or a flood during the next three years.'

Lance frowned, as though it would never have occurred to him that one's fortunes could depend on the weather. 'If that happens, I'll pay for you myself.'

'Oh, I couldn't let you do that!' she exclaimed, despite being thrilled that he had offered. 'The Browns always pay for themselves.'

Lance sighed. 'So I've gathered from Bud. Damn it all, Angie, you *must* come to Sydney.'

'Must I?' she croaked. Her eyes locked with his and her heart filled to overflowing. He feels the same as me, she thought dazedly. He just thinks I'm too young for him to say anything. This is his way of saying he'll wait for me.

'Not that I'm sure I'd like you going to Sydney Uni,' he muttered, but Angie wasn't really listening any more. She was drowning in his beautiful blue eyes, thinking how wonderful he was and that she wanted him to kiss her more than anything else in the world. She would just die if he went back to Sydney without kissing her.

'What course do you want to do?' he asked.

'What? Oh…er…an arts degree, majoring in psychology, if I get a high enough mark. If not, I'll do a degree in Social Welfare. I want to work with people, you see. I want to help solve some of the social problems of the world.'

'That's a tall order, Angie—solving the world's social problems. But I think it's fantastic that you want to try. So, tell me, what do you see as the world's main social problem?'

'That's a hard one. There are so many problems. Look, this is probably a simplistic approach but I think if people made their lives simpler they'd be happier. The Western world is moving too far away from the family unit and family values. I'd like to encourage people to be more serious about marriage and their commitment to raising children, to appreciate how much time it takes to do both well.'

'And do you want marriage and children for yourself? Or will you settle for a career?'

'I don't see why I can't have both. Of course, my career would always play second fiddle to my family. My husband and children would always come first with me.'

'Mmm, I see I'll have to keep a close eye on you when you get to Sydney, or some smart bastard will whisk you off to the altar before you can say licketysplit!'

'You…you won't have to worry about that happening, Lance. There'll only ever be one man for me.'

Having gone this far, she turned her head and stared him straight in the eye.

Those eyes flared briefly wide with surprise, before narrowing to an expression he'd never bestowed on her before. His darkened gaze moved slowly over her face, dropping at last to her softly parted lips then down to where her breasts were clearly outlined against the thin material of her top. Suddenly, she knew what it was like to be the target of a man's desire. A *man's*, not a boy's. She felt her body respond, everything all at once hot and tight and tingling. Her face flamed along with the rest of her.

'You're only fifteen,' he said abruptly, as though reminding himself.

'I won't be fifteen forever,' she returned breathlessly.

'True... But when you grow up, you might change your ideas about who and what you want.'

'No, I won't,' she said, her voice firming. 'Mum says I'm as stubborn as old Wally Robinson's bull. I'll feel the same way about you in three years as I feel now.'

She shook his head, obviously still troubled by the situation.

'Wait here,' she whispered, and, jumping up, raced inside to her bedroom, returning within no time.

'I wrote this the first week you came,' she said, and pressed the piece of paper into his hands.

He read the poem in dead silence before folding the page and putting it down on the step, shaking his head all the while. For a long moment Angie thought she'd made an utter fool of herself. But then he looked up at her and she knew… She just knew she'd been right. He *did* feel the same.

'Oh, Angie,' he said softly. 'Sweet…sweet Angie.' And he reached out to touch her face lightly.

His fingertips were like flicks of fire against her already heated cheek, at the same time igniting other flames throughout her body. The words fell out of her mouth—reckless, breathless words.

'Kiss me, Lance. Kiss me…'

'You can't stop there!' Vanessa wailed when Angie suddenly fell silent. By this time they'd reached the block of units in North Sydney where they lived, parked in the underground garage and were making their way up the internal staircase to their neat little second floor unit.

'What happened?' she persisted.

Once she recovered her composure, Angie smiled wryly at Vanessa's enthusiasm for her story. Underneath her hard-boiled exterior, she was a romantic—like most females.

'Nothing much. He kissed me, just once. It was quite brief, really.'

'It couldn't have been *that* brief if you still remember it. And if it's totally turned you off all other men ever since.'

'I didn't say I was totally turned off other men,' Angie explained. 'It's just that I've been waiting for their kisses to do for me what Lance's kiss did. I guess it's a matter of a standard of chemistry never being reached again.'

'So what was so special about the way this Lance kissed?'

'I don't think there was anything really special about his technique. I think it was the way the kiss made me feel that was so special.'

'And how did it make you feel?'

Angie stopped at their door, her heart squeezing tight again at the memory. She inserted the key in the lock but didn't turn it, her hand freezing as the words were wrenched from deep within her. 'Like the world had tipped on its axis,' she choked out. 'Like I'd died and gone to heaven...'

It was crazy, but even after all these years she could still remember the feel of his steely arms winding tight around her, the heady, intoxicating effect of his lips possessing hers, the blindingly electric shock that had charged along her veins when his tongue had momentarily dipped past her eagerly parted lips.

But it was what he'd said to her afterwards which had caused the lasting damage.

'I'll write,' he had said thickly, when he'd put her from him. 'And when you're old enough, we'll be together properly. I promise...'

Perhaps he'd almost meant it at the time. She could give him the benefit of the doubt after all these years. But that didn't change the inevitable outcome of his thoughtless arrogance in making a promise he must have suspected he would not keep, in condemning her to years of hopeless longing. In a way, that kiss had ruined her life.

'Wow, Angie! You really were in love with him, weren't you? So what became of him? Where is he now?'

Angie snapped back to reality, firmly pushing the still upsetting memories of Lance to the back of her mind. 'Happily married to a very rich, very beautiful woman,' she said with seeming calm. 'They live in Melbourne.'

'What did the poem say? Can you remember?'

Of course she could remember. Every heartbreaking, humiliating word.

'Not really,' she hedged. 'It was just a lot of sentimental twaddle, much better forgotten.' Which was true.

'I presume he didn't keep in contact after he left,' Vanessa said drily. 'No letters or anything.'

Angie threw her a cynical look as she turned the key and pushed open the door. 'Only a polite note to my parents, thanking them for having him to stay.'

'Bastard. There again, Angie, it was only to be expected. He was way out of your league.'

Five minutes later both girls were sitting at the small kitchen table, sipping a reviving cup of coffee. Angie was off in another world—worrying about Debbie—when Vanessa returned to the subject of Lance.

'Did you see him again after that summer?'

'Yes. A few times.'

'No kidding. Where? When?'

'The first time was a few months later at his and Bud's graduation ceremony. The whole family travelled down to Sydney to celebrate the occasion.'

'And?'

'He was polite to me, but distant. And of course there was this very sexy-looking redhead hanging off his arm all the time.'

'You must have been awfully upset.'

'Crushed. I'd still been making excuses for him in my mind, telling myself that he was like so many males when it came to writing letters. I thought once we saw each other again everything would be all right. He would see I was quickly growing up—having turned a whole sixteen by then. He would tell me he was still waiting for me.'

Angie's rueful smile hid a wealth of remembered misery. 'Silly me. But it was Bud who finally put the nail in the coffin of my one-sided love that day, when he told me that Lance had been voted Superstud of the Year at the party his faculty had held the previous night. Seems he'd had more girlfriends in the past three years than porcupines have prickles. The redhead was the latest—acquired at that very same party. Bud was already taking bets with his mates on how long she would last.'

'Hmm. Maybe you had a lucky escape, Angie—getting out with only being kissed. He could have screwed you and your life good and proper if he'd wanted to. You have to give him some credit for not taking advantage of your youthful hormones.'

'Yes, I did think of that. Eventually. I also believed I'd finally forgiven and forgotten, or at least gotten over him...till I literally ran into him in Sydney one day during my second year at university. I had a mid-morning lecture and my train had been late. I dashed out of Wynard Station, and was racing along the street for a bus when I collided with this man. You can imagine my surprise when I realised who belonged to the strong hands which reached out to steady me. I think Lance was just as surprised.'

'My God!' he gasped. 'Angie...'

Angie tried not to stare at him. But he looked so handsome, dressed in dark trousers and a cream sports jacket. And so sophisticated. Only twenty-seven, but the university graduate was gone forever, replaced by the elegant man-about-town he had always promised to be.

She hated her tongue-tiedness; she hated the way she couldn't stop staring at him; she hated the way her heart was instantly yearning and hoping once more. She hadn't gotten over him at all. Not for a moment.

His blue gaze swept over her, taking in her typical student dress of jeans and T-shirt, a canvas backpack slung over one shoulder, battered trainers on her feet. 'I see you made it to uni,' he said. 'Did you get into the course you wanted?'

'Yes,' was all she could manage. She'd pictured such a chance encounter happening ever since coming to Sydney, had run over in her mind how she would act. So cool, so casually indifferent.

But there was nothing cool or casually indifferent in the way she was gobbling him up with her eyes. Or the way her heart was pounding behind her ribs. God, what a fool she was!

'You're looking well, Angie,' he said. 'I was sorry I couldn't make it to Bud's wedding last month. I've been overseas on business. And I'm sorry I can't stay and talk. I'm on my way to meet someone.'

'Oh, that's all right. I can't stay either. I'm late too. Look after yourself. Bye.' And she was off, almost running.

'Where are you staying?' he called after her.

Her heart leapt as she ground to a halt and turned around. Oh, God, he wasn't going to ask her out, was he? Please, God, let him ask me out, she prayed.

'I need to know your address so that I can send you an invitation,' he elaborated.

'Invitation?' she repeated weakly.

'For my wedding. I'm getting married in October.'

'Oh…' Did she look as stricken as she felt? She must have, for suddenly he looked awfully apologetic.

His obvious pity was the saving of her.

Somewhere she found a smile, a bright, breezy smile to hide her inner weeping. 'Fancy that! Married! Well, congratulations. Look, why don't you send the invitation to Bud's place? I keep changing my digs. Must go, Lance. See you on your big day!'

'Surely you didn't go!' Vanessa exclaimed in appalled tones, glaring at her over the table.

Angie shrugged her admission.

'Gees, girl, you're a glutton for punishment!'

'You can say that again. What Lance can do for a dinner suit is criminal.'

'Why on earth did you go?'

Angie expelled a weary sigh. 'Curiosity, I guess. I wanted to see the woman who'd snared him. Besides, the whole family had been invited, including Mum and Dad. I really couldn't get out of it without having to answer some darned awkward questions.'

'And?'

'Sheer perfection, the bride was. Like a Dresden doll and just as expensive. I hated her on sight and worshipped Lance all the more. It was the worst day of my life.'

'What about your family in all this? Didn't they notice anything? Didn't they see you'd broken your heart over this heartless Don Juan?'

'I'm sure Mum was beginning to wonder. And I think Bud had guessed some time back. Perhaps as far back as the night of his and Lance's graduation. He'd made such a point of letting me know about Lance's reputation where the opposite sex was concerned. Even at the wedding he said he'd make a fortune if he took bets on Lance's marriage lasting.

He said Lance was a great guy but that he wasn't cut out for monogamy. He added, rather pointedly, I thought, that it wasn't always his fault. That a lot of the times silly girls—this said looking straight at me—threw themselves at him.'

'Pretty lame excuse, if you ask me. Hard to rape a guy, I say. Did you speak to lover-boy himself at the wedding?'

'I tried not to, but Lance seemed to deliberately seek me out. Lord knows why. Maybe he was finally suffering from a guilty conscience. He gave me this ghastly kiss on the cheek, then told me rather stiffly that he hoped life would bring me everything I'd ever hoped for, that he thought I was the nicest girl he'd ever met and that he wished the world could be full of people like the Browns.'

'Oh, dear,' Vanessa sighed. 'Hardly the thing to say to turn you off him, was it?'

Angie swallowed the lump that had suddenly filled her throat. 'No,' she confessed. 'Not quite…'

Vanessa was frowning at her. 'You're not *still* in love with him, are you?'

'No, of course not,' she returned impatiently, standing up abruptly to carry her empty mug over to the sink. 'That was donkey's years ago. Don't be silly.'

Vanessa joined her at the sink. 'I hope you're telling the truth, for it *would* be silly of you to still be in love with him. It's also silly for you to keep knocking back other men because of the way some rich creep once made you *feel*. Get your head out of the clouds, Angie, and get real. You're not getting any younger, you know. One day you'll wake up and you won't see a cross between Elle MacPherson and Sophia Loren in the mirror, and then it'll all be too late!'

Angie had to laugh. Vanessa had a turn of phrase which could be highly amusing. A cross between Elle MacPherson and Sophia Loren, indeed!

'You're going to your brother's birthday party tonight, aren't you?' Vanessa went on, with a devious gleam in her eye.

'Yes…'

'Is it a big party or just a small gathering?'

'Bud's parties are always huge.'

'What's your brother do for a crust?'

'Well, he did a business degree, majoring in computer studies and marketing. But he went into advertising and he's been surprisingly successful.'

'Then his party should be full of eminently suitable candidates, shouldn't it?'

'Candidates for what?'

'Your first lover.'

Angie was about to protest when she stopped herself, all those maudlin memories of Lance sparking an uncharacteristic surge of recklessness. Maybe Vanessa was right. Maybe even Debbie had been right this afternoon. Life was meant to be lived. To remain ignorant and inexperienced just because she was clinging to a crazy dream was indeed silly.

'At least go with an open mind,' Vanessa urged. 'Promise me that if a suitable candidate shows up, whom you're genuinely attracted to, you'll think about giving him a chance.'

'All right,' she said, suddenly making up her mind to do just that. 'I promise.'

'Now you're being sensible.'

Which was what Lance had said about her more than once that summer. How sensible she was.

Well, she was sick of sensible! Her resolve to follow Vanessa's suggestion deepened. She would find herself a real lover as opposed to a fantasy one. It was time. Yes, it was definitely time!

'I'm going to make sure I look smashing tonight,' she said through clenched teeth.

'Attagirl!' Vanessa crowed. 'Go for it, sweetheart. You only live once!'

Ten o'clock that evening found Angie regretting the trouble she had gone to over her appearance. She received enough male attention at parties at the best of times. Done up as she was tonight, and smothered in perfume, she seemed to have reduced potential candidates to panting pursuers, thereby ensuring her revulsion. She hated men who came on too strong, who delivered obvious lines then expected her to melt instantly at their feet. If one more intoxicated fool said 'your place or mine', she was going to scream.

There again, she supposed it was her own stupid fault if they all thought she was on the make. She should never have curled her long auburn hair and worn it provocatively over one shoulder. Or let

Vanessa talk her into borrowing her outrageous gold and crystal earrings, which were five inches long and looked incredibly sexy.

On top of that, she hadn't been able to wear a bra under the petticoat-style party dress she'd bought specially for the occasion, and her naked nipples were patently obvious under the silky material. She should have bought the black one she'd first tried on, but the salesgirl had talked her into the green, saying it matched her eyes and complemented her auburn hair.

If she'd tried the dress on instead of just holding it up against her, she'd have known that the green didn't camouflage her body as well as the black. Angie began to worry that from the back she might look totally naked under the dress, despite wearing tights with built-in knickers.

Spotting a glassy-eyed chap making a beeline straight for her across Bud's crowded living-room, Angie whirled and made a dash for safety, gripping her glass of wine firmly in both hands lest she spill it all down her front. She found a temporary sanctuary in the kitchen, where Bud's wife, Loretta, was happily refilling serving dishes with all sorts of party snacks.

'Oh, hi, Angie. My, but you do look slinkily glamorous tonight. Bud said you had all his workmates drooling. Now I can see why. You had a jacket on when you first arrived, didn't you? Darn, there goes the front doorbell again. Could you get it for me, love?'

'Sure.' Angie didn't mind at all. It was better than

going back into that room with all those heavy-breathing yuppies.

She sipped her wine as she made her way along the downstairs hall towards the front door, thinking as she went that Bud had really done very well for himself for a country boy from Wilga. A thriving career as an advertising executive, a lovely home in the leafy North Shore suburb of Turramurra, a very pretty wife and a delightful little boy, named Morris after their father. All this, and only thirty today. Remarkable.

Angie opened the door and promptly froze.

The man standing on the front porch, with his hands deep in his trouser pockets and an overnight bag at his feet, had his back to her. But she knew immediately who that well-shaped fair head belonged to. She'd have known him from any angle.

It was Lance.

CHAPTER FOUR

HE TURNED slowly at the sound of the door, moving with that lazy, indolent grace which she remembered oh, so well. There was no man who could mount a horse like Lance. There was no man who looked like him, either.

Even at thirty-one, Lance was still breathtakingly handsome. The lines around his eyes and mouth did not detract from the brilliance of those beautiful blue eyes, or the sensual appeal of that perfectly sculptured mouth. If anything, they added a very attractive maturity, which Angie preferred to his once almost pretty-boy look.

His body hadn't changed, though. Perhaps it would have been better if it had. A few pounds of flab to mar its male perfection might have provided some protection from the way it had always affected her.

How was it, she wondered caustically as her eyes travelled with an almost resigned fascination over him, that he could look so sexy in an ordinary pair of grey trousers and a simple white shirt?

A bitter taste invaded her mouth as she recalled the occasion of that unexpected meeting in Sydney, when she'd been flustered and tongue-tied. Angie vowed that this would not be a repeat performance, despite the way her heart was instantly racing.

Her green eyes stayed cool as they lifted to meet that brilliant blue gaze. 'Hello, Lance,' she said casually. 'Long time, no see.'

For a few seconds he didn't reply as he gave her as thorough a once-over as she had given him. It piqued Angie when his expression revealed a degree of surprise, plus something else that she couldn't quite identify.

'Yes, it is,' he said slowly. 'I see you've changed somewhat.'

'For the better, I hope,' came her almost challenging comment as she sneakily moved her glass to cover her left nipple, the one which her hair didn't reach.

His smile was wry. 'Hard to improve on perfection, Angie.'

He could not have said anything to annoy her more. For it was so insincere! She found a smile as wry as his. 'You always did know what to say to turn a girl's head, Lance. But, tell me, what are you doing here? Is Bud expecting you?'

'No.'

'You do realise it's his birthday today, don't you?' she said archly. 'And that we're having a party in his honour.'

'Yes, of course. That's why I came.'

She frowned down at the bag at his feet. 'You look like you're aiming to stay for longer than the party.'

'For a night or two. But only if Bud has room. I

can just as easily go to a nearby motel for the night. I have my car.'

She frowned some more. 'Are you saying you drove up from Melbourne just because it's Bud's birthday?'

'Partly.'

'What does that mean?'

'It means, Angie, my sweet, that my wife and I have agreed to a divorce and I felt the sudden need to get away and see old friends again.'

Angie congratulated herself on taking this news so nonchalantly. At least on the exterior. 'You've left your wife?'

'Aah, now, I didn't say that. She left me, actually.'

'Why?'

His casual air suddenly dropped, irritation flaring. 'For pity's sake, Angie, must I stand here answering questions? I've just driven all the way from Melbourne. I'm stiff as a board and damned tired. I need a shower and a drink. Your mother wouldn't have left me languishing on the doorstep like this. She would have given me a big hug and bundled me inside, posthaste.'

'Indeed. Well, I'm not my mother, am I? And I'm more into kissing than hugging. Would you like to kiss me hello, Lance?' she taunted, thrilling to the foolishnes of her words.

He stared at her. 'Are you drunk or something?'

'No.' But I'd like to be, came the savage thought.

'Then why are you acting like this?'

'Like what?'

'So unlike yourself.'

She laughed. 'How would you know what I'm like these days? The only Angie you ever knew was just a kid—a silly, impressionable kid who once thought the sun shone out of you.'

'Well, it's perfectly clear you don't any more,' he muttered testily.

She could hardly believe her ears. He was actually sounding disappointed that her once obvious hero-worship of him had disappeared.

'Oh, do stop scowling, Lance, and come inside. I'll go get Bud for you.'

Bud was as amazed as she was.

'Good God. Lance? *Here*?'

'His wife's left him,' she whispered to her brother.

'Hmm. Doesn't take too many guesses to work out why. I always said Lance was never cut out for monogamy.'

'Apparently he drove all the way from Melbourne today because he wanted to celebrate your birthday with you. Says he also wants to stay the night.'

'Well, of course he can stay the night. He's my friend! Go tell Loretta we have an overnight visitor, will you, Angie?' And he raced off towards the front hall.

Loretta was back in the kitchen, this time loading the dishwasher. She took the news of Lance's unexpected arrival and anticipated stay as cheerfully as

Angie's mother would have, giving Angie new insight into why she and Bud were so compatible.

'How nice for Bud. He hasn't seen Lance since his wedding.'

'Neither have I,' Angie said.

Something in her tone brought a sharp look from her sister-in-law. 'You're not still carrying a torch for him, are you?'

Angie blinked her surprise, and Loretta smiled softly. 'One would have had to be deaf, dumb and blind at that wedding not to know you were heartbroken that day. Bud told me later that he tried to make you see that Lance wasn't the right man for any girl, let alone his much-loved sister. Did he succeed?'

Angie shrugged. 'I'd be lying if I didn't admit I still find him awfully attractive. But I'm cured of anything more.'

'I hope so. Married men are always trouble.'

'He says he's getting a divorce.'

'That's as popular as the cheque's in the mail,' Loretta said drily.

'You don't have to worry about me, Loretta. I'm once bitten, twice shy where Lance Sterling is concerned.'

'I know Bud will be relieved to hear that.'

'I'll be relieved to hear what?' the man himself said as he came into the kitchen.

'That Angie's cured of Lance.'

Bud looked hard at his sister. 'She'll need to be, dressed as she is tonight.'

Angie bristled. 'Meaning?'

'Meaning Lance is not the sort of man to ignore the signals you've been giving out tonight, dear sister of mine. On top of that, he always did fancy you.'

'Come on, Bud, you're living in the past. And give me a break. I'm twenty-four years old now, not fifteen. I think I can handle myself where men are concerned—Lance included.'

Brave words, girlie, that voice mocked inside her head again. Want to put them to the test?

Her brother sighed. 'Yeah, you're right. I'm being paranoid. Lance seems to have changed too. He was very quiet just now—not at all like his old self. I think that marriage must have knocked the stuffing out of him.'

'Where did you put him?' Loretta asked.

'In the main guest-room. He's having a shower. I'm supposed to be mixing him a Scotch and dry and taking it up to him. Since you're so cured, Angie, you can do that. I really should get back to my other guests. You should, too, Loretta. You've been in this kitchen long enough.'

Panic claimed Angie immediately. She wanted to scream out that she wasn't that cured yet, but the idea of taking Lance up a drink while he was in the shower did have a certain perverse appeal. Who knew what she might accidentally see?

Memories of their swimming together in the creek at home came back in a rush. Lance had such a great body. A swimmer's body. Wide of shoulder, slender of hip, with long, tapering muscular legs. He'd been a champion swimmer at university, only missing out on the Olympics because he would never take training seriously.

That had always been a problem with Lance. He'd never taken anything really seriously. But that had been part of his attraction too. Serious-minded, deep-thinking Angie had been intrigued by someone who didn't seem to plan or worry about much.

Not that he had to. He'd been born clever and handsome and rich—the rich part being the most influential in forming Lance's attitude to life. Everything just fell into rich people's laps, it seemed. Everything had certainly fallen into Lance's lap—females included.

This last thought brought a sour grimace to Angie's face. She threw together a whisky and dry which would have made the heroine in *Raiders of the Lost Ark* finally slide under the table, and carried it upstairs, wondering what her motivation was in mixing such a stiff drink. Was she trying to anaesthetise Lance, or prime him for seduction later on?

She gasped with shock at this last thought, grinding to a halt on the top landing. But the shock quickly changed to defiance. Hadn't she promised Vanessa that if a suitable candidate showed up at the party tonight she would give him a chance to become her first lover? Who better than the man she'd wanted to be her first lover all along?

God, maybe she was drunk after all. How many

glasses of wine had she had before Lance arrived? Two? Three? No, only two. She wasn't drunk, but she also wasn't acting like her usual sensible self either, as Lance had so accurately pointed out at the door. Suddenly she felt even more reckless than she had earlier, and just a little bit wild. Wild as in angry.

Oh, yes, she was angry. Angry at Lance. He had no right to show up here tonight and spoil everything for her again. It wasn't fair! He would have to pay. She would make him pay. With his body!

She didn't knock, just bowled straight on in. But as luck would have it, Lance was out of the shower and almost dressed. He still looked very inviting, with his shirt open to the waist, giving her a splendid view of his golden and gloriously hairless chest.

His eyes snapped up at her abrupt entry, glaring his disapproval at her as he finished buttoning his shirt and then his cuffs. 'I'm sure your mother taught you to knock before entering a gentleman's room,' he said sharply, tucking the shirt into the waistband of his trousers.

'I'm sure she did,' Angie countered. 'I'll remember that next time I enter one.'

He sucked in a startled breath, his blue eyes darkening. 'Are you trying to pick a fight with me for some reason, Angie?'

Yes, came the totally unexpected but brutally honest thought. For if I don't, I just might throw myself at your feet and tell you that I still love you—have done all these years!

Angie turned away before he could see the stricken look on her face. Oh, God. It couldn't be true. It *shouldn't* be true. But it was…

She whirled back, a plastic smile on her face. Her head was spinning and she had no idea what she was going to do now. Her idea from a moment before, of a crazy seduction, suddenly seemed even more appropriate—maybe even essential.

For the first time in her life Angie wanted Lance to be as heartless a womaniser as he'd always been painted. For she didn't have much time. There was no doubt that he would return to Melbourne in a day or two. She would never have another chance. Maybe all she had was tonight.

'That *was* bitchy of me, wasn't it?' she said, trying to bring a seductively soothing quality to her smile. 'I was only teasing. Here's your drink. Bud asked me to bring it up to you.' She handed it over, then perched on the edge of the bed, hitching her dress up over her knees as she saucily crossed her legs.

'So what happened to make your wife leave you?' she asked, still smiling. 'Have you been a naughty boy again, Lance?' One part of her wanted him to say he'd been a very naughty boy. Another part wanted him to deny adultery, to claim he'd done his best to make his marriage work but found it couldn't because he'd never really loved his wife. He'd really been in love with someone else, you see. A girl named Angie.

He stared at her legs while he swallowed a deep gulp of the drink, grimaced, then placed the glass down on the nearby dressing-table. Still saying nothing, he picked up a comb and started combing his hair in the dressing-table mirror—his lovely, thick, wet dark blond hair. Angie watched it fall into perfect place, hating every single obedient lock, wanting to clasp great clumps of it with cruel hands while she pulled his mouth down on to hers.

A deep shudder ran through her. She had never thought herself capable of such feelings, of such a savage passion. It made her afraid of what she might do afterwards, if she went to bed with Lance and it was as incredible as she expected that it might be.

Suddenly she became aware that he was staring at her in the mirror. Not at her legs, this time, but deep into her eyes. 'Why do you want to know about my marriage?' he asked.

Her shrug was marvellously indifferent. 'I'm just curious, that's all. Bud always said it wouldn't last.'

His eyebrows shot up as he turned around. 'Is that so? And did he say why?'

'I dare say he thought the man voted Superstud of the Year wasn't good husband material.'

Lance went awfully still before shaking his head slowly and sighing. 'Dear old Bud,' came his dry remark. 'And I thought he was my friend.'

Angie bristled at the implied criticism of her brother. 'Bud *is* your friend,' she snapped. 'His saying that didn't make it so, Lance. If your marriage failed, look to yourself.'

'Oh, I do, Angie. Indeed I do. I made a big mistake marrying Helen.'

'I hope you're not blaming her now.'

'I blame no one but myself.'

'So you're definitely getting a divorce, are you?' Angie asked, hating herself for wanting to know so desperately. What difference could it possibly make to her, or her life? Lance was only up here for a night or two, then he would go back to Melbourne and his own world of high-fliers and other women like Helen. 'There's no chance of a reconciliation?' she added, in what she hoped was a carefree fashion.

'None,' he grated out, sweeping the whisky glass up for another gulp, followed by another pained grimace. 'Hell, Angie, what did Bud put in this? It's strong enough to kill a brown dog.'

'Don't blame Bud. I made it. I thought you looked like you needed relaxing.'

'You could be right there. But not this way.' And he placed the drink down. 'So, tell me, Angie, has life brought you all you ever wanted? Is there some eager young man waiting downstairs for you to return to his loving arms?'

At that moment, Angie wished she'd put arsenic in his drink. 'Actually no, Lance,' she returned with a coldly brittle smile. 'I'm between boyfriends at the moment. As for my other ambitions, I *am* only twenty-four, and only three years out of my degree. I need a little more time before I can change the whole world. Though I realise now that some things—and some people—can never be changed.' This with a sour look at Lance.

'Look, drop the acid barbs, will you? It's Bud's birthday, and if I remember Bud, there'll be music and dancing downstairs. I could do with some music and dancing at this moment, believe me.'

Taking Angie's nearest hand, he pulled her somewhat abruptly to her feet. She stumbled slightly and his other arm shot out to steady her, then snaked slowly round her waist. Startled, her green eyes widened as they flew to his, only to meet a decidedly cynical gaze.

'Don't look so surprised, Angie,' he drawled. 'Isn't this the sort of behaviour you would expect from an unconscionable rake like myself? I'm just taking you up on that hello kiss you offered me earlier on.'

Panic-stricken, Angie turned her face away from his descending mouth. 'Too late,' she muttered through clenched teeth as his lips brushed her cheek. 'I only give hello kisses at the door, not in bedrooms.'

He cupped her chin and brutally forced her face frontwards. 'Then call this a goodbye kiss,' he ground out.

No, she tried to cry out, but his kiss obliterated the word before she could do more than open her lips.

The memory can certainly play tricks with your mind, Angie thought dazedly as Lance's lips took violent possession of hers. She'd told Vanessa that his kiss had made her think she'd died and gone to heaven. Either she'd been mistaken, or things had changed dramatically. There was nothing at all heavenly about the lips which were clamped to hers at that moment, prying them apart with so much force that her lips were ground back against her teeth. It was sheer hell.

But no sooner had Angie decided that she'd been mad to imagine she'd loved him all these years than everything changed. The fingers gripping her chin suddenly gentled, then trailed tantalisingly down her throat. Another hand slid up her back and into the hair around her neck. The vice-like lips lightened their gruelling pressure.

And then—then, when she was sighing with relief and almost relaxing into him—*then* his tongue moved slowly and incredibly seductively into her mouth.

It dipped deep, then withdrew, then darted back, coupling with her own tongue in an erotic dance which went on and on and on.

Angie was polarised with the most intense pleasure—eclipsing everything she had remembered. Sensations were racing to every corner of her body, every last nerve-ending, every tiny fibre of her being. She felt shattered, yet at the same time almost complete. This was where she'd always wanted to be—in Lance's arms, his mouth fused with hers, their bodies pressed together. Only by making love would she be totally complete.

In silent yearning she reached for that end, her hands instinctively lifting to splay into his hair, to keep his mouth on hers, to press herself closer and closer. She heard his groan of raw desire, felt it rising against her. Her own desire rose to meet his, and her hips moved with instinctive need.

'Auntie Angie...'

The small voice pierced the fog of her passion with crippling effect. She gasped away from Lance's mouth, the wild wonder of it all immediately replaced by sordid reality as Angie was faced with the knowledge that she had only been moments away from letting Lance do whatever he wanted with her.

'I want a dwink of water,' three-year-old Morris cried, when his auntie looked over Lance's shoulder at him.

With a soft moan of self-disgust, she pried herself out of Lance's seemingly frozen arms and turned to her nephew, who was standing just outside the open doorway—another factor in Angie's mortification. My God, she thought, anybody could have walked by and seen us. What if Bud had come up?

Her insides churning, she scooped up Morris and carried him swiftly down towards the main bathroom and his bedroom. 'Your mummy and daddy won't be too happy with your being out of bed, young man,' she said breathlessly. 'I won't tell them if you promise to drink up your water real quick, then go back to sleep.'

'Who was that man kissing you, Auntie Angie?' Morris asked with a child's innocent puzzlement.

'He's a friend of your father's and mine,' she told him, hoping that would be a satisfactory answer. Morris was going through an inquisitive stage when he asked questions about everything.

'Why was he kissing you? Are you going to marry him, Auntie Angie?'

Angie felt sick inside. 'No. I'm not going to marry him, Morris. We haven't seen each other for a long time. People kiss each other when they haven't seen each other for a long time.'

'Yes, but—'

'How much water do you want?' she broke in, hoping to distract the child. 'A whole glassful or only half a glass?'

Angie managed to get Morris back to bed without any more embarrassing questions. She only hoped he wouldn't relay the news in the morning, of his Auntie Angie kissing one of Daddy's friends in the guestroom. Briskly she tucked him in, pecked him on the forehead, and was about to escape when Morris decided that he couldn't possibly go to sleep without being read a story.

Sighing, Angie did the honours with *Toby, the Tonka Truck* which proved to be quite a long story. By the time she finished it, Morris was sound asleep. For a long moment she stared down at the sleeping child, with his olive skin and black curls, the unbidden thought coming that a son of Lance's would probably be as fair as Morris was dark. Asleep, he would look like a golden angel.

Her heart turned over and, closing her eyes, she bent to kiss Morris on the forehead, her mind still full of that imaginary golden angel. 'Love you,' she whispered softly.

With a sad sigh, she opened her eyes, closed the book, put it aside and stood up. After carefully snapping off the bedside light, she had turned to tiptoe out of the room when she encountered Lance, lounging in the doorway. Clearly he'd watched the whole proceedings; the thought disturbed and then infuriated Angie. When would she rid herself of these stupid futile dreams?

She shoved him out of the doorway none too gently, and quickly closed the door before he said anything and woke Morris.

'Smart little tyke,' Lance said. 'Trust Bud to have a great kid like that.'

Angie eyed him with a mixture of surprise and annoyance. 'Jealous, Lance?'

'Of course.'

'In that case, why haven't you had children of your own?' she snapped. 'Or have you been too busy with your jet-setting life to fit them in?'

'If you're going to answer your own questions, Angie, then why should I? I might ask you the same question. Why haven't you converted that obvious maternal instinct of yours into first-hand reality? Why haven't you found some nice man to marry by now and had a couple of kids?'

God, he had a hide to ask her that! The man had to be thick as a brick! 'No doubt I will,' she said, smothering her hurt behind a cold smile. 'Eventually. But for now I happen to have a career.'

'Ah, yes…your career. Bud tells me you're directing schoolgirls along the path of right and righteousness.'

'Trust someone like you to sneer,' she countered tartly. 'People with no morals and standards always mock those who have.'

His eyebrows shot upwards. 'Watch it, Angie. People in glass houses shouldn't throw stones, you know.'

'Meaning what?'

'Meaning ten minutes ago you showed a tendency to loose morals yourself. You could have knocked me over with a feather when I found you'd become one of those females willing to open their legs after one kiss.'

Her hand flashed across his cheek, the sound harsh and biting. 'Bastard,' she hissed, everything inside her trembling wildly.

His own hand lifted rather indolently to rub his reddened cheek. 'Was that for just now, Angie, my sweet? Or nine years ago?'

'Both,' she bit out.

His gaze narrowed on her, his brilliant and deceptively intelligent eyes darkening to a deep thoughtfulness. 'Good,' he said at last, in an oddly satisfied voice.

'What's good about it?'

'Not all that much, I guess. Come on,' he said,

grabbing her hand and tugging her along the hall. 'Let's go downstairs and dance.'

Outrage had her wrenching her hand out of his and grinding to a halt. 'Just like that? You expect me to go downstairs and dance with you after you insulted me?'

His mouth broke into one of those old smiles of his, dazzling and totally disarming. 'Hell, Angie, *you've* been insulting *me* ever since I got here. What's a few insults among friends? Besides, I don't think what I said was an insult. I rather like females of easy virtue. Saves a chap a hell of a lot of lies.'

'Oh, you—' He shut her up with another kiss. A lightly teasing brush of lips which evoked a soft little moan of despair mixed with delight. 'You're wicked,' she whispered shakily.

'And you're gorgeous,' he drawled, his eyes narrowing sexily as he picked up one of the long curling strands of hair that covered her appallingly peaked nipple and drew it slowly between her lips.

A wild heat flooded those lips, and then her limbs. Weak with desire, she reached out to grip his shoulder, her lips falling apart as she unconsciously pulled him closer.

'Later, I think, sweet Angie,' he murmured, withdrawing the lock of hair and smoothing it down back over her breast, brushing over the pained peak as he did so. 'I have an aversion to starting anything I can't finish, and I have a feeling that brother of yours might shortly make an appearance.'

Angie's nostrils flared as she sucked in another indignant breath. 'And I have an aversion to men who make arrogant presumptions,' she flung back at him. 'I'm not as free and easy with my favours as you think, Lance.'

'No?'

'No.'

'How interesting…'

'Not really. You like your females easy, remember?'

'Usually. But for you, my sweet Angie, I'd be prepared to make an exception.'

'Stop calling me that!' she snapped. 'I'm not your sweet Angie any more. I'm not your Angie in any way, shape or form. I despise you, Lance, and all men like you. You wreak havoc wherever you go. You smile and you laugh and you dazzle, but you're all show and no substance. You come here tonight and try to seduce me within five minutes of landing, while your poor wife is probably crying her eyes out back in Melbourne.'

'I doubt that,' Lance snarled, all the dazzle gone from his face. 'I doubt that very much. Far from crying, Helen is probably at this very moment bonking her head off with her current lover.'

CHAPTER FIVE

For a second Angie was stunned, sympathy sweeping in for the angry man standing before her. Till the truth sank into her addled brain. Then sympathy turned to sarcasm. 'So she'd finally had enough, had she? Gave you back some of your own medicine.'

Lance simply stared at her. 'You're incredible, do you know that? You really think I'm a cross between Casanova and Bluebeard, don't you?'

'You can stop at Casanova,' she said drily. 'Murder is not your style. You're a lot of things, Lance, but violent is not one of them.'

'I wouldn't say that,' he muttered darkly. 'I can think of someone I'd like to strangle at this very moment.'

'Really?' she mocked. 'Yet only a moment ago you wanted to dance with me?'

His glare was savage, his eyes glittering dangerously. 'Who said I was talking about you?' he ground out. 'Let's go, lover.'

Any protest at this last tag was obliterated when Lance roughly repossessed her hand and hauled her downstairs. Neither did she object when he dragged her into a room where dance music was playing, and yanked her hard against him.

59

Their mutual anger lent a perverse edge to the unwanted desire that was still pulsating through Angie's veins. Soon, the throbbing beat of the music plus the heat of Lance's skin had her senses all awhirl, any common sense routed. Stupidly, she wound her arms up around his neck and sank against the body she'd always coveted, the body of the man she'd always loved.

But it was desire, not love, which was ruling her at that moment. It seemed to be ruling Lance as well.

Their eyes clashed—his hooded, hers widening. For she could feel his stark arousal pressing into her silk-covered stomach. Yet it was her own raw and highly primitive response to that arousal which surprised her the most. God, but she wanted him. And she wanted him *now!*

'Lance,' she breathed shakily.

'What?' he bit out, pulling back from her a little.

'I…I…'

'So here you are!' Bud broke in, his hand clamping on Lance's shoulder and spinning him away from a flushed Angie. Luckily the room was dimly lit, with disco-style lights flashing. That, plus the many other dancing couples, precluded Bud noticing too much. Thank heavens.

'I looked upstairs but couldn't find either of you,' Bud raved on heartily. 'For a second there, I thought you'd run off together.' Bud laughed, and so did Lance. Drily.

Privately Angie thought that her running off with

Lance somewhere was a distinct possibility. Right now, she would do whatever he wanted.

It was a mortifying realisation, and one which brought her real personal pain. How could she possibly counsel other people on matters of life when her own could spin out of all control so quickly? She should have more will-power, more self-respect. Twenty-four years old and she was acting like an immature, hormone-filled teenager!

Angie would have been quite happy about being reduced to a state of mindless passion if Lance had cared about her.

But he didn't.

At best, he was physically attracted to her. At worst, he was using her as a way of getting back at his wife. Either way his desire for her was a very casual and fleeting thing, to be indulged in this one night and forgotten in the morning.

Angie, however, would not forget it in the morning. She could see herself now—torn by remorse and regret, plunged into despair and self-disgust. Lance would go off on his merry way, leaving her again to die another thousand deaths in the wake of his empty charm and superficial sex-appeal.

But, oh...how his charm could charm—and how his sex appeal appealed...

Even now, all she wanted was for Bud to get the hell out of here and let Lance take her in his arms once more.

Exasperation came to her rescue. If the man affects

you physically like this, she lectured herself valiantly, then stay away from him, for goodness' sake. Don't look at him anymore. Don't dance with him. Don't go anywhere near him!

In fact, *go home*!

'If you'll excuse me,' she said swiftly, before she could change her mind. 'I…I have to go and see Loretta about something. You and Lance must have loads of things to talk about. I'll catch up with you later, Lance.'

Angie fled without looking back, surging past various gyrating couples and heading straight for the cupboard under the stairs where she'd put her jacket and bag.

Retrieving them both, she draped the black jacket over her shoulders, then closed the cupboard door and hurried towards the front door, opening her handbag as she went. It was a largish black patent leather number, with a zipper running along the top and one roomy cavernous area inside, filled to the brim with all sorts of female paraphernalia. Make-up. Tissues. Perfume. A nail file. Nail clippers. Bobby-pins. Safety pins. Comb. A mirror.

Plus her car keys.

Somewhere…

Angie ground to a halt, swearing under her breath as she blindly rifled through the mess with her hand. She encountered everything but her keys.

God, but that was so typical! Whenever one wanted to find something desperately, one never could. Speed was of the essence too. Any moment, Loretta or Lance or Bud might appear, wondering what she was doing and where she was going. Her brother would be annoyed with her for leaving his party so early but she would survive his disapproval. She might not survive something else if she stayed.

'Lord, where are those damned keys!' she groaned aloud.

Frustrated, she raced over and tipped the entire contents out on to the hall console; the keys were the last thing to clatter on to the marble surface.

'Looking for this?'

Angie gasped when Lance materialised to reach over her shoulder and pick up the condom Vanessa had mischievously dropped into her bag and which lay with garish clarity among her make-up and other possessions.

Whirling, she went to snatch it back, but he was too quick for her, slipping it into his trouser pocket. Angie glared at him. No way was she going to try to retrieve it from there!

Her cheeks burning, she spun back to the console and scooped everything but the keys into her still open bag. Picking up the keys, she dangled them in the mirror on the wall for him to see. '*These* are what I was looking for. But do keep the condom, Lance. No doubt you'll be needing it before the night is out. A superstud like yourself won't have any problem finding some pretty little thing to oblige you.'

'Do you always carry condoms around with you?'

he asked as she zipped up her bag and rammed it under her arm.

Angie turned to glare at him, livid at the look of hypocritical reproach on his face. 'Why not?' she flung at him, her defiant expression reminding her of Debbie that afternoon. 'A girl never knows when she's going to get lucky, after all.' Rather enjoying his ongoing air of shock, Angie lifted her chin proudly, then hurried down the hall and out through the front door.

The sight of a sleek black car parked behind hers in the driveway, barring her escape, brought a groan of dismay to her lips.

'Blast,' she muttered. 'Someone parked their damned car behind me.'

'I wouldn't think you should be driving anywhere,' Lance said quietly from behind her. 'You're obviously drunk.'

Now she really lost her temper. 'And why, exactly, must I be drunk?' she fumed, spinning round and planting furious hands on her hips. 'It wouldn't be because I've chosen to leave your not so salubrious company, would it? Or because I've decided to be the exception and not surrender to your oh, so irresistible charm this evening?'

'No,' he returned calmly. 'It's because I've finally realised you've been acting totally out of character ever since I arrived. Now, why would that be, I'm beginning to wonder?'

Her slow handclap reeked of sarcasm. 'Bravo,

Lance. You've had virtually nothing to do with me for nine years and you claim to know what my usual character is. Believe it or not, old friend, a girl changes somewhat between fifteen and twenty-four. This is me these days, Lance,' she said, scooping off her covering jacket with one hand, clasping her bag in the other then twirling round so that he could see every inch of her provocative dress. 'It wouldn't be that you can't cope with your "sweet Angie" being sexually active, would it? Even nice girls *do*, Lance. And *I* do—quite often, in fact!'

The moment the lie was out she regretted it. Crazy as it was, she hated seeing the disappointment in Lance's face.

Or was it something else she glimpsed behind those suddenly clouded eyes of his? Maybe it was...defeat?

The idea of Lance feeling anything like defeat bewildered Angie. Yet his shoulders were beginning to sag and there was an air of wretchedness about his slightly slumped form.

Maybe, she conceded with great difficulty, maybe he was more upset about his marriage break-up than she'd believed. Maybe he'd really been in love with his wife...

As much as Angie hated *that* idea, it showed that Lance was capable of feeling deeply about a woman. Bud had had little to do with his friend since their marriages, so his old opinion of Lance's character might be totally out of date. Angie herself had just made the point that people changed. Well, maybe Lance had changed as well.

She'd no sooner starting thinking sympathetic thoughts about him than he snapped out of his dejected demeanour, straightening up and throwing her a ruefully sexy smile.

'You're right,' he said. 'I'm being somewhat of a hypocrite. You're only young once, and you're just as entitled to sow your wild oats as anyone else. Any reason why you can't sow some of them with me?'

Angie just shook her head. So much for Lance having changed.

'Nope?' he mocked. 'Oh, well, can't blame a guy for trying. Come for a drive with me, then?'

Angie stamped her foot in total exasperation. 'What is it with you? Can't you see I don't want to go anywhere with you? I just want to go home. If I knew who owned that damned car I'd get him to move it and—'

She broke off when Lance smiled a smug smile.

'It's *your* car, isn't it?' she said frustratedly.

'Sure is. Actually, Bud asked me to go buy some more beer from the local grog shop. He said you'd show me where to go. I'm sure he had no idea you were thinking of going home. Why are you, anyway? The night's still young. Who knows? You might get lucky, after all.'

Angie chose to ignore Lance's last remarks. 'Why doesn't Bud go get the beer himself?'

'Because he's finally cornered a very important potential client. You know what advertising people are like, Angie. Much the same as insurance salesmen. They're always working.'

Angie felt that underneath his light-hearted attitude Lance was denigrating her brother's profession. 'Well, at least Bud *works*,' she bit out.

Lance looked taken aback. 'You think I don't?'

Angie shrugged, aware that she'd been abominably rude to Lance tonight. Whether or not he deserved her contempt was not the point.

'One day,' he grated, taking her elbow, 'I'm going to sit you down and tell you some cold, hard facts about my life. You have a very jaundiced view of it. But not tonight,' he added as he shepherded her down the steep driveway past her small red Lancer and over to the passenger door of his car. 'Tonight is Bud's birthday party, some more beer is needed, and his sweet sister is going to show me where to get it!'

'I will, provided there's no funny business,' she stated firmly at the passenger door. 'No passes. No suggestive remarks. No nothing. Just down to the grog shop and back again. Then I get to take my car home.'

'Scout's honour,' Lance said, and crossed his heart.

'Hmph!' Angie grunted. 'I doubt you were ever a Boy Scout, Lance Sterling.' And she wrenched open the car door.

She didn't recognise the make and didn't much care. It was a rich man's car, which smelt of real leather and had probably cost a fortune. She climbed in and belted herself properly, determined not to make a single complimentary remark. Let him think that she often rode around in rich men's cars! Let him think whatever he damned well liked about her, as long as he kept his hands off!

'Second street on the right,' she told him sharply, once he'd reversed out and was heading in the right direction. 'There's a drive-in bottle shop a couple of hundred yards down on the left.'

There certainly was, but its driveway was crammed with cars. Lance parked in the street, growling, 'Be back in a minute,' before he alighted and strode off to get the beer.

Butterflies invaded her stomach as she waited for him to return. She wasn't sure why. Was it that she didn't trust Lance—or herself? Sitting there quietly in the car was certainly not conducive to sensible thinking. It allowed that devil's voice back into her mind, the one which told her not to let Lance get away a second time, to take what was on offer, even if it was only sex. After all, it wouldn't be just sex on her part, would it? It would be making love as well.

Yeah, right, she argued back silently. And what do you think would happen as soon as he found out you were a virgin? A man of his experience would know for sure. You wouldn't be able to pull the wool over *Lance's* eyes. Too bad you're not the free spirit you've been painting yourself to be all evening, then there wouldn't be any trouble.

What irony, Angie conceded bleakly. Who would

have believed that her old-fashioned morality would cost her what she had always wanted most, besides Lance's love?

Still, her thoughts had calmed her agitation somewhat, and had made her see that to run off home like a frightened rabbit was totally unnecessary. Recalling her virginal state had strengthened her earlier resolve not to do anything with Lance. She would rather die than be on the end of his mockery!

He came striding back, smiling wryly over at her as he climbed into the car. 'You stayed,' he said somewhat drily. 'I thought you might run away again.'

'No,' she said. 'I'm done with running away for tonight.'

'And what, precisely, does that mean?' he demanded to know.

'It means, Lance, that I've decided not to go home after all.'

'You never did explain why you were leaving in the first place.'

'I guess I was worried you were lining me up as another notch on your gun.'

'Ah. Back to Casanova, are we?' He shook his head as he restarted the car. 'I can see I have no hope of changing your opinion of me. It's fixed in concrete in your mind. Still, maybe I can chip away at that concrete over time...'

Glancing over his right shoulder, he executed a perfect U-turn and accelerated back up the road, neither of them saying another word till he swung his car into Bud's driveway and braked barely an inch from Angie's bumper-bar.

'Very impressive,' she muttered caustically.

Lance laughed. 'Glad to see I've impressed you in some small way. There was a time, though, when I impressed you in just about every way, wasn't there? I could have said the world was flat and you would have believed me. I could have asked you to walk on water and you would have tried.'

Angie twisted to stare at him with pained eyes. 'That…that time is long gone,' she said, shaken by his words.

'True,' he bit out. 'But there *is* one way where I suspect I still make an impression. And that's this way,' he rasped, snapping off his seat belt and leaning over to capture her startled mouth with his before she could do a damned thing to stop him.

CHAPTER SIX

SHOCK held Angie compliant for a few seconds, giving Lance the opportunity to kiss her very thoroughly, and to very good effect. But, despite her pounding heart and swirling senses, Angie was just mustering her courage to bite his maurading tongue when it withdrew.

Unfortunately, Lance misinterpreted her moan of dismay.

'It's all right,' he whispered, raining soft wet kisses all over her face. 'I feel the same. This had to happen one day. You know it as well as I do.'

'No!' she gasped. Or was it groaned?

'Oh, yes,' he insisted, then kissed her again, as if to prove it. She did her best to ward him off, moving her head from side to side while her hands pushed at his shoulders, but both gestures proved futile.

'Don't be such a little hypocrite,' he muttered, grabbing her hands and pressing them into the leather seat on either side of her twisting head. 'You *want* me to make love to you. That's why you've been calling me names all night, because underneath you despise yourself for wanting me. That's why you tried to run away back there, because you were afraid to stay—afraid of what I might do.'

'I'm not afraid of you,' she spat at him.

'Then what is it you're afraid of?' he taunted. 'Surely not the consequences of our making love? Have you forgotten I've got your very own protection in my pocket?'

'I haven't forgotten a thing.'

'Which, of course, is the main thrust of your dilemma. I'm still being punished for what I did nine years ago. Would you believe me if I said I did what I did back then for you, sweet Angie? Would it be unthinkable to attribute me with some honour?'

'*Honour*?' she repeated in blank amazement.

'Well, maybe not honour,' he said drily. 'You always did produce dishonourable thoughts in me. But I tried to do the right thing in the end.'

Which just showed how much she had meant to him that summer. The only feelings she had inspired in him back then had been lust. Nothing more.

'And *now*, Lance?' she asked derisively. 'Are you trying to do the right thing now?'

'Hell, no, Angie. I can see this is my one and only chance to have what I've always wanted—in a fashion—and I aim to take that chance by fair means or foul.'

'Bud will throttle you if he comes out and sees us together like this,' she warned him.

'No one can see into this car. It has specially tinted glass. Besides, Bud isn't going to come out.'

'Wh—why not?'

'Because he's very, very busy with that potential

client of his. On top of that, he has no idea we're out here.'

'But—but...'

'Bud didn't ask me to buy any beer. I made that up on the spur of the moment to get you alone.'

'Why, you...you... If you kiss me again,' she hissed, 'I'll bite your damned tongue off.'

'Thanks you for the warning, lover,' he murmured through a menacing smile. 'I'll make sure I keep away from those pearly white teeth of yours, in that case.'

His mouth landed at the base of her throat, and Angie drew in a sharp breath when he started to suck on the fluttering flesh he found there.

Bittersweet sensations warred with her pride and self-respect. God, but she did so want to give in. That devil's voice was back again, tempting her, torment-ing her.

You love him. You want him. Let him.

Don't think about tomorrow. Don't think about be-ing a virgin. Don't think about anything.

Lance put the issue beyond question when his mouth slid down from her throat to where her breasts were rising and falling on either side of the confines of the seat belt. Pushing back the left side of her jacket, he began to lick at the already hard nipple through her dress, wetting the silk till it moulded the rock-hard peak like a second skin.

At that point he started scraping his teeth back and forth across the exquisitely sensitised tip, stopping

every now and then to moisten it again with his
tongue.

Angie had to bite her own tongue to stop herself
from crying out, so sharp were the sensations. An
electric excitement charged along her veins, heating
her blood and firing her brain. When he closed his
lips round the nipple, her back arched as far away
from the seat as the seat belt would allow, pressing
her breast further into his mouth. He obliged by drawing the entire aureole within the heated cavern beyond
his lips and suckling away like a greedy infant.

It blew Angie's mind.

'Oh, God, Lance,' she groaned.

He abruptly released her hands and they fell limply
to her sides. His mouth stayed at her breast, even
when both front seats suddenly sank from an upright
position to a semi-reclining one. Angie found herself
closing her eyes and sighing with surrender to whatever was going to happen. Nothing could stop her
now, not even an earthquake or the eruption of a volcano.

She was the volcano, she decided dazedly. Feelings
long dormant were being released, bubbling up within
her, straining for release. She could feel the pressure-
cooker tension behind the pleasure of the moment,
feel the simmering heat which at any moment threatened to flare out of control.

He was back kissing her mouth, her eyelids, her
ear, whispering erotic suggestions which sent small
explosions of desire popping in her mind.

'Yes,' she whispered back blindly. 'Yes, please.'
Only to wonder immediately what she'd agreed to,
what she'd begged for.

She seemed to have the answer when his hands
moved up under her skirt to begin peeling off her
tights. She even lifted her buttocks to help him. Soon
her shoes were gone and her tights were draped over
the dashboard and she was naked under her dress.
When his hands slid slowly back up her naked legs,
taking her dress with them, she was beside herself
with excitement. Any second now... Any second...

But he didn't touch her where she was dying for
him to touch her; his hands lingered tantalisingly on
her thighs, caressing her softly trembling skin, stroking the outside from hip to knee in long, teasing
sweeps till she couldn't stand it any longer. Her legs
moved restlessly apart, showing him what she
wanted.

And he obliged.

Dear God, how he obliged!

Angie could not believe she was allowing him to
do what he was doing. But, oh...the heaven of it all.
Her breathing quickened. Her heartbeat soared. Everything in her seemed to be rushing upwards, yet
inwards at the same time. She moaned under the spi-
ral of wild pleasure, her hands finding his hair, twisting it in her fingers, till finally she wrenched his head
up and away from her burning, bursting body.

'No!' she cried, not at all sure what she was saying

no to, except that it was all too much—too intense, too frightening.

'It's all right,' he reassured her huskily. 'I was just about to stop. That's not what I want at all, either.'

Angie lay there, staring with wide eyes up at him while he struggled to manoeuvre himself to her side of the car and crouch between her legs. He didn't undress properly but he did protect them both, undoubtedly with what he'd pocketed earlier.

For a few moments he caressed her again, this time with knowing fingers, till she was arching away from the seat again in desperate need. Only the seat belt kept her from threshing wildly against that torturous touch, so that when he stopped, to lift her ankles up on to the outside edges of the seat and ease her bottom forward, she was beyond thinking of anything but having him inside her.

Yet the moment he began pressing against her virginal flesh, she tensed terribly. His sharp intake of breath brought more panic, his second attempt to penetrate making her muscles spasm even more tightly shut.

'God, Angie,' he ground out, probing harder. 'Relax, will you?'

'I…I can't,' she choked out. 'Oh, God…I just can't. I don't know how.'

'What do you mean, you don't know how?' he rasped, all pressure easing as he totally withdrew. 'Hell…are you saying what I think you're saying?'

Angie wanted to die of humiliation and frustration.

She hated herself and her inexperience at that moment. Hated everything and everyone. She groaned with the deepest chagrin, lifting her hands to cover her face.

Lance swore again. Then again.

Angie cringed inside at the sounds she heard. Clearly he'd decided not to continue. Clearly uptight virgins were not Lance's style.

'Dear God in heaven, Angie,' he finally rasped, unsnapping her seat belt, grabbing her hands and yanking her upright. The soles of her feet shot off the seat down on to the floor, her bare legs practically wrapping around Lance, who was still squatting in the space between the seat and the dashboard. Thankfully her skirt fell down over her lap as Lance snapped her further forward, their faces only inches apart.

'Why didn't you tell me earlier that you were still a virgin?' he interrogated harshly. 'Why did you let me believe you were some kind of good-time girl who'd have sex with anyone she fancied at any place, any old time?'

Angie shuddered under Lance's fury. She'd never seen him like this before.

'Hell, do you think I'd have treated you like this if I'd known?' he flung at her as a finale.

'T-Treated me like wh—what?' she stammered, confused by this last outburst.

He stared at her, then shook his head. 'I'm not sure if you're a total innocent, or more calculatingly wicked than any woman I've ever known. Which is it? *Are* you a professional tease? Do you get your kicks out of dressing up like this and seeing how many men you can have panting after you? Did you perhaps get out of your depth tonight,' he scorned, 'with a man who doesn't tolerate teases—a man you once *really* fancied?'

'No!' she denied fiercely. 'And yet, yes…in a way…'

'Which is it? Yes or no?'

'No, I'm not a tease,' she denied hotly. 'But, yes, I did dress up seductively tonight, and, yes, you're right—I do fancy you. I always did.'

'No kidding! Well, the dressing up seductively part wasn't for me, though, was it? You had no idea I'd even be here. So what was on your agenda tonight which called for this vamp image?'

Angie grimaced, then shook her head.

'Either you tell me, or I'll ask Bud,' he threatened.

'Bud doesn't know.'

'Doesn't know what? That you're still a virgin? Or that you're some kind of sick man-hater?'

'I am *not* a man-hater!'

'Then tell me the truth!'

'I…I decided today that I was f-fed up with being inexperienced,' she confessed, blushing and stammering. 'I…I thought it was well past time that I lost my virginity. I knew there'd be a lot of potential partners here at Bud's party tonight so I dolled myself up and… Well, I just…I just…'

She shrugged, hoping she'd said enough to satisfy his curiosity.

'You just what?'

His persistence began to annoy her. What was it to him anyway? He didn't really care about her. He'd simply shown up out of the blue tonight at a highly opportune moment then tried to take ruthless advantage of it, even if he didn't know it.

'Oh, do shut up, Lance. I'm sure even Blind Freddie could get the picture. You turned up just when I was ripe and ready to take a lover, and for a short while tonight I thought it might as well be you, since you had been my first love, after all. By the time I decided not to boost your insufferable ego any further, you'd rather spoiled me for any other man here this evening. You have a habit of doing that in my life, Lance,' she bit out. 'Spoiling me for other men. One of the reasons I'm still a stupid damned virgin is because of you!'

She scowled at him but he didn't scowl back. All the anger seemed to melt from his face as a tender expression took over. 'I don't think there's anything stupid at all about being a virgin in this day and age,' he said softly. 'But since I've spoilt you for any other man so far, then the least I can do is undo the damage I've done.'

'What…what do you mean?'

'I mean, Angie, my sweet,' he said, kissing her lightly on the lips, 'that you're quite right. It *is* high time you lost your virginity, but I also think your first experience should be with someone you really fancy, not some bloke you've picked up at a party. There's nothing special about a one-night stand. Therefore I'm volunteering to be your first lover.'

'But I thought… I mean—'

'Don't think, Angie,' he cut in with a strangely gentle firmness. 'Just do as I say and everything'll be fine. Firstly, tonight is not the right time, and this car is certainly not the right place for such an important occasion in your life. We'll put all this fantastic bottled up passion of yours on hold for another twenty-four hours,' he murmured, encircling her mouth with a fingertip till her lips gasped apart and a shudder of delight rippled through her.

'God, but it's going to be good, Angie,' he promised huskily, taking his finger away to kiss her again.

'But I thought you'd be going back to Melbourne tomorrow,' she protested weakly, everything already going crazy in her head.

'No. I was never going to do that. As for now… I'm going to get out of this car, if I can. You'd better put your tights and shoes back on before you do, though. And do up your jacket. I've pretty well ruined that dress, I'm afraid. But no worries. I'll buy you another tomorrow.'

Angie sat there in a stunned state while he climbed over her out of the car. He groaned as he straightened, probably because of the muscle strain of being squashed up on his haunches for so long. Finally, as though mesmerised, Angie did as he suggested, pulling her tights back on and buttoning up her jacket so the undoubtedly ruined dress would not show. She was dimly conscious that underneath her clothes her body was still aroused, her nipples still distended, the area between her thighs acutely aware of the snugly fitting underwear.

But her still being turned on physically took second place behind the emotion which welled up within her soul when Lance leant into the car and took her hand in his. His tender smile sent tentacles of warmth curling round her heart, evoking all those old feelings which had besieged her that long-ago summer—feelings which had nothing to do with lust. When he drew her from the car and upwards, everything around him went out of focus. Her eyes locked on to his and nothing else existed for her but Lance—his face, his eyes, and the love she imagined she saw in their brilliant blue depths.

It was his mouth crashing back down on to hers which snapped her back to reality. For Lance didn't love women. He only made love to them.

Oddly enough, this renewal of her knowledge of Lance's character no longer had the power to turn Angie off. She'd gone beyond that now. Once back in his arms, she was too weak to fight his incredible appeal.

She did what he told her to do. She stopped thinking. Her arms wound around his waist then up his back. Her tongue darted forward to move past his and into his mouth, sending wild tremors of pleasure down her spine.

It was Lance who drew back first, his face actually flushed, his breathing ragged. 'Hell, Angie, we have to stop this, or I'll never last the distance.'

'*We*, Lance?' she teased softly, while trying to get her own rampant desire under control. '*You* kissed *me*, remember?'

'Yeah, but did you have to be so co-operative?'

'Yes.'

Their eyes clashed, Lance shaking his head then smiling with rueful acceptance of her honesty. 'You always were a one-off experience, Angie. Come on, let's get inside before someone realises we're missing.'

'What time is it?' she asked as they made their way together up the driveway.

'Eleven-thirty.'

Angie ground to a halt. 'Is that all?' She recalled seeing the time on a wall clock when she'd been arguing with Lance in the hall. It had been ten to eleven.

They'd only been gone from the house forty minutes.

It felt like an eternity.

CHAPTER SEVEN

LANCE was right. Bud didn't even notice that they'd been absent. He was too busy being the life of the party, telling jokes and generally having a wow of a time.

Loretta, Angie wasn't so sure about—her sister-in-law having given her and Lance a suspicious stare as they wandered into the main party room together. She seemed to make a point of excusing herself from the group of people she was chatting to and coming over.

'I've been wondering where you two disappeared to,' she said. 'Been catching up on old times, have you?'

'Not exactly,' Lance replied smoothly, before Angie could think of a suitable excuse. 'I had Angie show me where to buy Bud some beer for his birthday. I came without a present, you see. Speaking of presents, what did you give Bud, Angie? I seem to recall your family had a rule in the old days that presents could not exceed thirty dollars. It was to be the thought that counted. Does that still apply?'

'It certainly does,' Loretta jumped in, seemingly relieved by Lance's answers. Apparently she agreed with Bud's view that Angie should share nothing but friendship with a man like Lance.

Too bad, Angie thought with a sudden fierce resolve. Lance was going to become her lover and to hell with what everyone else thought. Maybe it would only last for a night, or a weekend, or a week. But that short time with him would mean more to her than a lifetime with any other man.

Lance might be a compulsive womaniser but he had other qualities besides his sex-appeal to be treasured. There was a core of tenderness in Lance which was as captivating as it was rare. A sensitivity and sense of compassion which she had once appreciated, and which she was sure still lived within his soul.

Oh, yes, he was still easily moved to lust by a good-looking female—herself included—but just lust would have taken her virginity back there in his car. It would not have backed off, or begun planning something special for her initiation into sex. It would have ploughed on selfishly, and to hell with her discomfort or pain.

Lance might not love her, but he cared about her. Angie sensed that caring now more than ever and hugged the secret knowledge to her heart.

'So what did you buy him?' Lance asked, and Angie smiled mischievously.

'Something very useful.'

'What?'

'A pair of glow-in-the-dark boxer shorts. They have an arrow pointing to the appropriate spot.'

Loretta dissolved into giggles. 'I always did have to draw your brother a map,' she said, and Angie

almost choked with laughter. Lance was chuckling
too when the man himself joined the group.

'Must be a good joke if Loretta is laughing at it.'
He smiled broadly as he put an arm around his wife's
quaking shoulders. 'I love her dearly but her sense of
humour leaves a lot to be desired sometimes.'

'Angie was telling us about her birthday gift to
you,' Lance confessed with a wry grin. 'Loretta was
saying she's always needed to draw you a map.'

Bud's smile seemed to freeze on his face. He recovered quickly, but Angie thought she detected an
acid note in his reply. 'Well, no one could say the
same about you, mate. You'd find your way around
a woman's body blindfold.'

An awkward silence descended on the group for a
few embarrassing seconds, till Lance laughed. 'Blindfold, eh? Now, there's a thought. Though, personally,
I like to keep my eyes open when I make love.' And
his eyes moved slowly to Angie's.

'Make *love*?' Bud scoffed. 'That's not what you
used to call it, old chum. Still, I suppose it *is* a four-
letter word. Hasn't quite got the same colourful flair,
though, has it? Neither does it truly reflect your superstud status.'

To give Lance credit, he didn't react. He merely
smiled with seeming indulgence and dry amusement
at his friend. Angie had to admire his forbearance.
Another man might have flattened him.

Loretta, perhaps sensing that the atmosphere was
becoming strained, decided it was time to produce

Bud's birthday cake. It was a welcome distraction for Angie, who felt so angry with Bud that she had a job giving him a birthday kiss after the singing and candle-blowing was over.

It wasn't like him to be so rude, and she couldn't understand his motivation. It wasn't as though he suspected anything between herself and Lance. Loretta's earlier suspicions seemed to have been doused as well, especially as Lance had moved off and started chatting up a tall, voluptuous blonde, who could hardly contain her delight at his attention.

Angie wasn't at all delighted. Jealousy stabbed deep into her heart. Jealousy, plus insecurity and a general feeling of inadequacy. Maybe even now Lance was deciding he would be a fool to have anything to do with a naïve and totally inexperienced virgin. He would probably prefer to spend his break in Sydney with someone who could cater to his undoubtedly sophisticated tastes in bed. The more Angie watched him with that woman, the more she was convinced any attraction she held for him was already on the wane.

When the blonde lightly touched Lance on his arm, then laughed up at him, her fears increased. There was something incredibly intimate about that laugh. And something incredibly sexy. Were they making plans for a secret assignation—maybe even later tonight? Angie could practically see them now, laughing in a motel bed together, their naked bodies entwined, the blonde's long legs wrapping around Lance as he bent his head to her very large breasts.

Angie choked down the bile which rose in her throat and launched herself across the room towards him. Lance seemed startled when she grabbed his arm and said she wanted to go home and needed him to move his car.

Quickly recovering, he excused himself from the blonde, who didn't look so pleased now.

'And where are you two off to?' Bud pounced as they made their way together towards the front door.

'Angie wants to go home,' Lance explained patiently, 'and my car's parked behind hers.'

Bud's obvious relief reminded Angie of how disapproving her brother would be of her becoming sexually involved with Lance. Not that she intended telling him.

Still, maybe that would never happen, now that Blondie had come on the scene. Angie's insides began to churn. She wished Bud would just disappear, so she could get Lance alone to tackle him on the subject.

'Goodnight, then, love,' Bud said, giving her a kiss on the cheek. 'Thanks for coming. I'm not sure I should thank you for that rude birthday present, though. Just wait till your next birthday comes along. I'll find you something that will make you go as red as a beetroot!'

Angie laughed. 'I'll look forward to it. Say goodnight to Loretta for me, will you, Bud? I really must go home. I have this awful headache coming on.'

'Do you really have a headache?' Lance asked her after he'd moved his car and returned to where she was standing by her own.

'Yes,' she snapped. 'And it has blonde hair and big boobs!'

'Ah…' He grinned at her. 'You're jealous.'

'And if I am?'

'If you are, sweet Angie,' he said, drawing her into his arms, 'then that's good. That's very good.'

'You wouldn't think it was so good if you were on the other end. There again, I suppose you're never jealous, are you?'

'I could be…'

'You're not going to sleep with that woman tonight, are you, Lance?' she asked, true anxiety in her face and words.

Lance lurched backwards as though she'd struck him, his arms dropping away, his eyes suddenly stormy. 'Damn and blast, but I'm getting fed up with this! What is it with you? Do you think I have such little control that I can't go one night without sex? I'm not some randy ram who ruts around indiscriminately. I do have *some* standards. Believe it or not, I like to know and respect a woman before I go to bed with her. I haven't had a mindless one-night stand since the night of my uni graduation party.'

'Oh! I…I'm sorry, Lance,' she apologised, confused by his heated defence of his own character. And not altogether convinced he was telling the truth.

'And so you should be,' he ground out. 'I've had about as much second-hand insult from the Browns tonight as I can take. It's got to stop, Angie. I'm not what you think I am. Hell, don't you have any respect for me at all? Have you agreed to have an affair with me only for the sex?'

Angie's confusion changed into total fluster. She dithered and hesitated and blushed till he solved the problem for her.

Lance stared at her. 'Hell, it *is* just the sex, isn't it?'

'No, of course not,' she denied through her fluster. 'I...I like you a lot. I've always liked you. You know that, Lance.'

'You *loved* me, Angie. That's a lot more than just like.'

'I *thought* I loved you,' she countered. 'I was only a child, for pity's sake.'

'You were more an adult woman at fifteen than my wife was at twenty-four!'

Angie gasped and stared up at him. He reached out and cradled her cheeks, drawing her gently up on tip-toe till their mouths met. 'You *loved* me,' he whispered into her softly parted lips. 'Don't deny it.'

A sob of admission fluttered from deep within her throat.

'Maybe you still do?' he suggested huskily.

She gasped again and drew back, green eyes wide

and heart pounding. 'No,' she choked out, a wild panic claiming her.

'No?' he repeated, blue eyes narrowing on her.

'No, I don't still love you,' she stated, with a firmness which belied her inner upheaval. 'As you just said, I don't even know you any more.'

'Then you will,' he vowed somewhat darkly. 'Starting tomorrow.'

'Only biblically speaking.'

Frustration flared in his face. 'If you think that, then you don't know anything about really making love.'

'I don't pretend to,' she said sharply.

'Then don't pretend to know what will transpire between us tomorrow. Now, go home, Angie. I've run out of patience for this kind of conversation tonight. I'll pick you up tomorrow morning at eleven.'

'Eleven!'

'Yes, eleven.'

'Why so early?'

'Have you anything else you have to be doing tomorrow?'

'No...'

'Then be ready at eleven.' He went to spin away when she called him back. 'What?' he snapped.

'You...you don't have my address.'

'I'll get it from Bud.'

Angie grimaced. 'But I...I don't want Bud to know...'

His glare made her feel vaguely ashamed. 'I see,'

he said rather coldly. 'Very well, tell me your address. Believe me when I assure you I won't forget it.'

She told him and he was immediately striding away from her, not looking back, his body language showing extreme annoyance. He'd obviously taken her last request as another insult—this suspicion confirmed by his banging the front door shut behind him.

Angie groaned her dismay out loud. She would have liked nothing better than to tell the world Lance was going to become her lover. *If* he loved her. If there was some guarantee that tomorrow night would be the beginning of a real relationship, not just a sexual rendezvous.

But Angie was not about to fool herself. Lance's claims didn't change the fact that his record with the opposite sex was hardly enviable. Maybe he had stopped having one-night stands after leaving university. But that didn't mean he hadn't had a huge turnover of girlfriends. His marriage failing after four years was hardly a recommendation for relationship-forming, either.

His promiscuity over the years probably wasn't all his fault, she conceded. His inherited wealth, plus the many talents God had given him, made him a compulsive target for women. Clearly they threw themselves at his feet all the time. Still, she doubted he'd been a faithful husband. She doubted a lot of what Lance had said to her.

Sighing, Angie turned and climbed into her car. Time to go home. Time to try to get some sleep.

Tomorrow was not many hours away. It was, in fact, she realised as she glanced at the clock on the dashboard, already here.

'You're pulling my leg!' Vanessa exclaimed.

It was five past nine and both girls had struggled out of bed shortly before, then padded out to the kitchen in pyjamas and slippers for some reviving coffee. While the kettle came slowly to a boil Angie had told her flatmate about the night before. And Lance.

'I'm beginning to wish I was,' Angie said, a rush of sick nerves claiming her stomach. 'I'm never going to be able to eat any breakfast, the way I'm beginning to feel.'

'Now, let me get this straight,' Vanessa resumed, once they'd settled at the kitchen table with their coffee. 'Lover-boy Lance has left his wife and—'

'His wife left him,' Angie corrected.

'Do you know why?'

'There's another man, I gather. From what Lance said, there'd been more than one.'

'You're telling me that Mr Irresistible's wife has been having affairs?' Vanessa said sceptically. 'After only four years?'

Angie shrugged. 'Maybe she was a slut.'

'And maybe her superstud husband was so busy servicing every attractive female he came across, he didn't have time for the little wife back home.'

'He says he's not like that any more.'

'For heaven's sake, Angie, he had you flat on your back within an hour or two of meeting you again. That's pretty good going, don't you think? And hardly the action of a recently faithful husband.'

'It might very well be the action of a recently faithful husband,' Angie argued, her face flushing with indignation as Vanessa voiced her own fears out loud. The cold light of morning rather made one see things differently. 'If he was completely conscienceless, he wouldn't have stopped once he found out I was a virgin.'

Vanessa gave her a pitying look. 'You don't believe that any more than I do. He's merely exchanged a few seconds of passing pleasure for a whole night's worth of proper bonking. He gave you a line of bull, darling, and you fell for it.'

Angie put her mug down with a clank. 'Hey! *You* were one who said I should get myself laid, remember? Well, I'm going to. Tonight. And Lance is going to do the honours.'

Vanessa gave her another pitying look. 'You still love him, don't you? It's the only explanation for your putting yourself through this torture.'

'What torture? Lance makes love like a dream. I ought to know. I had an advance sample last night in his car.'

'He might make love like a dream but the afterwards will be a nightmare! Hell, Angie, you pined over one bloody kiss for nine years. Lord knows what one entire night's expert lovemaking will do to you!

On a scale of one for a kiss and ten for the real thing, you'll be a cot-case for ninety years!'

Tears suddenly flooded Angie eyes. 'You think I don't know that?' she choked out, jumping to her feet and running for the bedroom. She was already sobbing uncontrollably by the time she hit the unmade bed, face-down.

Vanessa wasn't far behind. 'Oh, dear,' she sighed, sitting down on the side of the bed and putting a sympathetic hand on her weeping friend's shoulder. 'You really should stop all that bawling. It's going to make your eyes red and puffy. Cinderella can be covered in chimney dust when Prince Charming arrives, but her eyes are never red and puffy. Look, don't take any notice of me. I'm probably just jealous. You go and bonk your brains out with him. Who knows? It might get him out of your system. Even if it doesn't, it might get *you* into *his*. Maybe, when the night is over, he won't want it to be over. Do you get my drift?'

Angie rolled over, blinking as rapidly as her heart was suddenly beating. 'Do you really think that's possible, Vanessa?'

'Hell, honey, if I were a guy and you presented yourself to me on a silver platter, I reckon I'd want to keep you on that silver platter for more than one miserable night. You're the genuine article, and genuine articles don't come along very often these days.'

Angie sat up and threw her arms around a startled Vanessa, hugging her fiercely. 'Oh, thank you for saying that!' she exclaimed excitedly. 'Thank you, thank you, thank you.'

'Lordie, Miss Claudie!' Vanessa said, extracting herself from Angie's fierce embrace. 'You are an emotional little thing under that cool exterior of yours, aren't you?'

Angie smiled as she dashed away her tears. 'Our family's rather given to hugging, that's all.'

'Does dear Lance know what he's getting tonight?' Vanessa asked drily.

Her question bewildered Angie. 'What do you mean?'

'Never mind,' Vanessa muttered. 'What are you going to wear for this momentous occasion?'

'I have no idea. Lance is picking me up at eleven.'

'Eleven!' Vanessa wrinkled her nose. 'Oh, yuk. There's nothing worse than doing it in the daytime. Takes all the romance out of it.'

Angie laughed. 'You are funny! But I don't think that's what Lance's plan is. He has some idea about my getting to know the new him first.'

Vanessa's eyebrows shot up. 'Really? That sounds promising.'

'I thought so too…at the time…'

'And now?'

'Now I just feel sick.'

'You can always back out. Ring him and say you've changed your mind.'

Angie shook her head vigorously from side to side. 'I could never live with myself if I did that.'

'Will you be able to live with yourself if this comes to nothing more than that kiss did all those years ago?'

'I'll have to, because there's no going back, Vanessa. And no changing my mind. I'll survive losing Lance again. I won't survive not doing this.'

'I suppose the experience will add perspective to your counselling abilities,' her flatmate said drily. 'My mother always said one should look for the plusses in every negative.'

'I doubt many women would rate sleeping with Lance a negative,' came Angie's equally dry retort.

'Really? I must get a gander at this god-like creature when he arrives to pick you up. Do let me answer the door.'

'Be my guest. My knees will be knocking by then.'

'Oh, no, they won't be. You'll sail out of here looking and acting as cool as a cucumber, because that's the way you are. Or at least seem to be on the surface.' A devilish gleam glittered in Vanessa's dark brown eyes. 'I'd sure love to be a fly on the wall later on when lover-boy takes you to bed. If he thinks he's getting a shy, quiet little virgin then he might be in for a shock or two. I suspect there might be a hot little number somewhere behind those prissy clothes you wear to school.'

'I wasn't exactly dressed prissily last night,' Angie reminded her friend.

'No, and look where it got you. Almost being raped in the front seat of a car!'

'I wasn't nearly raped at all. I was all for it till the last moment.'

'Which reminds me. Have a couple of glasses of champers or something equivalent before the real thing tonight. Relaxation is the name of the game, girl.'

'All right. I'll do that.'

'And I'll pop a few you-know-whats in your hand-bag in case Casanova has a memory lapse. Nothing kills passion more quickly than having to dash out to the chemist at the last moment.'

'Yes, Teacher.'

'Don't knock it, honey. I wish I'd had an under-standing flatmate to give me all this good advice be-fore I did it for the first time. There again—' she stopped to flash Angie a wicked grin '—I didn't have a flatmate at fourteen.'

'Fourteen!'

Vanessa shrugged. 'I always was a precocious child. Now, shouldn't you be hot-footing it into the shower? Time and tide waits for no man. Neither does man wait for woman.'

Angie was still smiling when she closed the bath-room door. But as she stripped off her pyjamas and saw her naked reflection in the vanity mirror, her smile faded.

A nice body wouldn't be enough to capture Lance's heart. He'd had enough nice bodies to last a lifetime. And proving to be a hot little number wouldn't im-

press, either. No doubt he'd had some women who
had been so hot they'd melted their satin sheets.

No, there was no point in Angie doing herself up
sexily today. Or in trying to outdo all his other lovers
in bed. She wouldn't be able to, anyway. It would be
like trying to win an Olympic medal at a sport she'd
only just taken up the week before the games.

But she could give Lance what perhaps he'd never
had before. A truly loving experience. A night full of
warmth and affection and genuine gratitude. For she
was indeed grateful to him. No matter what his mo-
tive, he was about fulfil part of her deepest dream—
the one she'd once expressed in the poem she'd given
him nine years ago.

Angie still hugged that secret dream to her heart,
and tonight—tonight, a small part of that dream
would come true.

CHAPTER EIGHT

ANGIE'S flat was on the second and top floor of a rather old building in North Sydney, in a handy street tucked away behind the main business district. It was not far from the station, but unfortunately without any view of the nearby harbour or bridge.

The block had twelve flats in all, four on each floor. Angie's was number eleven. Its living-room window overlooked the street below, which proved to be an asset if one wanted to spy on people arriving or leaving.

At five to eleven Vanessa took up her position behind the half-closed venetian blind.

'What kind of car does he drive?' she called out to Angie, who was still in the bathroom, deciding if she should wear her hair up or down.

'Black,' came back the answer.

'Yes, but what kind?'

'I have no idea. It's not a sports car, but it's sleek and foreign-looking.'

'With roomy bucket seats in the front,' Vanessa added drily.

'And tinted windows.'

'It's just pulled up outside.'

'It *has*?' Angie squawked, dashing out of the bathroom, holding her hair on top of her head.

Vanessa looked her up and down. 'I just hate people who can wear any old thing and still look fantastic.'

'This dress is not any old thing!' Angie protested. Made of a bright orange linen, it was halter-necked and very fitted, hugging her figure down to just above her knee. 'It cost two hundred dollars new.'

Admittedly, she had bought it a couple of years ago, and worn it to death. But it always made her feel good, and was the least prim and proper thing she owned, other than the green silk party number she'd worn the previous night. Angie was only human, and had decided in the end that she wanted to look sexy for Lance.

'Should I wear my hair up or down?' she asked in desperation.

'Up. With little wispy bits hanging around your face and neck. Not too tidy or tight, either. Loose is sexy. And earrings are a must. I've got just the thing. Oo-ee. Lover-boy just got out of the car—which is an Audi, by the way—and you're right. He's scrumptious!'

'What's he wearing?'

'A bluey grey suit. Wow, Angie, I've got the hots for him already.'

'Hands off, Vanessa. He's mine.'

Vanessa laughed. 'Do you honestly think he'd look twice at me with you in the same universe? I'll just go get those earrings—and those other things I promised. You whack some pins in your hair. Then when lover-boy arrives don't come out for a full five minutes.'

'Stop calling him "lover-boy",' Angie groaned. 'His name's Lance.'

'OK. Lance what?'

'Sterling.'

'It would be. Here's the earrings.' And she held out a pair of amber and gold creations which would hang to her shoulderblades.

Angie shook her head at them. 'No, Vanessa. They're too much. I'll just wear these simple gold drops, if you don't mind.'

'I don't mind, but just remember whose earrings you were wearing when you snaffled his attention last night.'

Angie declined telling Vanessa that Lance had also thought her a tramp of the first order last night, and that maybe the saucy earrings had contributed to that first impression. 'Maybe, but that was a party. This is daytime. Oh, God, there's the doorbell.'

Vanessa swanned off towards the door while Angie fled back into the bathroom.

Her hands shook as she pinned up her hair, resulting in the haphazard style Vanessa had suggested more by accident than design. Still, she felt surprisingly satisfied with the final result. She looked classy but sexy. Cool, yet subtly sensual.

Grace Kelly, with auburn hair.

Collecting herself with several deep steadying breaths, Angie finally found the courage to leave the sanctuary of the bathroom and face her destiny.

He looked as gorgeous as Vanessa had said, his almost dazzling glamour seeming out of place in their small and cheaply furnished lounge-room. He was standing with his back to the half-open venetian blind when she entered the room, his suit jacket open, his hands slung lazily into the depths of his trouser pockets.

The slats of sunlight coming through the window glinted a line of gold on his glossy head, and picked up the silk sheen in his expensive Italian suit. His shirt was the palest blue, his tie and kerchief a bold mixture of blues and yellows and greens in a splotchy design.

The only other time Angie had seen Lance formally dressed had been at his wedding, which wasn't the same as encountering it in one's own living-room at eleven in the morning. She realised with a suddenly sinking heart that she could have bought ten of her orange linen dresses with the money it had taken to buy that suit.

Lance's wealth had never bothered her before. But then neither had she harboured this kind of hope about him before. Now she saw his multi-millionaire status as a major hurdle in their ever becoming more than just transitory lovers. Girls like Angie Brown didn't marry men like Lance Sterling. At best, they became girlfriends of a sort.

Or mistresses…

Angie realised she was standing there frowning at him, and that Lance was frowning at her frowning at him while Vanessa was frowning at them both. Carefully placing that stupid dream of hers back where it belonged, she found a plastic smile from somewhere.

'You're very punctual,' she said crisply.

'And you're very beautiful,' he returned silkily, bringing a small sigh from Vanessa's lips.

Angie glared at her, then bent to pick up her cream handbag from where it was sitting on the coffee-table. It wasn't an exact match for her cream shoes, which hadn't bothered her earlier but now did. She wished she'd gone out and bought new shoes and bag. She wished she'd bought brand new underwear. She wished her earrings were real gold and not gold-plated.

Damn it all, she almost wished she were rich!

'Shall we go?' she suggested airily.

'Nice to have met you, Vanessa,' Lance said, extending a polite hand.

Vanessa did likewise. 'And you. So where are you two off to today?' she asked before Lance could propel Angie out of the door.

Angie found herself pulling away from the possessive and highly disturbing touch on her elbow to look into those brilliant blue eyes of his. 'Yes, where are we off to today, Lance?' she echoed, amazed at how calm and casual she sounded.

Vanessa was right. She *had* developed a rather controlled façade over her years living in Sydney, and while it was a good cover for feelings best hidden she wasn't at all sure that she liked it. Where had the simpler, more honest country girl gone to? Would *she* have wanted to be rich? Would the Angie of old have felt somehow inferior because her stupid damned shoes weren't exactly the same colour as her bag?

'I thought I might take you shopping,' he said, his sensually sculptured mouth curving back into a slight smile. 'I did promise to replace your dress, remember? Then I thought we'd go somewhere for a long lunch.'

'Oh, so Angie will be back for tea, will she?' Vanessa persisted, her own smile extremely naughty. 'It's my turn to cook, you see, and I need to know if it will be for two. Or maybe three?' And she threw Lance a quizzical look.

'I wouldn't be expecting Angie home for tea,' he returned with silky smoothness, the amused gleam in his eyes showing that he knew exactly what Vanessa was up to. 'I wouldn't be expecting her till very late tonight, actually. I've also made plans for this evening. You *are* free this evening, aren't you, Angie?' he directed straight at her, cleverly bypassing Vanessa.

'Yes,' was all she could manage. Dear God, why had she agreed to Lance picking her up this early? The day stretched ahead as hour after hour of sheer torture. She wasn't even sure she would enjoy the evening, when it finally came. Maybe by then she would be too nervous.

'Excellent,' Lance pronounced. 'Goodbye, Vanessa.'

'Goodbye? That sounds like we won't be seeing each other again.' Angie flinched at the cynical implication behind Vanessa's remark.

'Does it?' Lance drawled. '*Au revoir*, then. I'm sure that won't be the case.'

'I *hope* not,' she muttered, and Angie rolled her eyes at her behind Lance's back. Vanessa responded with an immediate but patently false smile. 'Well, off you go,' she gushed. 'And don't forget what I said about drinking, Angie.'

'I won't, Vanessa,' she bit out, taking Lance's arm and practically pulling him out of the flat before that mischief-maker said another word.

Lance gave a dry chuckle once the door was shut.

'What's so funny?' Angie almost snapped.

'Your friend. Anyone would think you were Little Red Riding Hood about to venture into the woods with the big bad wolf. What on earth did you tell her about me?'

'Only the truth.'

'Your version of the truth bears little resemblance to the real truth, Angie. Not that it's your fault. Bud's been feeding you a warped view of me for years. I told him so last night. I also told him that it had to stop.'

Angie sucked in a shocked breath. 'You didn't tell him you were taking me out today, did you?'

'No, though, damn it all, I was tempted to. The

only reason I didn't was because I'd promised you. Still, I knew I'd say something I'd regret if I stayed there, so I went to a motel for the night.'

Last night's visions of Lance and that blonde rolling around on a motel bed immediately flashed into her mind, and, try as she might, Angie couldn't get rid of them. *Or* the suspicion that Lance's reason for going to a motel for the night had nothing to do with a spat with Bud and everything to do with ridding himself of the frustration she herself had caused.

She continued walking down the stairs in a black silence, hating her doubts yet grabbing at them with a wild despair.

'You've gone all silent on me,' he said with a weary sigh. 'What is it, Angie? What have I done now?'

She stopped at the bottom of the stairs, gripping her handbag in tight hands as she turned to face him. 'Swear to me you didn't sleep with that blonde last night,' she cried brokenly. 'Please, Lance. Swear it!'

Angie was taken aback by the savage fury which swept into his eyes. When they heard a group of people coming down the stairs, Lance grabbed Angie's arm and bustled her outside, then over and into his car. Once he'd climbed in behind the wheel he swivelled to face her, his face full of bitter reproach.

'And if I did so swear?' he challenged. 'What would that prove? If I were the kind of person who would do that, then I would also have no compunction about lying. But if it makes you feel better, Angie, I do swear. I did not sleep with that blonde last night, or any other woman. To cover all contingencies, I also did not kiss any other woman last night,' he went on testily, 'or have sex with her, or have her go—'

'Stop!' she groaned. 'I…I believe you.'

'Do you, now? How nice.' Sarcasm dripped from every word and Angie cringed.

'Oh, God, Lance, I'm so sorry. Truly I am. I do believe you. I do! It's just that you're so attractive to women and I got so jealous when I saw you talking to that blonde, and…and…'

'And I'm still lumbered with my old superstud reputation,' he finished ruefully for her. 'God, but if I could only go back in time I'd go to some blasted monastery for my education rather than that uni. I have no excuses for my truly appalling behaviour during that time, except that I was a silly, spoiled young fool with more hormones than sense.

'But I *did* change in that regard, Angie. I stopped taking advantage of this empty talent I have for attracting the opposite sex. After uni I had girlfriends, not one-night stands. Helen was my only bed-partner during the year leading up to our marriage.'

'And during your marriage, Lance? Were you faithful to her?'

'I'd be lying if I said I was. But she drove me to it. She stopped sleeping with me over a year ago. I wanted her to have children, and she refused. Hell, I'd been wanting her to have children since the day we married. She compromised by saying she would have a baby after two years. Then she extended it to three. Finally, she refused altogether. I can't tell you how furious I was. She didn't trust me to use protection after that so she simply moved out of the bedroom till I supposedly came to my senses.'

'But why wasn't she on the Pill?'

Lance's laugh was cold. 'She told me it ruined her libido and made her put on weight. Like a trusting fool, I believed her. But, of course, the Pill is no protection against other hazards besides pregnancy—especially if one wants to be wildly promiscuous.'

'Helen started having affairs?'

'She'd been having them since shortly after our honeymoon. The private detective I finally hired to investigate her a couple of months ago showed me all the times and dates of her various daytime hotel assignations, dating back nearly four years. She ruthlessly but recklessly signed and paid for them all with the credit card I gave her. Sometimes, when business called me overseas, she gave the house staff time off and actually had her current lover to stay in the house with her. They made love in our marriage bed.'

Angie could only stare at Lance.

'When I showed her the report, earlier this week, she admitted she'd never loved me but thought that I would make her a very rich divorcee. At which point I left the house before I killed her. While I was gone she packed all her things and moved out.'

'Oh, my God, Lance, that's awful! And yet... almost incredible!'

'I can show you the report,' he said drily, 'if you don't believe me.'

'It's not that I don't believe you. Of course I do. I simply can't understand any woman marrying any man she doesn't love—or any woman married to you who would ever want another man.'

Now it was Lance's turn to stare, his startled eyes slowly melting as he reached over and stroked her cheek. 'You are so good for me, my darling girl. God, but if only all females were like you. If only—' He broke off to straighten, a deep frown creasing his high forehead as he appeared to drop deep into thought.

'Lance?' she asked softly at long last.

He snapped out of his reverie to smile over at her. It was the saddest smile she had ever seen Lance give anyone, and it made her heart bleed for him. People might think he had everything in life, but in fact he had nothing of real worth, if worth was measured by the values of family love and loyalty. Angie had long known that his parents had little time for him, and he didn't have any brothers or sisters. Angie suspected that his mother had stopped having children at once when she'd produced a male heir. She'd met the woman at Lance's wedding and had been struck by her cold snobbery.

Lance's wife had obviously never really loved him, either. From what Lance had said, it was likely she'd seen dollar signs from the moment she'd met the Sterling son and heir.

Angie had opened her mouth to tell him that *she*

loved him, when something held her back—some last, lingering worry which whispered that to tell him of such an enduring and almost blind love would be to give him great power over her. As much as Angie did admire Lance in many ways, his moral fibre had to have been corrupted by his background, plus that ghastly marriage.

'Let's not talk about Helen any more,' she said instead. 'Let's not talk about anything serious today. Let's just have fun.'

His answering smile was much more like the Lance she remembered. His perfect teeth sparkled, his blue eyes flashed, that cheeky and charming dimple of his dimpled cheekily and with great charm.

'Best suggestion I've had all year!' he pronounced heartily.

He drove over the bridge into the city, where he turned into the driveway of the Prince Hotel—one of the new boutique establishments springing up all over Sydney. Angie only recognised the place because she'd seen a small spot about it on the television recently. Described as a classic of old-world charm and grace, it was reputed to be scandalously expensive, and patronised only by the very wealthy or the very famous. Strict privacy was what they offered, plus discretion and red carpet service.

'Er…what are we coming in here for?' Angie asked hesitantly. 'Will we be lunching here?'

'No. I'm staying here.'

'Since when?'

'Since I rang and made a booking this morning. It's supposedly within walking distance of the shops and the theatres, not to mention the quay and Darling Harbour. It should make a perfect base for our activities today.'

Activities?

Angie had heard it called a lot of things but never…'activities'. An insane little giggle threatened to burst from her lips but she smothered it just in time and gave Lance what she hoped was a perfectly unreadable look. She must have succeeded for he frowned at her, the kind of frown a man gave a woman when he didn't know what was going on in her mind but would dearly have loved to.

'I thought you said you wanted to have fun,' he muttered. 'If that's the case, do you think you might try smiling at me?'

She did, and when he smiled back a warm wave of love rushed through her.

'That's better,' he said in a satisfied tone. 'Come on. Let's get out and go inside. The valet wants to park the car.'

Angie was all eyes as she climbed out, standing there gazing all around her while Lance instructed the pompously uniformed porter about his bag then gave the equally pompously uniformed valet his car keys. 'Have you stayed here before?' she whispered as Lance took her arm and guided her through the heavy glass doors.

'No. Never. And why are you whispering?'

'This is a whispering sort of place,' she said, still in hushed tones, at the same time glancing all around her with wide-eyed fascination at the rich wood-panelled walls, the plush red-carpeted floor, the deep leather chairs and the many bronze statues—all of old-fashioned-looking ladies in various stages of undress. Angie found the décor a little much, and while she could imagine a lot of men liking it, she didn't think it reflected Lance's taste. 'Er…why did you choose it?'

'Because it was the only hotel in Sydney where the honeymoon suite wasn't booked out for tonight.'

Angie ground to a halt, her stomach fluttering. 'The…the honeymoon suite?' She stared up at Lance, searching his face for an explanation.

'That's right,' he said, his voice as softly caressing as his eyes. 'I decided our first night together required something really special—something reflective of how I think about you and what you mean to me.'

A great lump filled her throat. Tears threatened, but she valiantly battled them away. 'That…that's very sweet of you, Lance.'

His low laugh had a drily cynical note to it. 'It's not sweet at all, Angie. I haven't been brought up to be sweet. I'm selfish and arrogant, and at times utterly ruthless. I'm pulling out all the stops to make sure you never forget tonight. Or me. If you thought I'd spoilt you for other men before then, believe me, by tomorrow morning you're going to be well and truly spoilt for other men for the rest of your life! Now, sit down over in that armchair,' he ordered, smiling an utterly ruthless but devastatingly attractive smile. 'I'm going over to check in. Then I'm taking you shopping!'

CHAPTER NINE

'YES, we'll take that one too,' Lance said from where he was sitting in a comfy winged chair, supervising Angie's try-ons and sipping the cup of coffee the staff had brought him. They were in a very exclusive fashion boutique in the Centrepoint Building where, naturally, Lance had been given first class treatment from the moment he walked in with Angie in tow. He was that kind of man.

Angie frowned, knowing that the gold brocade suit she was wearing cost a small fortune—much more than the black velvet dinner dress he'd just given the nod to. Angie had not minded the velvet number, as Lance *had* ruined her green silk dress last night and it wasn't too expensive. When he'd suggested she try on the brocade outfit, which had been highlighted in the display in the window, she had done so, thinking he was giving her an alternative choice to the velvet.

In truth, she *did* prefer it. The sleek straight skirt and hour-glass-style jacket suited her longish body to perfection, and the lowish V-neckline between the satin-edged lapels showed off her nice bust to advantage. Angie had fallen in love with it, till she glanced at the price tag in the changing-room.

Still frowning, she walked over to Lance and bent

down to whisper in his ear. 'Lance…this suit is very, very expensive. I couldn't possibly let you buy it for me.'

He replaced the coffee-cup in the saucer with a small sigh. 'Yes, you can,' he told her firmly, though in a discreetly low voice. 'You can do anything you want, Angie; *have* anything you want. You're with me today as my woman, and I am a very rich man. Indulge me, my darling. Let me pamper you and spoil you. It will give me great pleasure to dress you— almost as much as it will give me to undress you this evening.' This last remark was made with a not so discreet glance at the shadowed valley between her breasts.

Angie blushed fiercely as her head jerked up and their eyes met. 'You…you shouldn't say things like that,' she said, shaken by his calling her his darling, and very shaken by the images his other words had catapulted into her mind. A wicked heat started firing her blood and flushing her skin. Desire quickly became a throbbing pulse in her veins.

His smile was vaguely triumphant. 'Perhaps not,' he drawled. 'But I simply couldn't resist. I've never been with a female before who would react as you just did. It's enchanting. But then you *are* enchanting, sweet Angie. In every way…'

'I…I asked you not to call me that,' she said, trying to sound stern, but failing miserably.

'But why, when it suits you?'

He smiled, and she couldn't help it. She smiled back. 'You're a wicked man, Lance Sterling.'

'Well, you can't have everything, darling. Rich and good just don't go together.'

A fact which she'd already realised. Angie wondered if he was paving the way to turning her into his mistress. Perhaps he was already corrupting her, getting her used to things she could never afford but which he could continue to give to her provided she continued to give him what she would give him tonight.

'I'm not going to become your mistress, Lance,' she said, hoping that saying the words out loud would prevent the reality happening.

He seemed taken aback. 'Is that what you think this is?' And he waved down her expensively clad body with his free hand.

'Would I be wrong?' she challenged.

'You would,' he said sharply, but did not elaborate.

Angie's surprise quickly turned to bewilderment. 'Then, what is it?'

'It's fun, Angie.' He smiled an engaging though enigmatic smile. 'What you said you wanted today.'

'Fun,' she repeated blankly, till the penny suddenly dropped. Yes, of course! How silly of her! Nothing so serious and semi-permanent as making her his mistress.

Tonight, for all Lance's softly seductive words, was really just a one-night stand, dressed up to look like something else. His arrogant claim that he would spoil her for any other man was just that. An arrogant claim. It contained no promise of tomorrows. It contained nothing but the promise of a night she would never forget.

But oh, dear heaven, how she was looking forward to that night. Even now, as she gazed down at the handsome man draped elegantly over the chair before her, she wanted to beg him to stop this fiasco, to take her back to that honeymoon suite immediately. She did not want to waste another moment of her short time with him being dressed up like some Barbie doll, or eating a stupid lunch she had no stomach for.

'What if I told you I'm not finding this much fun?' she choked out. 'What if I told you that I'd much rather we... That I'd prefer to... That I want you to...to...' Her voice trailed away as she simply could not confess the desire now running rampant through her. But she must have still conveyed the shameful truth to him by her flushed cheeks and glittering eyes, by the way her lips stayed softly apart to allow the shallow panting caused by her rapidly beating heart to escape.

He stared up at her over the rim of the cup, holding her captive with his eyes and thrilling her with the sudden passion which blazed away in their brilliant blue depths. It was as though her bumbling confession had stripped away the cavalier façade he'd been wearing all day, and suddenly she saw what making love to her meant to him. She was both incredibly moved and incredibly turned on.

'Lance,' she breathed shakily, everything around him going out of focus, as it had the previous evening.

'Yes,' he rasped back. 'I know.' The cup clattered back into the saucer once more, and he seemed to have to drag his eyes away from her before rising slowly to his feet. 'The lady will take the outfit she has on,' he told the hovering saleslady in a brusquely commanding voice. 'She won't be changing back into her other clothes. Wrap her orange dress up with the black one. Here's my credit card.'

When he turned back to Angie she was actually trembling. A mixture of nerves and excitement had taken hold of her, making her feel sick with anticipation of what was to come. There was something incredibly thrilling about the unknown. Yet also something incredibly frightening.

When she flashed Lance a torn look, he took her arm within a steadying grip and steered her over to the sales desk. Five minutes later he was bundling her into a taxi for the short ride back to his hotel.

He seemed to know not to speak to her during this brief journey, or in the hotel lobby, or even on the lift ride which carried them up to the honeymoon suite. Angie was grateful for his silence, aware that she was incapable of making sensible conversation at that moment.

The lift doors opened, and before she knew it she was standing at a heavy wooden door while Lance inserted the key into its brass lock. For the first time her mind turned to what the honeymoon suite might look like. She wasn't sure what to expect after the décor downstairs, but it wasn't what met her eyes when Lance pushed open the door and ushered her inside.

Everything was white or cream or gold. White walls and furniture, cream carpet and curtains, gold lamps and cushions. There was quite a bit of glass too. All the table-tops were glass. One whole wall was glass, with a splendid view of the harbour bridge and surrounds. A huge crystal and gold chandelier hung from the ornately plastered and very high ceiling.

'Oh!' she gasped on entering, all carnal desire momentarily pushed to one side. 'What a lovely room!'

It was more than just a lovely room. It was a honeymoon suite to exceed all honeymoon suites. Gracious. Spacious. And touchingly romantic. Angie moved in somewhat of a daze through the large sitting-area into the dream of a bedroom. She stared at the huge white four-poster bed, with its flouncy lace valance, the pearly satin quilted spread and the multitude of small lacy cushions propped up against the four satin-covered pillows. Truly a bed fit for a bride on her wedding-night.

'You like it?' Lance said softly, coming up from behind her and curving his hands over her shoulders.

'It...it's exquisite,' she managed to get out in a strangled tone. Oh, God, she wasn't ready for this. She'd thought she was but she wasn't. She was petrified. Almost literally! She felt like a frozen piece of wood. Or a statue.

'Try to relax,' Lance suggested softly, and bent to kiss her on the neck.

Angie stiffened even further. 'I...I need to use the bathroom.'

Lance's lips left her constricted throat and she practically fled into the bathroom, shutting the door behind her.

For a long moment she leant against the door, her eyes shut, her heart thudding. When at last she opened her eyes it was to take in the largest bathroom Angie had ever seen. And the most opulent. Great expanses of creamy gold-veined marble, with three vanity bowls, an enormous shower, a sunken spa bath, plus a matching toilet and bidet.

She shook her head at the gold taps which were in the shape of cupids, the water being shot out of their arrows. She was also stunned by all the other provisions. Every conceivable complimentary item was supplied, from 'his and her' hairdryers, to toiletries, toothbrushes and tissues. A telephone hung on the wall next to the toilet. The towels and robes were plush and white, small satin cupids embroidered on various corners and pockets.

This was not a honeymoon suite for any old Darby and Joan from Woop-Woop, Angie conceded. This was a honeymoon suite for a multi-millionaire. One night here would cost a mint.

A new burst of nerves really did necessitate a brief using of the toilet and bidet, after which Angie got a grip on herself and returned to the living-area. There, she was amazed to find Lance in the process of filling two crystal flutes from a bottle of champagne. An elaborate silver ice-bucket was resting on a side-table, along with a huge platter of assorted fruits, cheeses and crackers. None of these things had been there, Angie was fairly certain, when they'd come in.

Or had she just not seen them? Had she been so full of blind passion when she'd first walked in that she'd been oblivious to such minor details? It was possible. She'd been ready for anything back then. Now, the time delay, plus a resurgence of nerves, was dampening her desires, making her worry that she might make a fool of herself.

Lance had had so many beautiful women—all undoubtedly more experienced than herself. His wife had been absolutely gorgeous—a young Elizabeth Taylor, with black hair, creamy skin and wide violet eyes. Helen's ultimately proving to be a slut did not lessen the fact that she must have known everything there was to know about pleasing a man in the bedroom. Lance would not have married her if he hadn't been very satisfied in that regard.

'All this came while you were in the bathroom,' he said, looking up and holding one of the flutes out to her. 'Compliments of the hotel.'

'Oh.' Angie was relieved that she hadn't been so besotted that she'd failed to see something so obvious. She also remembered what Vanessa had said about having a couple of drinks to relax before the big event, and came forward to take the proffered glass.

Lance smiled as he clinked her glass with his. 'To my beautiful bride,' he toasted, and everything inside her contracted anew, her own glass freezing in mid-air.

'Don't,' she whispered, her eyes dropping away to the floor lest he see the sudden tears pricking behind the lids.

'Don't, what?' he asked, a dark puzzlement in his voice.

'Don't make fun of me...of this...'

He swore, and her blurred gaze flew up to meet his stormy one. But once he'd witnessed her very real distress, he groaned. 'You think I would do that? There is no fun in this moment, Angie, only a very deep regret that I have waited this long. I should have done this years ago,' he murmured, curling his free hand round her neck and gently caressing it. His eyes moved from hers to her trembling mouth, then back down to where her breasts were rising and falling in a raggedly syncopated rhythm.

'God, but you *are* incredibly beautiful,' he said thickly, putting his own glass down and taking hers from her oddly frozen fingers. Odd, because the rest of her was quivering madly. 'I don't deserve you,' he said. 'But that's irrelevant at this vital stage. I must drink of this cup...' And he took a sip of the champagne. 'And so must you...'

He held the glass to her lips till they parted, then

tipped a little of the champagne inside, watching her through narrowed eyes as she swallowed, then as her tongue darted forward to lick up an escaping droplet.

'More,' he commanded huskily, and pressed the glass back to her lips, his hands shaking slightly. The crystal rim tinkled against her teeth, and her hands fluttered up to enclose his, both of them trembling as she helped him to tip more of the sparkling liquid into her mouth.

Angie had never experienced anything as blisteringly sensual as the feel of the champagne filling her mouth and throat, before she was forced to gulp it down. After the first swallow Lance filled her mouth anew, the action repeated till not one but both glasses were empty and Angie's senses were spinning. The champagne had hit her empty stomach with a quite savage force, fizzing into her bloodstream with incredible speed. She began to tingle all over, swaying on her high heels. Lance put the second glass back down, then scooped her up into his arms.

'My hero,' she said, then shuddered with a type of surrender.

He didn't say a word, simply carried her into the bedroom and laid her down on the snow-white quilt. She closed her eyes when he sat beside her on the bed and started undressing her. Her head—and the room—had begun to spin slightly. Not that she felt sick at all. She felt glorious, and very, very accommodating.

When he told her to sit up, she sat up. When he

told her to lift her bottom, she lifted her bottom. When he told her to lie back down, she lay back down.

It was only when she was down to her strapless bra and panties, and he appeared to have abandoned her, that her eyes flew open. But it seemed he'd only stopped to begin taking off his own clothes. His jacket and tie had been already discarded; his shirt was hanging open to the waist.

Their eyes locked—Angie's blinking, his guarded. 'You feeling OK?' he asked.

'I'm not sure,' she admitted, aware the room was not entirely steady.

'You'll be fine in a minute or two. You drank that champagne too quickly.'

'You made me,' she accused.

'Yeah, right, Angie. Just as I made you come here.' He smiled a wry smile, then stripped off the shirt, giving her an unimpeded view of the same beautiful bare chest which had fascinated her all those years ago.

Her mouth went dry as she contemplated its glorious contours, from the width of his shoulders to his well-defined chest muscles and the washboard flatness of his stomach. The thought that shortly she would be able to run her hands at will over his body sent little tremors running through her. Her nipples peaked hard inside her bra, poking at the cream satin which confined them.

Lance's gaze zeroed in on them as though they had

red lights built in. Seemingly entranced, he sat down next to her, his right hand reaching out to take possession of the closest peak between his thumb and forefinger. Angie's eyes widened as he rolled the nipple left and right. Such an action might have been painful if she'd been naked, but the nipple's satin covering softened the feeling to an exquisitely sharp sensation. When he squeezed gently, Angie betrayed her pleasure with a deeply sensual moan.

His right hand moved over to her other breast while his left took over with the already sensitised peak, and Angie sucked in a strangled breath at the doubled delight. When he slipped his thumbs under the bra to rub across her naked nipples her back arched away from the bed, her lips gasping apart.

He bent to cover those lips with his, sending his tongue between them, stunning her with his wildly urgent thrusting. Till then, he'd seemed so controlled, but now, suddenly, his own desire was off the leash.

Angie's body leapt with an answering savagery of her own. Her hands reached up to clasp tightly around his neck, keeping his lips hard upon hers, keeping that devouring tongue deep within her mouth. She thrilled to his moan of raw response, to the way he roughly rid her of her bra while he kissed her, his hands wonderfully brutal on her bare breasts. She didn't want him to be gentle with her. She wanted him wild!

When he finally tore his gasping mouth from hers, she groaned her disappointment. But she wasn't disappointed for long. His lips swept down her throat to her aching breasts, where he punished the already aching tips with broad sweeps of his tongue, giving each nipple a brief but barbaric suckling before abandoning them to move further down her body.

His mouth traced a feverish though tantalising path as he peeled her panties down her legs, kissing and licking her skin as he went but deliberately avoiding that molten area between her thighs.

But, despite his teasing, Angie knew what was coming, memories of the night before in the car making her stomach tighten in anticipation, a fierce heat racing through her veins as she recalled how it had felt when his mouth had made love to her down there. She would never forget the delicious screaming of each nerve-ending as he'd sucked on her most sensitive spot. She wanted to experience that screaming again. She longed for the wildly tormenting tension, the electrifyingly sharp sensations, the utterly addictive torture.

Tossing her panties aside at long last, he began working his way back up her legs, but this time with his hands only. To begin with, Angie felt slightly disappointed—she wanted his mouth—but by the time he reached the soft flesh of her inner thighs her heart was beating like a threshing machine. With a merciless and devastating expertise, he explored the moist valley between her thighs, teasing and tormenting her till her legs fell wider and wider apart, wanting more…asking for more…aching for more. Her eyes grew heavy with desire, the lids fluttering half closed on a low moan.

When his touch finally probed at her virgin entrance, her buttocks instinctively clenched tightly together. They lifted slightly from the bed, pressing herself with wanton abandon against his fingertips, inviting a deeper penetration. He obliged and she accepted him avidly, without hesitation, without discomfort.

Where she'd resisted last night, clamping her muscles in rejection, now she flowered open, wallowing in the less painful and much less threatening penetration. In fact, she could not get enough. When his mouth unexpectedly joined in, his tongue homing in on the swollen apex of her desire, everything quickly spiralled out of control and over the edge. Spasm after spasm racked her body, making her cry out, making her head thrash from side to side on the pillow.

It was the most intense, most incredible experience she had ever lived through, but it was over much too quickly. Her eyes flew open on a groan of dismay when his mouth and hands immediately abandoned her, leaving her lying there, awash with a mixture of ambivalent feelings. As much as her orgasm had been glorious, it was not really what she'd wanted. She'd wanted him joined to her, deep inside her, climaxing with her.

When Lance went to stand up, she sat bolt-upright and clutched at his arm, the desire to be as one with him still incredibly strong. There was an emptiness within her body and her soul that only he could fill.

'Don't leave me,' she cried.

He returned to kiss her trembling mouth and laid her back against the pillows. 'My sweet Angie,' he murmured. 'I'm not leaving you. I'm just going to undress.'

'Oh…oh, all right, then. But don't be long.'

'I'm not going anywhere. While you're waiting,' he added, smiling wryly, 'select one of these!' And he drew several small foil packets from his trouser pocket and dropped them nonchalantly on to her naked stomach. 'I couldn't make up my mind which kind might take your fancy so I brought one of each.'

His naturalness totally defused any embarrassment in Angie. She picked up each one in turn, the last one making her eyes snap up to his. '*Passion-fruit* flavoured?'

He grinned wickedly while he unzipped his trousers. 'It seemed an appropriate flavour. Besides, I seem to recall you were very partial to passion-fruit.'

Now Angie *did* colour with embarrassment. And perhaps something else. She knew she wouldn't need any incentive to do whatever would please him. She couldn't wait to explore his body as he'd explored hers, to kiss and possess every inch of him, to make him shudder with desire for her.

At last he was naked, and he was as magnificent as she'd known he would be, and wonderfully uninhibited about being nude before her, despite his intense arousal. He returned to sit beside her, dispensing with all the condoms but one, then doing what he had to do with a stunningly swift expertise which left Angie floundering. Before she could feel any real dismay, however, he bent to kiss her mouth again, caressing her body at the same time till she was trembling with desire for him.

'Now, close your eyes, my darling,' he whispered into her softened lips. 'Lie back and think of nothing but you and me, together in each other's arms, loving each other. We've both waited for this for a long time, and you deserve the very best...'

His words had the most powerful effect on her. Her love for him rose to fill her heart to overflowing. She reached for him, pulling him down, on to and into her body. Her cry was a cry of pure joy, despite the flash of pain. When he hesitated, she clung to him, pulling him deeper and deeper, till they indeed were one.

For a long moment they stayed that way, their mouths searching for each other to complete their union, their hearts beating to the same beat. He speared her fingers with his and lifted her hands high above her, stretching their upper bodies full-length till he covered every inch of her chest and arms with his. Again, he stayed that way for several moments, and she gloried in his weight upon her, a feeling of warm surrender washing through her.

When he began to move within her, her legs lifted automatically, to wrap high around him so that he might sink even more deeply into her, and quite instinctively she began to move with him. Their rhythm became a drum-beat, first in her head, then all through her body. *She* became the drum, stretched tighter and tighter, and Lance the drummer.

Soon the beat grew louder and faster. Angie became hotter and hotter, beads of perspiration breaking out all over her body. She feared everything inside her might burst if Lance didn't slow down, or stop. Then something did explode, deep within her, and suddenly everything was very, very right.

She cried out, and clung to him all the harder as spasms of the most exquisite delight racked her insides. They went on and on, squeezing and releasing Lance, till he too cried out. Angie felt the great shudders of his climax, and tears sprang to her eyes. Perhaps they were tears of release and relief, but she liked to think that they were tears of love. For she did so love this man who had just made the most beautiful love to her. Loved him so much that to contemplate life without him was unendurable.

Now the tears flowed fresh, and Lance was kissing them from her face, cradling her to him and stroking her back.

'Don't cry, my darling,' he told her. 'You were wonderful. You *are* wonderful. God, I wish I didn't have to go back to Melbourne tomorrow. I wish I could stay here and make love to you forever.'

CHAPTER TEN

ANGIE froze momentarily in his arms before sighing her resignation to his words. Lance's voicing the transitory nature of their affair should not have shocked or distressed her, since she'd known the reality all along. But it *was* hard to reconcile reality with what they had just shared. To Angie it had been an out-of-this-world experience—so damned wonderful, in fact, that she'd begun to harbour stupid hopes again, romantic fool that she was!

She sighed again, and Lance's head lifted.

'Are they sighs of satisfaction, exhaustion, or something else?' he asked.

She smiled softly and reached up to comb his hair back from his forehead with her fingers. 'What do you think?' she said.

'I don't know,' came his pensive answer. 'That's why I'm asking.'

Angie felt slightly flustered by the question, a nervous laugh escaping from her lips. She foresaw their having an argument if she started telling him how much she loved him, and how much she wanted to be a part of his life on an ongoing basis. If all she was ever going to have with Lance was the rest of today and tonight, she wasn't about to do or say anything to spoil their short time together.

'All three, I guess,' she said. 'I'm very satisfied, very exhausted, but also very disappointed.' This last bit she delivered with a softly seductive pout.

It threw him. 'Disappointed?'

'Yes. I'd like you to be able to stay and make love to me forever too. But if you have to go back to Melbourne tomorrow then that's that. We still have the rest of today and tonight, don't we? Gosh, Lance, I wouldn't have left it this long if I'd known sex was so fantastic. Though perhaps it's the man I'm with who's fantastic. You're an incredible lover—do you know that?'

He was frowning down at her and she wondered what she'd said that was wrong. He muttered something under his breath, then abruptly withdrew, making her gasp. Desolation swept in at the empty feeling he left behind, not just in her body but in her soul. Her heart sank ever further when he rolled from her, stood up, then strode off into the bathroom.

Clearly she'd said something to offend him. But what?

The blackest depression descended while she listened to the bathroom sounds—the flushing of the toilet, then the turning on of taps. But when the taps remained on, she began to frown. When Lance wrenched the door open, standing there naked and glowering, she sat up. 'What is it?' she said. 'What have I done? Why are you mad at me?'

'Well you might ask,' he growled, and stalked over to haul her unceremoniously up and over his shoulder like a sack of potatoes. 'We're going to have a spa bath together, Angie Brown. And while we're in there, we're going to talk.'

'Talk?' she squeaked, all the breath having been knocked out of her body.

'Yeah, *talk*, lover,' he snarled as he carried her into the bathroom, both his arms clamped firmly around her thighs and buttocks. 'What did you think? That you'd add an underwater screw to your tally of new experiences for today? Perhaps you'd like me to screw you in the shower as well, or on the floor, or up against the vanity? Mirrors can add a real dimension to sex, you know. Oh, yes, I forgot... We still have the passion-fruit-flavoured experience to go as well. Hell, I'm really looking forward to that one. Make it good and I'll dash out for some strawberry as well!'

'Why, you...you...' She began to pummel his bare buttocks with balled fists. 'I'll have you know that—'

She broke off with a squeal when he dragged her off him and dumped her into the hot frothing bath, bubbles and water splashing up the walls and on to the floor.

'You'll have me know what?' he ground out, plonking himself down in the furthest corner of the bath away from her and crossing his arms.

Angie glared at him over the expanse between them. 'You're a damned hypocrite, Lance Sterling,' she stated, lifting her chin in cool outrage. 'It's all right for you to have sown your wild oats but I'm not even allowed one night's wild oats without your looking down your nose at me.'

'That's right. Because you're *not* me. You're my sweet Angie, and I want you to stay that way.'

'Oh, piffle!'

'*Piffle*?' he bellowed.

'Yes, *piffle*!' she repeated, just as loudly, folding her arms as well and curling her top lip at him. 'I've never heard such a load of rubbish in my whole life! You were all for bringing me here and deflowering me, Lance, and now, suddenly, just because I really liked it and want a whole lot more, you've gone all prim and proper. What is it? Conscience getting the better of you all of a sudden? Or are you just sorry that you have to go back to Melbourne and some other man might get the benefit of your splendid initiation?'

'You're not to sleep with any other man,' he growled. '*Ever*!'

'Really? And how do you aim to stop me?'

'By making you my wife!'

Angie was staggered, as much by Lance's unexpected announcement as by her immediate and furious rejection of the idea. 'And what makes you imagine that I'd even *consider* marrying you?'

'Because you love me!' he said, blue eyes blazing.

No mention of his loving her, she noted bitterly.

That's because he doesn't, that dark voice in her

head whispered. His offer of marriage is just a means to an end. You in his bed. Exclusively.

Her laugh carried disbelief at his presumptuous arrogance. 'You have to be joking. As I said last night, Lance, how could I possibly love a man I don't even know? I had a crush on you once, and there's still a chemistry between us. But that's not love.'

'Who says it isn't?'

'Well, even if it *is* a form of love—and I question that—it's not the kind which lasts. It's certainly not the kind that makes a good foundation for marriage.'

'Is that your final answer?'

Was it? Panic raced in as the reality of what she was doing hit her. The man she loved had asked her to marry him and she'd just turned him down. Her indecision turned to anguish. How *could* she blindly commit her life to Lance when what she'd said was true? She didn't know him. Not as yet, anyway.

Gathering all her common sense and courage, she ground out, 'For now, it is.'

'And in the future?'

She swallowed convulsively. 'That's up to you, Lance. You might try working on winning my love and letting me get to know you better. I'm sure what I feel for you could easily turn to true love, given the chance.'

'I see,' he said thoughtfully.

'Do *you* love *me*?' she asked, and held her breath. Their eyes clashed and his face hardened. 'I'm not in the habit of telling women I love them after they've just rejected me.'

'But I haven't rejected you. I've told you to work at winning me, if you really want me. The trouble with you, Lance, is that you've had everything given to you on a silver platter. You must learn that some things don't come easily.'

'You were pretty easy today,' he snapped.

'And so were you,' she countered.

They glared at each other and slowly, very slowly, Lance's mouth curved back into a smile. 'You're turned into a tough little cookie, haven't you?'

'No, Lance, I've just grown up.'

'And very nicely too,' he said, his eyes dropping to her breasts, which weren't totally covered by the bubbles. Angie was irritated to feel her nipples respond. She gulped when Lance closed the distance between them, stiffening when he curled a soapy hand around her neck and started drawing her mouth towards his.

'What…what do you think you're doing?' she said, despising her voice for shaking on her.

'Exactly what you told me to do. I'm setting about winning you.'

'And you think this is the way?'

'Hell, Angie, a man has to use whatever limited talents he's got in a situation like this. You yourself said I was an incredible lover. I guess I have to believe you, because my Angie wouldn't lie. She's as honest as the day is long…'

The fingers caressing her throat gradually exerted enough pressure to close the small distance between their mouths. It was a lightly teasing, impossibly tantalising kiss, an annoyingly effective kiss. Angie yanked her head back and he chuckled ruefully. 'Hopefully, this day will prove to be *very* long, because I can see I've still got a lot of winning to do…'

Angie lay in bed on her side, watching Lance's chest rise and fall in the steady rhythm of sleep. Her own chest rose, then fell in a weary sigh. The light trickling through the curtained window showed that dawn wasn't very far away.

'Well, Lance,' she murmured to his unconscious form. 'You've won. I know now I can't risk letting you go back to Melbourne today without me, can't risk your never asking me to marry you a second time, can't risk that I might never lie like this with you again…'

She sighed another soul-shattering sigh and rolled on to her back, fearful of her future if she married this man. Would he be faithful to her? Would he make a good father? Would he share his life with her in every way, like her father did with her mother?

For that was what she wanted. Not an empty high society marriage, where the wife was little better than a social hostess. She also wanted her children always with her, not sent off to some toffee-nosed boarding-school. She definitely wanted her husband to come home every night, not to be jetting off all the time on so-called overseas business trips.

Angie accepted unhappily that she might never have all that if she became Mrs Lance Sterling. The kind of marriage he would offer her would probably prove to be hell. But not to become Lance's wife would be condemning herself to an even worse hell.

She closed her eyes and contemplated that alternative fate. Never to feel his arms around her again, or his lips on hers, or his body blended with hers. Never to hear the wonderfully seductive words he'd whispered to her over and over.

'You're so beautiful...I adore you...I've always wanted you...I'll always want you...I'm crazy about you...'

Lance had undoubtedly pulled out all the stops each time they'd made love during the long day and the long, long night. He'd spent limitless time on foreplay, always making sure that she was so aroused by the time they moved on that she would agree to whatever demands he'd made of her, and whatever position he'd suggested. When his supply of protection had been exhausted he hadn't stopped making love to her, he'd simply stopped seeking satisfaction for himself. He had seemed to gain as much pleasure from seeing her climax as from having one himself, although, in hindsight, Angie doubted that was so. It had simply been his way of corrupting her further to his will. Of totally seducing, then winning her.

And how well he'd succeeded, she conceded with

bittersweet realisation. She'd told him proudly that some things would not come easily. What a laugh that was! She obviously hadn't anticipated her own sexual weaknesses.

The sound of the telephone ringing beside the bed startled her. Who could it be? The only person who knew she was here was Vanessa, Angie having called her flatmate the previous evening to tell her where she was and that she wouldn't be home that night. Vanessa hadn't sounded at all surprised, though Angie had been relieved that Vanessa was on her way out on a date and didn't have time for more questions.

'Answer it,' Lance mumbled beside her. 'Maybe the hotel's on fire.'

Angie reached for the receiver. 'Yes?' she said, a frown on her face and in her voice.

'That you, Angie?'

Bud! Oh, God, it was Bud! Angie clamped her hand on the phone and groaned.

'Who is it?' Lance immediately demanded, propping himself up on one elbow.

'Bud,' was all she could manage.

Lance's swear-word told it all.

Angie gulped and lifted her hand. 'Yes, it's me,' she said simply.

'Gees, Angie, I couldn't believe it when Vanessa told me where you were and with whom. I can't tell you how disappointed I am in you, and how disgusted I am with Lance.'

Angie's mind began racing. Vanessa would never

have told Bud where she was and with whom unless there was a real emergency. Certainly not at this hour of the morning. She would have made up some excuse for her friend. 'Never mind the lecture, Bud,' Angie said impatiently. 'What's happened? What's wrong?'

'Mum's had a heart attack,' he said bluntly.

Everything inside of Angie seized up with shock. Her mother had had a heart attack? But she was only forty-eight years old. It didn't seem possible.

A sick pounding began in her temples, and her heart.

'She...she's not dead, is she? God, Bud, don't tell me she's dead,' she cried.

'No. She's not dead. But she's in hospital. Dad says it's still touch and go.'

Angie broke down in a flood of tears, Lance taking the receiver out of her suddenly shaking hands.

'This is Lance, Bud,' she heard him say. 'Angie's too upset to talk. What's all this about?'

Angie still could not believe it. Her mother... maybe dying. What would she do if she died? What would Bud do? And Dad? Dear God, Dad wouldn't be able to cope. Not at this stage. It was too soon. A hundred years too soon!

'For pity's sake grow up, Bud, and get your priorities right,' Lance suddenly snapped. 'What in hell does it matter if Angie and I spent the night together when your mother might be dying? Now, get your butt into your car and start driving up there. And don't damned well speed! It won't do your dad any good if you wrap your stupid bloody neck around a tree.'

Angie blinked at the forceful tone in Lance's voice. She was surprised, and impressed, despite everything. He was normally so easygoing and laid back in his dealings with Bud. Crises sometimes brought out the best or the worst in people. It was clearly bringing out the best in Lance.

'No, don't waste time coming in here to pick Angie up,' he resumed, in that same masterful tone. 'I'll drive her up there myself. And you'll keep your mouth shut about Angie and me if you know what's good for you. If you say one derogatory word about us to your parents, I'll skin you alive. You've pushed our friendship as far as I can take it this weekend, Bud, and I won't take any more!'

He reached over Angie and slammed the receiver down, his tough expression melting at the sight of her tear-stained face. 'My poor darling,' he crooned, taking her in his arms and rocking her gently back and forth. 'I know what your mother means to you…to all of you. She's a grand woman.'

Angie was touched by his sympathy, and had to battle not to break into further sobs. Eventually, and reluctantly, she extricated herself from the comfort of his embrace.

'You…you'll really drive me all the way up there, Lance?' she asked. 'Don't you have to go back to Melbourne today?'

'I should, but I'm not going to. How could I possibly leave you at a time like this? You need me, Angie.'

Her eyes filled again. 'Yes…yes, I do. Lance, I—'

'No,' he cut in abruptly. 'Don't say any more. This isn't the right time. You're all emotional at the moment, and what you feel might not be real. Now, pop up and have a shower, love, and I'll order us some breakfast. I dare say you'll want to drop in at your flat on the way through to pick up some clothes, so shake a leg. Time might be of the essence.'

Lance's last remark sent Angie's mind flying back to her mother, lying ill and possibly dying in hospital. The thought that she might never see her mother alive again sent her hurrying out of bed and into the bathroom.

Less than an hour later, she was letting herself into her flat. As she walked into the living room the clock on the wall said twenty-five past six.

'Is that you, Angie?' Vanessa called from the bedroom.

'Yes. It's only me.'

Vanessa appeared, bleary-eyed and nightie-clad. 'I…I hope you're not mad at me,' she said worriedly. 'I wasn't going to tell that pompous brother of yours where you were, but when he told me about your mother I just had to.'

'Of course you did.'

'Where's Lance?'

'He's waiting for me in the car. He's going to drive me up home.'

'I suppose this isn't the right time to ask you how it went with you two?'

'No,' Angie returned stiffly. 'It isn't.'

Vanessa nodded. 'Is there anything I can get you? A cup of coffee or anything?'

'No, nothing.'

'I hope your mum pulls through,' she said, hovering while Angie stripped off and pulled on some white shorts and a black and white striped top.

'I hope so too,' she said, slipping her feet into a pair of black sandals.

'She always sounds so nice on the phone.'

'She is.'

'My mum's a right bitch, and I still love her.'

Angie's chin started to wobble.

Vanessa came forward and put her arms around her. 'It's all right, sweetheart. Cry. You don't have to be brave around me.'

Angie cried.

Ten minutes later, she was back in Lance's car and they were speeding north.

CHAPTER ELEVEN

'WHAT exactly do you do, Lance?'

His blue eyes whipped round at her question. They'd been travelling in virtual silence for nearly an hour, the only sound in the car some faint music from the radio.

'You don't have to talk for the sake of talking,' he said, returning his eyes to the road ahead.

'I realise that. I want to know. Bud told me once you worked in the export division of Sterling Industries. But what exactly does that entail?'

He slid her a sharp glance. 'Then you don't know?'

'Know what?'

'I moved on from that position twelve months ago. I now run Sterling Industries. I'm the managing director.'

Angie blinked her astonishment. 'No. I didn't know. I...I naturally thought your father occupied that position.'

'He did. Theoretically. Unfortunately, he hadn't been a hands-on CEO for many years, and Sterling Industries was beginning to suffer. His choosing to live in Sydney wasn't conducive to good management, considering all the companies' head offices are in Melbourne. But that was my mother's doing. She refused to live in Melbourne, and what she wanted, she got. By the time I took over, Dad's neglect plus the recent recession had put some areas of the business into deep trouble. I've been lucky enough to turn things around and we're now in a position to take advantage of the growing economy.'

Angie was both surprised and impressed. 'So how did you come to take over, Lance? Did you talk your dad into taking early retirement?'

'No. He died.'

Angie sucked in a shocked breath.

'It was in all the papers,' he added. 'The business section, that is.'

'I don't read the business section very often,' she murmured.

'I had no idea you didn't know. Bud knew, because he rang me at the time. I presumed he must have told you.'

'No. He didn't. He never mentioned it. Oh, God, I…I'm so sorry, Lance. You must have thought me very rude for not contacting you, or sending a card or something. How did your dad die? Had he been ill?' She recalled a tall, handsome man at Lance's wedding who'd not looked a day over fifty, although he had probably been older.

'Yes. Very ill. He had cancer of the pancreas and liver. There was nothing the doctors could do. He died less than three months after the original diagnosis.'

'How awful for you all. Your poor mother must have been devastated.'

'Oh, absolutely,' came his caustic reply. 'So devastated that she had to take herself off around the world to recover—her trip starting the day after the funeral. Last month she became Mrs Jonathon Winthrop the third. Fortunately, for me, Mr Winthrop lives in Texas, and can't travel due to some rare blood disease he has. I would say the next time I see my darling mama will be at my new step-papa's funeral. Though maybe not,' he added with savage sarcasm. 'If I'm a minute or two late I'll probably miss her. She'll have moved on by then.'

Angie was about to defend his mother with some soothing platitude but decided not to. She hadn't liked the woman—had despised her, in fact—and didn't blame Lance one iota for feeling the way he did. She'd been a cold and unloving mother, and, it seemed, a miserable wife—a beautiful but cold bitch, whose priorities in life were money and social status.

'I see,' was all she said, which brought another sharp look.

'Yes, you would,' Lance said, admiration in his voice. 'Any other woman would have made some inanely sympathetic remark and not meant a single word of it. But not you, Angie. You're your mother's daughter. Straight down the line. You've no idea how much I appreciate that. A man would always know where he stood with you. There'd be no deceptions. No lies. No bull.'

She felt warmed by his compliments, yet perturbed at the same time. What she wanted was the same from Lance. No deceptions. No lies. No bull. Ever!

'Then tell me what you do, Lance,' she insisted. 'Give me a run-down of a typical day in the life of Lance Sterling. Or, better still, a typical week.'

He slid a wry smile her way. 'Ah, that sounds like Angie Brown, psychologist and counsellor, taking over. This *is* the way you people get to know your patients, isn't it? By getting them to tell you about themselves. Maybe we should pull over and I could lie down in the back seat and pretend it's a couch.'

'And maybe you should just keep driving and answer my questions.'

He sighed. 'You might not like the answers.'

'I'll risk it.'

She didn't like the answers at all. She was appalled by them. Lance's normal daily schedule was horrendous. He worked eighteen-hour days during the week, with little time for anything else. Then, at the weekend, he seemed to be still working, even when he was playing golf or going to dinner or the theatre. They were business rather than social engagements. She began to appreciate where his marriage might have gone wrong. And said so.

'Ah, but you forget,' he argued back. 'For the first three years of my marriage I didn't hold this gruelling position. I had plenty of time for my marriage, and my wife. For the first two years whenever I went overseas Helen went with me.'

Angie ignored the stab of jealousy this evoked to concentrate on the facts Lance was relaying.

'By the time my father died, my marriage was already on the rocks. Helen was refusing to accompany me just about everywhere. She'd started refusing to sleep with me. She lived her own life and went her own way.'

'I must be honest, Lance,' Angie said painfully. 'Your present lifestyle is not conducive to a happy family life, even if your wife loved you.'

'Is this still Angie the counsellor speaking? Or Angie the woman considering my proposal of marriage?'

'Both.'

'So you see no hope for us, if I continue as managing director of Sterling Industries?'

'I...I won't marry that man,' she stated bravely. And meant it.

Lance must have heard the conviction in her voice, for he swore under his breath. 'Would you become that man's mistress?' he asked brusquely, slanting her a narrow-eyed look.

Angie had never felt so dismayed in all her life. Or more disappointed. She should have known that this would be Lance's next move. His aim, after all, was not so much to install her as his loving wife, but as a permanent bed-partner.

'Well?' he persisted harshly. 'Would you?'

Angie gulped. 'Yes, I probably would,' she confessed with a bitter honesty. But she refused to meet his eyes. She felt too ashamed.

For being a man's mistress was based on lust, not love. It wasn't a real relationship. Lance was offering her sex, and nothing more. Love didn't come into it.

Yet it was love which would propel her into such a role. A love which refused to die. A love which could make her untrue to herself, and the values she had been brought up with.

The most awful silence descended on the car.

Angie kept her head turned away from him and the miles flew past. They stopped only once, and briefly. Lance drove on and on—not speeding, but pushing the car to the limit all the time. The countryside grew browner, and Angie saw first-hand the drought that her father had been complaining about all year.

A good farmer, Morris Brown had made enough money to send both his children to university in Sydney, but while he could protect his crops from disease there was little he could do about the lack of rain. Luckily the Brown farm was bounded on one side by a river, but even that was down to a trickle in parts.

Not that her father would be worrying about drought at this moment, Angie conceded unhappily. His mind would be on other worries. As were her own.

'Am I to take you home?' Lance asked at last as they came into the main street of Wilga, which was fairly deserted at noon on a hot December Sunday. 'Or do you want to go straight to the hospital?'

'To the hospital. There might not be anyone at home.'

'Which way, then?'

Angie gave him directions and soon he was parking his car in the hospital car park. The heat blasted Angie as she opened the door, a testimony to the car's excellent air-conditioning. Thankfully, the hospital was air-conditioned as well.

It was a fairly modern building, extensions and renovations having been made only two years ago—not so much because the town of Wilga was growing, but because the hospital had to service a large area. Recent government cutbacks had forced several smaller hospitals and clinics in adjoining towns to close, which meant that patients were sent to the Wilga hospital from up to a hundred miles away.

'There's Bud's car,' Angie pointed out on their way through the car park. 'Oh, and there's Dad's utility!' She wasn't sure if this was good news or bad. Were they all at the hospital because her mother was still deathly ill? Or because she was better and they could talk to her? Either way, it did seem likely that Nora was still alive. Angie desperately hoped so.

Lance placed a supportive hand on her shoulder as they pushed through the heavy glass doors which led into Reception. 'She's a fighter, your mum,' he said soothingly. 'She'll be all right.'

But Angie was worried. Even if her mother pulled through this attack, she could see further health problems down the road. The doctor had told her mother years ago to lose weight because of her high blood pressure, but Nora hadn't seemed able to give up the rich foods she loved. Angie had no doubt that this had been a contributory factor in her mother's coronary. She also doubted whether Nora would take a blind bit of notice if told to go on a special low-fat diet.

Her voice was shaking when she asked the woman behind the reception desk about her mother. 'Mrs *Nora* Brown,' Angie repeated. 'She…she had a heart attack. I'm her daughter. From Sydney.'

The woman's smile brought some welcome reassurance. 'Oh, yes. I had your brother and father in here not long ago. Mrs Brown's been moved from Intensive Care to a general ward so I think you can take that as good news. She's in Ward C, room ten. You take the lifts over there to level three, turn right and follow the signs.'

Angie almost burst into tears with relief. Somehow, she held on, but her 'thank you' was choked out, and she was blinking madly as she hurried over to the lifts.

Room ten in Ward C was a private room, though small. When Angie went in, her mother appeared to be asleep, lying grey-faced in the white hospital bed. Angie's father was sitting by her side, holding her hand. Bud was standing at the small window, looking out at the limp trees beyond. Both men's eyes snapped up to hers as she entered, her father's brightening, Bud's still full of reproach.

'Angie's here,' Morris Brown whispered excitedly to his wife, and her eyes shot open.

'Angie,' her mother rasped, in a voice so hoarse and shaky that Angie almost broke down. When her mother held out her hands to her, she succumbed to those long-threatening tears and threw herself into her mother's arms.

'There, there, Angie, love,' her mother crooned, stroking her daughter's hair. 'I'm all right. It'd take more than a silly old heart flutter to kill me.'

'Heart flutter, my foot,' her husband rebuked, but gently. 'You'd have been as dead as a doornail if I hadn't got you in here as quick as I did.'

'What an exaggerator your father is, Angie,' Nora said, lifting her daughter's tear-stained face up and wiping away the wetness with the bedsheet. 'All I had was a little clot stuck in the wrong place for a little while. The doc says the ECG shows no lasting damage.'

'The doc also said that if she doesn't take herself in hand where her diet is concerned she might not be so lucky the next time.'

'Diet, diet, diet,' Nora sighed. 'That's all I've been hearing about ever since I woke up. I think diet is the most offensive four-letter word ever invented.'

'"Dead" is worse,' Bud grumbled. 'For pity's sake, Mum, you have to do what the doctor said. Diet does not mean starve. It means eating different things, that's all.'

'Oh, piffle!' she scorned.

'So that's where she got that word from,' Lance

muttered, from where he was standing just inside the room.

Nora Brown's eyes turned to him for the first time. 'Well, Lord be praised, if I didn't know better I'd think that was Lance Sterling over there! Angie, tell me I'm not seeing things.'

Angie sat up straight and threw a wry smile over her shoulder at Lance. 'I wish I could, Mum, but I'm afraid you're quite right. It is Lance. He turned up at Bud's birthday party on Friday night, like the pro-verbial bad penny, and was still in Sydney when the news about you came through. He was kind enough to drive me up here.'

Angie watched the wheels in her mother's intuitive head start going round, but she was darned if she was going to explain how Lance had come to be on the spot in the early hours of this morning.

'Well, well,' was all her mother said, but it spoke volumes to anyone who knew her. She stared at Lance, then at a suddenly blushing Angie, then back at Lance again. 'That was extraordinarily kind of you, Lance. Now, come over here, you handsome hunk, and give your second-best girlfriend a hug.'

Lance laughed, then did just that. 'Hello, Mrs Brown,' he greeted her warmly. 'Glad to see you haven't changed.'

'Can't say the same for you, my lad. You look mighty peaky. What you need is a good night's sleep and some fresh country air. Why don't you stay up here at the farm with Dad for a while?'

'I'd love to, Mrs Brown, but I have urgent business back in Melbourne to attend to tomorrow, which really can't wait. I'll have to drive back to Sydney first thing tomorrow morning, then take a plane.'

Angie contemplated telling her parents about the death of Lance's father, then decided it was hardly the time or the place.

'Pity,' Nora said. 'You young people don't know how short life is. Don't waste the one you have doing things that don't make you happy. And don't keep putting off doing the things you know you should have done years ago.'

Angie might have imagined it, but she thought her mother was directing a definite message at Lance with those last words.

'Scares like the one I've just had rather make one reassess life,' she went on. 'Dad and I have decided to go on that holiday we've been putting off for years—haven't we, Dad?'

'We certainly have, Mother. Hang the expense. *And* the overdraft.'

A hatchet-faced nurse with a bosom like the bridge on a battleship bustled in at that moment and ordered all visitors out, putting paid to any more conversation about holidays or wasted lives.

'Doctor says Mrs Brown is to rest,' Sister Sourpuss stated firmly when Angie's dad objected. 'And that includes you, Mr Brown. You need some rest as well.'

'The chooks and dogs need feeding anyway,' Nora

reminded him. 'I'll see you tonight, perhaps?' she said, looking at Sour-puss for permission.

That gesture alone showed just how much this attack had dented Nora's confidence. She normally never looked for permission to do anything from anyone. Still, old Sour-puss would have a deflating effect on just about anyone, Angie thought.

'I suppose you can have visitors tonight,' came the grudging concession. 'But only for an hour or so.'

Angie hated saying goodbye after so little time. Neither did she like leaving her mother in the hands of such a tyrant, but she could see the sense in her mother resting. Her father looked tired too. Wrecked, in fact. No doubt he hadn't eaten properly since her mother's attack and might need looking after himself.

She decided then and there not to go back to Sydney with Lance in the morning. She would stay and look after her father for a while. The school wouldn't fall apart at this time of the year if she had a week off—all the Year Twelve students had already left, and in two weeks the summer break would begin.

She would probably have to return the following week to tidy things up. And, given the situation with Lance, she might even have to hand in her resignation. She assumed that becoming his mistress would necessitate a move to Melbourne. Much as she didn't want to move to Melbourne to live, she'd passed the point where such considerations mattered. She would go wherever Lance was, to be with him as much as possible. End of story.

'Why don't you take Dad home, Bud?' she suggested to her brother as they all walked along the hospital corridor. 'Lance and I'll buy some take-away food and follow you as quickly as we can.'

'Fair enough,' came his curt reply. 'Get plenty of it, though. I'm damned hungry.' He stalked off, his body language telling its own story. Clearly they were not yet forgiven for the horrendous transgression of becoming lovers.

'I'll talk to him,' Lance said.

Angie sighed and shook her head. 'I doubt it will do any good. He's very angry with me.'

'No. He's very angry with *me*. And with good reason.'

She halted, her head snapping round to stare up at him with questioning eyes.

'That summer,' he explained with a weary sigh, 'after we got back to uni, Bud had some photos developed that he'd taken of all of us during my stay at the farm. They showed in living colour what he hadn't noticed in the flesh; that you and I had… feelings…for each other. He accused me of having already seduced you. I assured him that I hadn't, but he still went right off his brain. He told me if I ever touched you he'd kill me. He pointed out how young you were, and how innocent. He made me see you deserved a whole lot better than a cad and a spoiled bastard like me. Frankly, Angie, I agreed with him. I still do. And so do you. That's why you won't marry me.'

Angie was shaking her head and trying not to cry. So that was what had happened all those years ago...

'But I'm not as bad as Bud's made me out to be,' Lance added ruefully. 'I think I might even be redeemable. I just hope it's not too late.'

Angie looked up at him again, frowning her confusion at his cryptic remarks. 'Too late for what?'

'Too late to win what I want,' he said seductively, the brilliant blue of his eyes darkening as they caressed her. 'You, Angie. I want you...' And his mouth bent to hers.

She flinched back from his kiss in the end, frightened by his growing sexual power over her. For she wanted him back—right now and in the most basic way. How could she possibly want him like that? *Here*, of all places, with her mother lying ill down the hallway, and with his giving her nothing but bewildering and probably hollow promises about redeeming himself.

What kind of redemption was there for a man like him? she thought savagely. He was still going back to Melbourne tomorrow. In the end, any feelings he had for her weren't strong enough to keep him here, by her side.

No doubt he would send for her. Till she could move down there permanently there would be plane tickets and hotel reservations for romantic weekend rendezvous. And, weak fool that she was, she would fly to him and let him use her shamelessly. She actually felt perversely excited by the prospect.

Her laugh carried both nerves and a bitter acceptance of her own folly. 'Then you've got what you want, Lance. I've already agreed to become your lover.' She refused to use the word 'mistress', which had connotations she did not like. It was too removed from love, sounding like a business arrangement rather than a personal one.

'An agreement I will never let you back away from,' he ground out, pulling her into his arms. 'No matter what.'

His kiss, this time, allowed no room for escape. It dominated and devoured, giving her a further taste of what was to come. She was trembling inside by the time he let her go, and it wasn't all from desire.

Dear God, what had she done, becoming involved with Lance like this? She might not have told him in so many words that she loved him but he knew it. Everything he did and said betrayed that knowledge. She wanted to scream, but instead she wound her arms up around his neck and pulled his mouth back down on hers, kissing him as violently and possessively as he had kissed her. When she finally wrenched her mouth away, her heart and head were pounding.

'Don't go thinking my agreeing to be your lover is a licence to treat me badly, Lance,' she bit out breathlessly. 'I will have your respect, or you can go to hell!'

'If I ever fail to respect you, my darling, I'll willingly go there myself!'

Angie was taken aback by the fierceness of his
vow. If she'd been a complete fool, she might almost
have thought he truly loved her. Common sense, however, told her that Lance didn't have the capacity for
that kind of love. He'd never grown up with it and
had married without it. His wanting her didn't mean
that he loved her.

But she could pretend, couldn't she? Pretend he
loved her as much as she loved him. He did care for
her, in his way. And he did want her. That much she
could attest to. If last night was anything to go by,
he wanted her one heck of a lot!

Thinking about sex had a very agitating effect on
her, and she whirled to set off down the corridor.

Lance was hot on her heels. 'I take it we're off to
buy some food. Or are we looking for somewhere
private?' he added on a drily amused note.

Colour zoomed into her cheeks as she ground to a
halt and glared up at him, her mouth opening, ready
to reel off a ream of castigating words. But as she
looked up into his face suddenly all she could see
was that wickedly sexy mouth, all she could think
about were the wicked delights that mouth could de-
liver.

Self-disgust at her wayward thoughts had her eyes
and mouth hardening. 'Don't go letting that kiss go
to your head, Lance. Or anywhere else for that matter.
I was merely making a point!'

'And you made it very well, too,' he returned with
a twisted grimace.

'Then stop being provocative.'

'I wasn't trying to be. I thought a touch of humour might defuse some of the tension flying around here.'

'Well, it hasn't!'

'Yes, I can see that.'

'I'm beginning to wish you hadn't brought me up here.'

'I can see that too.'

'I don't want you kissing me any more. Not up here.'

'I don't want you kissing me, either. It's too bloody uncomfortable.'

'I won't. Don't worry.'

'Good. Let's go, then.'

Angie ground her teeth when he took off and she practically had to run to keep up with him. 'Slow down,' she grumbled.

'Sorry. There isn't time. I've wasted too much as it is.'

He surged on ahead again and she raced on after him, her thoughts whirling. Wasted it on me, does he mean?

Angie would have asked him, but his expression forbade her asking. Besides, she might not like the answer. She made a decision there and then not to ask Lance too many questions about anything. She had a feeling that she would never like the answers he'd give her, or the lies he might be forced to tell.

CHAPTER TWELVE

'MR BROWN...'

Everyone looked up from their plates when Lance spoke. They'd been seated at the kitchen table for a full ten minutes, eating their fill of the take-away food Lance and Angie had brought back to the farm.

No one had said much, everyone seeming to have private thoughts as they munched away on fried chicken, chips and fresh bread rolls. Angie was extremely irritated with Bud, who kept giving her and Lance scowling looks which would have raised considerable questions in her father if he hadn't been so distracted.

'Yes, Lance?' Morris Brown said.

'About that holiday you and Mrs Brown are planning...'

'Yes, what about it?'

'I know you're a proud man, and would never accept charity, but it would give me great pleasure to give you that holiday. Please look upon it as a thank-you for the kindness you and Mrs Brown showed me when I stayed here that summer all those years ago. It was the best holiday I've ever had, and I've never forgotten it.'

Bud made some kind of snorting sound, which

brought a startled look from his father and a black glare from Angie.

'You don't think I should take Lance's offer?' Morris asked his son in a puzzled tone.

Angie sent her brother a pleading look and he relented, if a little ungraciously. 'Of course you should. He can afford it—can't you, Lance?' he added, clapping Lance around the shoulders in a pretend buddy-buddy gesture. 'A few grand is a mere drop in the ocean to a Sterling.'

Morris shook his head. 'That's not the point. It's very kind of you, Lance, but I'm not sure Mother would like the idea. She doesn't like being beholden to people. She's never been keen on expensive presents, either.'

Angie reached out to cover her father's hand with hers. 'Dad, don't be silly. As Lance said, you and Mum gave him a free holiday, and now he's giving you one back.'

'I suppose so,' he sighed. 'But nothing too expensive, mind. And not too much travelling. Somewhere here in Australia. Somewhere really beautiful and peaceful.'

'I know just the place,' Lance said. 'Orpheus Island. It's one of the most northern and most beautiful of the Barrier Reef Islands, but also one of the most private.'

And one of the most expensive, Angie thought, but kept her mouth shut. Bud didn't say a word either, thank heavens, though his dark eyebrows arched in a way which suggested that he knew what a stay on Orpheus Island would cost.

'Mother's always wanted a holiday on one of those islands,' Morris mused.

'Then she shall have one,' Lance pronounced firmly. 'Angie, if I give you the money will you organise it? I think around May next year would be best. Your mum will be feeling up to it by then, and the weather up there is great at that time of the year.'

Angie heard the first-hand experience in his voice and was reminded once again of the difference between their lifestyles. Lance had always been able to indulge whatever whim or fancy came his way— which included jetting off to all the exclusive romantic hideaways in the world. Who knew? Maybe she was just his latest whim or fancy?

'May would be good,' Morris agreed. 'I'll have picked the summer crops by then. And the neighbours would look after the animals for us.'

'That's settled, then,' Lance said, sounding pleased.

Morris scraped back his chair and stood up. 'If you young 'uns don't mind, I think I'll go for a walk down to the river. I have a damned awful headache and that usually clears it. I won't be too long.'

Angie watched her father's dejected stoop as he pushed open the screen door and stepped out on to the side veranda. She hoped her mother was genuinely on the way to a full recovery because Morris Brown just wouldn't be the same without her. They shared that kind of love.

'It must be nice to be able to buy whatever you want,' Bud said nastily, his small dark eyes gleaming at Lance with a bitter enmity. 'Friendship. Approval. *My Sister*! God, Angie, haven't you got any pride?

Don't you know that you're only one of hundreds? When he grows bored with screwing you he'll toss you aside like a used tissue. You're nothing to him but a challenge, because you're the only female he didn't sleep with at the time of first fancying you. And now you're no longer a challenge. You're just another silly little fool who couldn't wait to get her pants off for the great Lance Sterling!'

'That's enough!' Lance snapped, spreading his hands out on either side of his plate and levering himself to his feet.

Suddenly Angie was afraid. She'd never seen Lance look so threatening, or so furious. She dimly recalled Bud telling her that Lance had dabbled in many sports back in his uni days, including the martial arts. With his naturally athletic physique he wouldn't need to recall too many of those skills to make mincemeat out of Bud if he chose to.

'Outside, Bud,' he bit out.

'Lance, no!' Her cry sent those blazing blue eyes flashing to her. 'Please don't,' she pleaded.

'I'm not challenging your brother to a duel, Angie. I simply want to straighten out some things.'

'Are…are you sure?'

'For Pete's sake, Angie!' Bud exploded irritably. 'We're adult men, not children. Besides, I can bloody well look after myself. I don't need my kid sister to come to my aid. If Lance wants to shove my teeth down my throat, then let him try. A lot of water's gone under the bridge since he was the super athlete of Sydney Uni. I can hold my own these days, in more ways than one. I'm certainly no longer the easily impressed country yokel who was only too happy to lick Lance's boots in the old days.'

Angie shook her head at her brother but said nothing. If he didn't watch it, his teeth *would* get shoved down his throat. Fear filled her heart as she watched her brother and her lover stalk out into the yard, then over into the barn, shutting the doors behind them. She rather expected to see the walls shaking and dust flying out from under them, as one saw in cartoons, but all remained ominously silent for a good twenty minutes, then the doors slowly opened.

They emerged together, Bud looking a little stunned but none the worse for wear. He wandered off in the direction of the river while Lance whirled and strode back towards the house. Angie raced out to meet him on the front veranda.

'What happened?' she burst out. 'What did you say to him?'

He stared at her for a few excruciatingly long and tense moments, before answering, 'That's between Bud and me, Angie.'

'But...but...'

'Don't try to pry it out of Bud, either,' he interrupted curtly. 'It'll put him in a very awkward position. Look, I've decided to drive back to Sydney straight away, Angie. The sooner I get back to Melbourne, the better. That way I should be able to return to Sydney by next weekend. What are your plans regarding your mother? How long will you be staying up here?'

Angie's head was whirling. She wasn't at all sure

what was going on. 'I...I thought I'd stay at least a
week.'

'So you won't be back in Sydney next weekend?'

'No. I dare say Bud will have gone back by then,
but I thought I'd take the Sunday night train back. I
really will have to be back at school for the last week
of the term. Lance, what's going on?'

'What do you mean? Are you still talking about
what happened between Bud and me?'

'No, I'm talking about *you* and me. What is it you
want of me, Lance? What do you expect?'

'Are you going back on what you agreed in the car
on the way up here?' he demanded, blue eyes immediately wary.

Her chin lifted even while her heart contracted.
'No. I'm not.'

His triumphant expression unnerved her, as did the
way his eyes slid down her body then up again. 'You
know what *I* want, Angie, but I'm not quite sure what
to expect from *you*. Yet. Time will tell, though. I'm
a patient man.'

'Stop talking in riddles!' she snapped. 'You know
I hate that kind of thing. Spell it out for me. Are you
planning on flying up to Sydney for dirty weekends?
Or do you expect me to resign and move to Melbourne? Don't go thinking you'll set me up in some
sleazy flat somewhere. I won't stand for that kind of
hole-and-corner relationship. If I'm to be your girlfriend, it will be a normal man-woman relationship,
nothing nasty. I pay my own way and you pay yours.'

He whistled at her tough stance. 'That's my Angie!
All right, I'll tell you all I can for now. I don't expect

you to resign and move to Melbourne. *I'm* going to move to Sydney, as soon as that can be arranged. You can stay living exactly where you are and working where you are...for the time being.'

Delight raced through Angie. And relief. Tears of happiness danced in her eyes. 'I can? Oh, Lance, that's wonderful! Oh, you've made me so happy.'

He said nothing for a moment, merely stared at her. Then he took her in his arms and kissed her with a passion that sent tremors rippling through both of them.

'Tell me you love me,' he rasped against her swollen quivering mouth.

There was no hesitation this time, no thoughts of self-protection. 'I love you,' she said, her voice shaking.

'And you'll never love anyone else?'

'I never have and I never will.'

'That's all I need to know,' he ground out. 'What time will you get back to your flat after work on Monday week?'

'Around four-thirty.'

'I'll be there,' he said, and, whirling away from her, hurried down the steps and over to his car. He didn't look back at her, didn't say another word.

It wasn't till the black car was speeding off down the valley road that Angie realised one crucial thing. Lance had not said he loved her back.

CHAPTER THIRTEEN

'LANCE gone, has he?'

Angie looked up from where she was sitting on the front steps, her eyes dull with depression. 'Yes,' was all she could manage without bursting into tears.

It was some seconds before she realised that Bud was staring at her, a most peculiar look on his face. He seemed both astonished and puzzled, as though he was trying to see into her soul but without much success.

'Don't look at me like that, Bud,' she snapped. 'You don't understand. I love him. I've always loved him. Ever since that first summer. I know you don't think he's worthy of being loved like that, but he is. Down deep Lance is a fine man. You just don't understand him.'

He raised both his hands, as if to ward off the defensive daggers in her words. 'You're wrong there, Angie. I think I understand Lance very well. Maybe even better than you do.'

Angie jumped to her feet, her eyes spitting fire at her brother. 'God, not that superstud stuff again, Bud. That's ancient history. What is it with you, that you feel compelled to run Lance down all the time? You're supposed to be his best friend. Fine friend you turned out to be. You know what? I think you're jealous of him. I think you've always been jealous of him!'

Angie planted furious hands on her hips as Bud started looking her up and down, a stupid grin on his face. 'I think I'm beginning to see what Lance sees in you, Angie. You've turned into one hell of a fiery female! I guess I was stuck in a time-warp, still thinking of you as a quiet, shy little teenager—so innocent in the ways of the world, needing your big brother to protect you from wolves like Lance.'

'Lance is *not* a wolf!' she protested hotly. 'He wasn't back then, and he isn't now. You make it sound like he had to seduce me or something. I assure you he didn't. I was only too willing to be seduced!'

'So he said.'

'He did?' Angie frowned at this news. She didn't like the sound of it. 'What else did he say about me?' she demanded to know.

'I'm not at liberty to tell you.'

Disgruntlement curled her lips. 'What on earth does that mean? Why can't you tell me what he said? Why do you both have to be so damned secretive all of a sudden?'

'That's the way Lance wanted it.'

'Since when do you do what Lance says? I'm your sister, for heaven's sake. Your first loyalty is to me.'

Bud laughed. 'Really? Then you don't know anything about true mateship, do you?'

'Oh, piffle. You and Lance haven't been true mates for donkey's years.'

'Fat lot you know, little sister. Men aren't like women. They don't have to see each other every week for their friendship to remain solid. Lance and I sorted out a lot of things today, and we're better friends now than ever.'

Angie scowled at her brother. 'Well, bully for you!'

Bud laughed. 'I'd watch that language, if I were you, madam. Any woman gracing Lance Sterling's arm wouldn't be expected to go around tossing off Aussie slang all the time.'

'Is that so?' Angie said archly, infuriated at this about-face in Bud.

'Yes, that's so. He has a certain position to uphold, you know.'

'Well, stone the crows, Bud,' she drawled, in the broadest Aussie accent, 'maybe I should just grace his bed, then, and not his arm. I'm sure the almighty Lance Sterling won't care what language I come out with there. I reckon I could be as colourful as I like and he wouldn't object.'

Bud's face darkened. 'Cut it out, Angie.'

'Why should I? Now that you're back licking Lance's boots you might as well know the whole score. I don't know what Lance told you in that barn, but the truth is he asked me to marry him and I turned him down. I told him I wasn't prepared to be the wife of some high-powered wheeler-dealer who spent more time in the air than on the ground. Of course,

Lance wasn't fazed one bit by my knocking back his proposal of marriage. He merely moved on to his next proposition to get me permanently into his bed. He asked me to be his mistress! How do you like dem apples?' she flung at him.

'Who's running Lance down now?'

'I'm entitled to. I'm the one who loves the bastard!'

He glared at her for several seconds before slowly shaking his head, a rueful smile splitting his round face. 'You know what, Angie? I almost pity Lance. All these years, I thought you needed protecting from him. But I was wrong. It's really the other way around. The poor bastard,' he said, chuckling as he walked away. 'Who would have believed it?'

A tap on Angie's office door sent her eyes to the wall clock. It was three thirty-five, a little early for Vanessa, who was a conscientious teacher and never dashed out of the classroom straight after the bell.

Angie rather wished Vanessa might be less conscientious today, with Lance coming to the flat at four-thirty. She hadn't heard from him since his departure from the farm over a week ago, either by letter or telephone—a situation she found unnerving. Yet, despite that, she had no doubt he would turn up today, as he had said he would.

'Come in,' she called, when the door-tapper didn't automatically enter.

It was Debbie, looking sheepish but happy. 'Sorry to bother you, Miss,' she said, hovering in the doorway. 'I know I don't have an appointment but I just wanted you to know I...I didn't do it. You know...with Warren. I thought about what you said and I decided to wait till someone more special came along.'

Angie's eyes misted before she could stop them.

'I also wanted to ask if you'll be here next year...' Debbie blathered on, God bless her. 'I mean...you're the third counsellor we've had in three years, and they all seem to leave after a year. We all like you a lot, Miss, and think you're real cool. Even Gloria likes you!'

Angie had to laugh, for she knew what Debbie meant. Gloria was the meanest, toughest, bitchiest girl in the whole school.

'That certainly is a true compliment,' Angie said, green eyes gleaming, but with laughter now, not tears. 'Yes, Debbie, I'll still be here next year.'

'Gosh, that's great. I'll tell all the others. We thought, after you were away last week, that you might have been getting sick of us, and took time off to look for another job.'

'No, it wasn't anything like that. My mum was ill. She had a heart attack. But she's getting better now. In fact, she came home from hospital yesterday.'

'Gee, Miss, we didn't know. No one told us,' Debbie said, resentment pursing her pretty young mouth. 'No one tells us anything! If we'd known we'd have bought a card or something. It's not as though we don't care.'

Angie felt warmed by the girl's sentiments. Moments like this made what she did worthwhile.

'I know you care, Debbie,' she said, a lump filling her throat. 'And I'm so proud of you for the decision you made. It was a very mature one.'

Debbie grinned. 'Yeah. I thought so too. But don't tell anyone else. I lied my teeth out and said sex was fantastic!'

Vanessa popped her head in the door moments after Debbie had disappeared. 'What did that little raver want?' she said scornfully. 'Do you know she's been going round telling everyone she lost her cherry last weekend? What kind of girls are parents bringing up these days? I ask you!'

'Not a very different kind from our generation,' Angie said wryly. 'We all struggle along, trying to work out what sex and love are all about, and we all make the most horrendous mistakes.'

Vanessa's dark eyes narrowed suspiciously. 'Are you saying you made a mistake becoming involved with lover-boy again?'

Angie stood up and began tidying her desk. 'Of course. He won't ever give me what I want, Vanessa.'

'Which is?'

'A normal family life, with a house and kids, and a hubbie who comes home every night.'

'Yuk! Give me penthouse suites and wild orgies and private jets any day.'

'You fibber! I saw the way you were batting your eyelashes at Bret Johnson today. And you couldn't get a more normal, down-to-earth bloke. So what's going on between you and the economics teacher?'

'Not much. Yet,' Vanessa added with a wicked grin. 'But he likes me. He *really* likes me.'

'And why not? You're very likeable...for a feminist and a maths teacher. You can tell me all about him on the way home. It'll keep my mind off Lance.'

'Nothing,' Vanessa said drily, 'is going to keep your mind off him, love. You know it and I know it.'

Angie groaned. 'You could be right.'

CHAPTER FOURTEEN

THE sight of Lance's black Audi already parked outside their block of flats showed Angie that her confidence in his turning up today had all been a sham.
Underneath, she'd been terrified he wouldn't.

'Hey, watch it!' Vanessa warned her sharply, when
the car drifted dangerously close to a van going the
other way.

'Sorry. I was distracted there for a second.'

'Yes, I can see myself what caused it. I thought
you said he wasn't due till four-thirty,' Vanessa finished drily.

'That…that's what he told me.' Angie did her best
to control her shaking hands, voice and insides, but
without much success.

'Well, it's only twenty-three minutes past four. He
seems keen, Angie.'

'Yes, but for what?'

Vanessa's head whipped round, her dark eyebrows
arching. 'My, my—I thought I was the only cynic
around here.'

Angie sighed. 'I'm fast catching up.'

'Men do that to you. Especially men who look like
that.'

Both women watched Lance emerging from his car
as they drove down the street towards him. He was

casually dressed this time, in blue jeans and a navy short-sleeved golf shirt with a crisp red stripe around the open-necked collar. Despite his everyday clothes, he still managed to look rich and perversely glamorous. Maybe it was that gorgeous hair of his, glinting gold in the sun, or the gleam of real gold on his wrist and fingers. Or maybe it was just the way he carried himself.

Were wealthy men born with that air of lazy arrogance? Angie wondered. Or did it just develop over the years of being treated as superior beings?

Even Vanessa was shaking her head. 'That is some man, Angie,' she said with rueful acceptance. 'I can understand why you flipped over him. If he asked me to be his mistress, I'd say yes like a shot. There again, I'd have agreed to be his wife. I have to admire your strength of character in saying no, there. Still, perhaps it's your saying no that's made him so keen. I can't imagine too many women saying no to him over the years.'

'Mmm,' was all Angie could say, her eyes locking with Lance's as she slid the car into the kerb behind him. 'Would you mind putting the car in the garage for me, Vanessa?' she asked her flatmate. 'I'd like to speak to Lance out here for a minute.'

'Spoilsport,' Vanessa grumbled.

'I'll bring him up for coffee shortly.'

'OK. I'll put the kettle on.'

Lance walked over to hold the car door open for Angie as she swung her legs out, his gaze flicking down then up her body as she did so. She couldn't tell if he liked the way she looked or not; his expression was quite bland.

Her work image was a far cry from the glammed-up party look Lance had encountered the night of Bud's birthday, and from the way she'd been dressed the following day. She always wore simple suits and tailored blouses to school, which didn't stand out among the uniforms and didn't bring too much attention to her natural good looks. Make-up was kept to a minimum, her long hair brushed straight back and secured at the nape of her neck with a clip or bow.

Today she was wearing a fawn suit with a knife-pleated skirt and a blazer jacket with cream buttons. Her blouse was cream, and a tortoiseshell clip held her hair tidily in place. She never bothered to curl it for work, leaving it quite straight.

'Hello, Angie,' he said. 'Vanessa,' he added, nodding at her as she too climbed out and began walking around the car towards the driver's side.

'Lance,' Vanessa replied succinctly, smiling a wry smile. 'Your punctuality is impressive.'

He merely smiled, saying nothing. Angie felt the tension behind his smile, and immediately succumbed to all kinds of doubts and fears.

He's come to tell me that it's over between us, she panicked. That he's decided not to move to Sydney. That I'm more trouble than I'm worth.

Yet if that was the case, logic argued back, why had he come in person? He would surely have chosen to give such bad news over the telephone, or by letter.

'Did...did you get all your business done?' Angie

asked, once Vanessa had driven off and they were alone on the pavement.

'As much as was possible,' he returned cryptically. 'There are still some loose ends to tie up. But if you mean have I moved to Sydney to live,' he added, his eyes never leaving her worried face, 'I have.'

Her relief seemed to please him. But it didn't please herself. God, but she was hopeless. She might as well just serve herself up to him on a silver platter if she meant to go on like this, with an attached note which said, 'To be used and disposed of as you please!'

Love and pride were bad bedfellows, she decided unhappily. They made fools of each other.

'Would you like to come up for some coffee? Vanessa's going to put on the kettle.'

'I'd rather not, Angie. I'd like to talk to you alone,' he said, with a seriousness that sent those doubts and fears churning in her stomach again. 'Is there somewhere we could drive to? Some nearby park?'

'I…I suppose so. Let me just run upstairs and tell Vanessa, or she'll think I'm terribly rude.'

She returned to find Lance already behind the wheel of his car. Under her directions they drove to a small reserve down on McMahon's Point, where there were several park benches on a grassy verge overlooking the harbour. It was a chilly spot during the winter months, but on a warm summer's afternoon it was a delight, with a cooling breeze and a view to soothe even the most troubled heart.

And Angie's heart *was* troubled—so troubled that she found it hard to keep silent while they walked together towards the only vacant bench. When they finally sank down upon the rather hard wooden slats she immediately turned to face Lance.

'Lance, I…I'm not sure that I…that I—'

'Don't go on, Angie,' he cut in abruptly. 'Listen to what I have to say first. Then you can have your say.'

'All right.' She just knew she wasn't going to like what he had to say.

'I haven't been strictly truthful with you.'

Angie's heart fell.

'I made a proposal to you that I had no intention of going through with.'

Her heart fell even further.

'I just wanted to find out if you still loved me. Once I did, believe me when I say I had no intention of letting you become my mistress. I had no intention of letting you become anything but my wife and the mother of my children.'

Angie's eyes flew up from where they'd dropped to the ground.

Lance reached out to touch her cheek gently, and her heart flipped over. 'I love you, Angie. I've always loved you…ever since that summer…'

'But…but you never came back for me,' she cried. 'And you married someone else!'

He shook his head, his hand falling from her cheek down into his lap. 'I foolishly allowed other forces to shape the course of my life. I thought I was being cruel to be kind. I thought I was unworthy of you.'

'How could you think that?' she groaned.

'Oh, Angie, Angie, have you any idea how different your family is from mine? That summer….I was given a taste of something so alien to everything I had ever known, something so damned wonderful that it ate me up with longing and envy.

'I'd already had an advance taste of the Browns with Bud, who was more openly honest and full of the love of life than any person I had ever met before. He was his own man, and I liked that. There were no pretensions about him, or airs and graces, as your mother would have said. He took me for what I was, not for what my parents owned. He liked nothing better than to bring me down a peg or two—a tendency he's perhaps taken too far over the years,' he added with a touch of acid.

'But truthfully,' Lance went on, reaching over to take her two hands in his, 'I could understand Bud's outrage where you were concerned. What brother would have wanted the man I was then for his fifteen-year-old sister? Hell, I wasn't really a man—I was nothing but a spoiled, arrogant, sex-crazed idiot, whose only feelings for girls up till then had resided firmly between my legs.

'It was so easy after I left the farm to tell myself I'd imagined those other feelings you engendered in me, to confuse the beginnings of a real love with the stirrings of lust, to excuse *your* feelings as little more than a schoolgirl crush which would fade in time.'

'I tried telling myself that as well,' Angie said, a sob catching in her throat. 'But I simply could not forget you.'

'Or I you. Though I tried damned hard. I avoided all girls who looked even remotely like you. Yet at the same time I was obviously looking for the kind of relationship you'd promised. When I first met Helen, she cleverly worked out what I wanted in a woman and played the part to the hilt. She convinced me that she wanted nothing but to be my wife and the mother of my children.

'It was all an act, of course. She came from a family who'd had money once but whose fortunes had declined after the property market crashed in the eighties. She married me for my money, and my money is all she got.

'I must take some blame for her subsequent behaviour, because it must have quickly become obvious to her that I loved her no more than she loved me. I did my best to make a go of the marriage but it was doomed from the start. After a few months of Helen refusing to sleep with me I hired that private detective, and put the final denouement into motion.'

'And it was during this time that you slept with someone else?' she asked carefully, needing to know the answer. 'Or were there a lot of women, Lance?'

'No, only one. Believe me when I tell you it meant nothing, Angie—either to me or to her. She was a hard-nosed career-woman in her mid-thirties. We met through business and she made it perfectly obvious that she was available. She used sex to de-stress her life, she said. I didn't much care what her motives were as long as she gave me what I wanted.

'That week, after Helen left, I finally took stock of my life. I looked at myself in the mirror and decided I did not like what I saw. Then I looked at something else, and I'm not ashamed to admit it, Angie—I cried.'

Angie's heart went out to him. 'What did you look at, Lance?'

'This, Angie…'

She sat, intrigued, as he drew his wallet out of his back pocket and extracted a folded and rather battered piece of paper. With careful and oddly tender movements he unfolded it and handed it over to her. Angie's breath caught as she realised what it was, the printed words leaping out at her from the page.

'It's my poem,' she choked out, her eyes blurring. 'The one I gave you that night…' She looked up at him through wet lashes. 'You kept it…all these years?'

'How could I ever throw it away? No one had ever loved me like that, Angie, or written me anything so beautiful. When I read it again that morning I couldn't contain my despair. But then slowly, over the next few days, my despair gradually turned to determination. I decided if there was even the slimmest chance for us I would take it.

'I knew you weren't married. I hoped and prayed you still felt something for me. It took me a few days to screw up the courage to actually act—Bud's birthday being the catalyst. I knew Bud's habit of always having a party, and I knew you'd be there.'

'So when you came to Bud's party…you really were coming for me at long last?'

'Yes,' he confessed, and Angie's heart swelled with happiness. 'One part of my mind kept telling me I was being an optimistic fool to pursue you after all these years. But once the idea took hold, I couldn't seem to rid myself of it.'

He smiled a drily amused smile. 'Of course, I still had a rather old picture of you in my mind. You've no idea of the shock I got when you answered the door that night. You rather dashed my hopelessly arrogant hopes in one fell swoop. This ravishing creature, I immediately realised, had not been waiting for yours truly to arrive on her doorstep. She certainly hadn't been pining for some old lost love in any way, shape or form.'

'But I had, Lance,' she cried, clasping the poem to her chest and looking at him with all the love in her heart. 'Truly.'

'Yes, I know, my love, and that's why I've done what I've done. I would move heaven and earth to make your dream come true, Angie, because it's my dream as well. I only hope it's enough.'

'What? What have you done?'

'Three things. I've resigned my position as acting managing director of Sterling Industries. I've put my house in Melbourne on the market, and I'm going into business with Bud up here in Sydney.'

Angie's mouth dropped open with shock.

'It's not such a huge sacrifice on my part,' he insisted. 'And I will not regret it later. With Dad dead and Mum gone, I have few feelings left for the family business. I've hired good people to run the various companies, and I can keep a general eye on proceedings from up here without it taking up much time. I might have to attend a few meetings a year. That's all.

'As far as my marital home is concerned...I don't have any fond memories there. I'll be only too happy to buy a new place up here. And as for going into business with Bud...I've always fancied myself doing something creative, and I think I'd be good at it. Bud told me the night of his party that he would start up an agency of his own if he could find a backer, so when we were speaking that day in the barn I proposed we go into business together, with my money and his expertise. Once he realised how serious I was about you, he agreed.'

Angie didn't know what to say. She was flummoxed and flabbergasted.

'Now I'm asking you again to marry me, Angie,' Lance said firmly. 'If you say yes, we'll go buy a ring straight away. We won't be able to get married for twelve months, till my divorce comes through, but meanwhile we can look for a house and plan the sort of wedding your mum would want for you.

'If you say no, however, I won't give up. I'll do everything in my power to get you to change your mind. I'll pursue you, seduce you, even buy or blackmail you if I have to. You will be my wife, Angie Brown. Make no bones about it. So what's it to be right at this moment? Yes? Or no again?'

Angie stared, first at Lance's handsome and impassioned face, then down at the poem she'd written all those years ago. Not that she really needed to read the words to remember its content. It was firmly imprinted in her brain. But there was something incredibly moving about seeing them in their original form—the large, simple print shouting out the tender innocence of the poem's creator, the battered piece of

paper showing just how many times Lance had unfolded this page to read them.

Every day I shall think of you -
Every night I shall dream of you -
One day you will come for me -
One night you'll be one with me -
Love burns eternal when it's true -
It does not die. I'll always love you.

'Angie?' Lance said, his voice husky. 'What's your
answer to be? Tell me, for pity's sake.'

She struggled for control as she looked up, emotion
welling up within her. She tried for a smile, but she
suspected she was crying.

'Yes,' she managed to get out, then suddenly broke
into a dazzling smile. 'Yes, my darling. Oh, yes!'

And she threw herself into his arms.

*   *   *   *   *

A WEEKEND
TO REMEMBER

by

Miranda Lee

CHAPTER ONE

A LIGHT drizzle started falling soon after the road began its long winding route up the Blue Mountains. Hannah flicked on the windscreen wipers and glanced over at her passenger.

He was still sleeping, thank heavens. The drive from Sydney up to the cottage was difficult enough at the best of times. On a Friday evening, in the dark and in the rain, it was downright dangerous.

Her hands tightened on the steering-wheel, her stomach muscles following suit. What in hell was she doing? Common sense told her to turn round and go back, take Jack home, confess all and throw herself on his mercy.

I'm terribly, terribly sorry, she could hear herself saying. *I don't know what came over me, but of course I'm not your fiancée. Just a very worried secretary who simply couldn't let that cold-hearted ambitious bitch take you for another ride. When that tile fell on your head this morning and you lost the last six weeks from your memory—including your whirlwind romance—I thought at first that might be the end of Felicia. But then a nurse at the hospital said a fiancée had been mentioned and would I please call her. In my mind's eye I saw Felicia swanning in and*

5

winning you all over again with her looks and her lies, so before I knew it I'd opened my stupid mouth and said *I* was your fiancée.

Hannah's heart almost jumped into her mouth when Jack shifted in his seat and muttered something under his breath. She sighed with relief when he settled back again, his head lolling to one side, his eyes still shut.

God, for a second there, she thought she'd been speaking out loud instead of in her head. As much as common sense kept ringing warning bells over her reckless deception, no way was she going to heed them.

She didn't care if she lost her job over this.

And she probably would.

Hannah was determined that till Jack got his memory back—the doctor had said that that could happen at any time during the next few days—the only person with him would be herself. She was determined to keep that two-timing witch out of the picture till she could tell Jack the whole appalling truth about the woman he'd been going to marry at the end of the month.

As it stood, dear Felicia was probably at this very moment fuming over the fax from Jack saying that he was having second thoughts about their engagement, and that he was going away for a few days to think things over. The fax also added that she was not to try to contact him, and that he would contact her when he returned.

Any guilt Hannah felt over doing such an outrageous thing, including forging Jack's name, was cancelled when she thought of what she had discovered last night. That woman deserved no consideration. None at all.

Hannah shuddered to think how close she had come to not going to Jack's engagement party and finding out the truth. She'd arrived home from work yesterday to be greeted by her final divorce papers in the mail, which hadn't exactly put her in the mood for partying. She'd literally had to force herself to dress, then drive down to Kirribilli, where the party was being held in a fancy high-rise unit overlooking the harbour, courtesy of a property developer friend of Jack's.

Even before knowing what she knew now, Hannah had harboured misgivings about Jack's choice of bride. She'd only met Felicia a couple of times in a very casual way at the office, but she had just known the woman wasn't right for Jack.

It wasn't jealousy on her part. Hannah had only been Jack's secretary for a little over a year, and there was nothing between them but a strictly work-related relationship. Her feelings for Jack Marshall stopped firmly at liking, respect and gratitude. Oh, yes…she was grateful to him. *Very* grateful.

When she'd applied for the job as private secretary to the boss of Marshall Homes, Hannah had honestly thought she hadn't stood a chance. Good Lord, it had been years since she had used her secretarial skills outside of the home.

But it seemed that Jack had been looking for someone mature, who could be relied on, not some flighty young flibbertigibbet—his word, not hers—who would leave either to go overseas, get married or have babies. She'd assured him she would do none of those things, since she hated travel, had already been married one time too many, and had had babies—two boys, now thirteen and fourteen, both in boarding-school.

Hannah had been so proud of herself when Jack had rung the next day to tell her she had the job.

Pride was something she'd been deficient in for quite some time, and in gratitude for the chance he'd given her Hannah gave him absolute loyalty in return. In her eyes, Jack could do no wrong. He deserved the best, in her opinion, and the best was not a two-faced two-bit soapie-star by the unlikely name of Felicia Fay.

Hannah's top lip curled in contempt at the mere thought of the woman.

Really, she was beneath contempt—the worst excuse for a woman Hannah had ever met. She'd begun to suspect as much the moment Jack's fiancée had opened the apartment door to her the previous evening…

'Well, if it isn't the efficient Hannah, running late for once. Whatever will Jack say!'

Startled by her sour tone, Hannah's hazel eyes blinked wide for a second, before narrowing to appraise further the woman her boss was to marry in four weeks' time.

There was no doubt that Felicia was physically beautiful—more so tonight than ever before. She looked a million dollars, in fact. Masses of blonde streaked tresses framed a perfectly made-up face before cascading down over slender shoulders. Her tall model-like figure was encased in a suede trouser suit in a deep blue which complemented her big blue eyes. A long rope of real-looking pearls hung between her high, firm breasts, matching drop earrings swinging sexily from her lobes as she tipped her head to one side and returned the appraisal.

'I see you haven't had time to change,' she drawled. 'I must tell Jack not to work you so hard. Poor Hannah. Still…black always looks well on older women, doesn't it? It's kind on the complexion and so slimming.'

Poor Hannah was stunned into silence by such an ill-concealed display of bitchiness. The black dress she was wearing was understated but definitely after-five—not the sort of garment she would ever have dreamt of wearing to the office. And her shoulder-length brown hair was stylishly done up in a French roll, not the simple topknot she favoured for work. Despite all this, Hannah knew she didn't hold a candle to the bright butterfly standing before her. So why the attempt to put her down?

'I must thank you for the sweet little engagement gift you sent via Jack,' the butterfly swept on, with a cloying smile. 'One can't have too many ornaments, can one?'

Hannah tried not to choke. The 'ornament' she'd sent had been a very elegant and very expensive Lladro!

'Now, don't just stand there, Hannah, looking out of place. Do come in. Jack's busy talking to some important people at the moment, so you'll have to mingle, I'm afraid.'

Hannah absorbed all the subtle and not-so-subtle slights of Felicia's welcome with a rueful dismay. This was the first time she'd been alone with Jack's fiancée for more than a minute, and the cat's claws were well and truly out. Rather telling, Hannah thought, since she was hardly the sort of secretary to worry a prospective wife. The woman had to be a natural bitch, who believed all other women were the same.

'I don't mind mingling,' Hannah returned as Felicia shut the door behind her.

'Don't you? Funny, I always think of you as such a shy little thing. It amazes me sometimes why Jack has so much confidence in you. You don't seem the type to be a super-secretary.'

Hannah bristled. 'What type would you say I am?'

Felicia's laugh was light and tinkling. Presumably it was meant to soften the malice behind the words. 'Oh, you know. The little-woman-at-home type. You are married, aren't you? You wear a wedding-ring and I heard someone call you Mrs Althorp the other day.'

The fingers of Hannah's left hand automatically curled over into a tight, tense fist. 'Actually, no, I'm not any more,' she said tautly. 'My divorce came through today. I just haven't bothered to take off my rings. Maybe I never will. With the number of males who come through the office, sometimes it's handy to be thought of as married.'

Felicia's glance was sharp. 'So you've become a man-hater, have you?' she asked hopefully.

'I wouldn't say that, exactly. But I have no intention of ever remarrying, if that's what you're asking,' she added, hoping to put the woman's unfounded fears at rest.

Her smile still had an edge to it. 'In that case, I'll make sure I call you Mrs Althorp when I'm in the office. Funny, I know a plastic surgeon called Althorp. Has a practice on the North Shore. But of course, he can't be *your* Althorp. Such a handsome, charming, cultured man.'

Hannah could hardly believe the venom she was hearing. What had she ever done to this woman but be polite and pleasant?

'I must get back to Jack. You can look after yourself, can't you?'

With gritted teeth, Hannah agreed that she could, all the while wondering if dear Felicia was the twenty-nine she claimed to be. Hannah's ex-husband was a dab hand at facelifts, and all sorts of other cosmetic surgery. Dwight's practice depended largely on ladies in the public eye who wanted to look young forever, and other poor put-upon women whose husbands and boyfriends wanted them to look like the models in *Playboy* magazine.

The epitome of feminine desirability these days seemed to be large-breasted, tiny-waisted, slender-hipped, tight-buttocked, firm-thighed, long-legged, small-nosed, big-lipped, wide-eyed, no-wrinkles, clear-skinned beauties, with the public sweetness of angels and the private talents of whores.

Hannah didn't quite qualify. Admittedly when she'd married Dwight, at nineteen, she'd been very pretty and her figure excellent. She was still pretty enough, she supposed, with neat features and nice big eyes. And, being fairly tall, she still looked good in clothes. But the birth of two boys by the time she'd been twenty-one, plus another fourteen years, had taken a certain toll. As for her talents in the bedroom... Well, least said, best said about that.

Felicia, however, obviously did qualify—in every way. Her face and figure were second bar none. Her public demeanour in front of Jack was feminine and accommodating. As far as her private demeanour was concerned... Hannah had no doubt that Felicia's talents in the bedroom were superb as well, to have Jack doing what he'd vowed never to do. Getting married.

Hannah sighed. God, she just hated to think of Jack married to that woman! Felicia was like this apartment—all surface glamour and glitz, but with no soul.

In a way, she reminded Hannah of Dwight. Both of them were social climbers, who cared more for appearances than anything else. Jack would find no more happiness with Felicia as his wife than Hannah had with Dwight as her husband.

But it was none of her business, was it, whom her boss married? He was a grown man, thirty-four years old, with a mind of his own. If she dared venture an adverse opinion of his new fiancée, he wouldn't be at all pleased. It might even reverberate on her and the job she valued. Really, there was nothing for it but to smile sweetly and keep her mouth firmly shut.

Hannah moved from the marble-floored foyer down three cream-carpeted steps and into the first of the large living-rooms. It was peppered with small groups of people, all with drinks in their hands, several with cigarettes as well. She cringed as the smoke haze teased her nostrils, setting off that old tell-tale pang of need. Irritated with herself, she swept a flute of champagne from the tray of a passing waiter and pressed it to her lips, taking a few swift sharp swallows. It wasn't as good as a cigarette, but it was better than nothing.

Glancing around, she quickly spied Jack across the heads in the next room. Nothing strange about that. At six feet six inches tall, Jack's head usually stood above all others. His longish wavy jet-black hair was hard to miss as well. Hannah stood, sipping her drink and quietly watching him from a distance.

Not a classically handsome man, Jack nevertheless

had a face one remembered, with its large, strong features, deeply set blue eyes, squared jaw and uncompromising mouth. One also remembered the scar that ran from his left eyebrow across his cheekbone to his left ear—the result of a run-in with a knife when he was a lad. Or so the rumour went.

Looking at him objectively, Hannah had to concede that a pretty boy, Jack wasn't. But, with shoulders and a body to match his height, he was physically a very impressive and intimidating individual.

She could still remember catching her breath in surprise when, during her job interview, Jack had suddenly stood up to attend an incoming fax. Prior to that he'd been leaning back in his swivel-chair, his long legs stretched out under the desk. She hadn't realised how tall he was. Even now, when he strode into the office some mornings, she could still be awed by his size.

Hannah was not used to physical men. Dwight possessed an elegant, slender frame—nothing like Jack, who was a big bull of a man. No, not a bull—a bear. But, like a lot of big bears, underneath all the huff and bluff, lay a soft heart.

Too bad it had to be snared by the likes of Felicia.

Hannah moved through the archway which separated the two rooms, her eyebrows lifting in surprise once Jack came into full view. For he was dressed as she had never seen him before, in a sleek black dinner suit with satin lapels that would have done an ambassador proud.

Hannah stared, amazed that Felicia had persuaded Jack to wear what he always called a 'penguin' suit. His usual garb was shorts and a T-shirt if it was hot, jeans and a sweatshirt if it wasn't. Occasionally he sported a pair of casual trousers and a proper shirt if he was going to a restaurant. No tie, though. He despised ties. Yet here he was, with a bow-tie choking his muscular neck.

There was no doubting the power of love!

Or sex, Hannah added with silent cynicism. Men's brains went from their heads to their groins when it came to sex—especially with women who looked like Felicia. Feminine instinct warned Hannah that her boss didn't really love his new fiancée. He was sexually besotted, that was all. As for Felicia... Hannah felt certain that she didn't love Jack either.

But there was nothing she could do about it.

Hannah stopped her progress towards her boss once she saw who Jack was talking to. It was Gerald Boynton, the owner of this unit and a highly successful property developer. About forty, he was one of those sleazily handsome men, with slicked back hair, a pencil-thin moustache and dark oily eyes which slid all over you.

Hannah couldn't stand a bar of him.

Recently he'd bought great tracts of land around the Wyong area, and wanted Jack to build his quality homes on the various developments he had planned. He insisted that together they would 'revolutionise' housing on the Central Coast.

That was the way Gerald Boynton talked. Very big. Still, there was no doubt he got things done, and it looked as if Jack would sign up with him. Hannah felt that it was the second dubious partnership her boss was about to enter into.

The urge to have a cigarette consumed her again, and she swivelled round to see whom she could cadge a cigarette from. The need quickly became a compulsion. Her fingers itched. She licked dry lips. It had been two whole months since she'd gone cold turkey, and she'd hoped she'd moved beyond this. It was clear that she hadn't.

Giving in to temptation with a rush of rebellion, she headed straight for a group of smokers, only to have someone grab her by the arm and pull her to a halt.

'Oh, no you don't,' a deep male voice growled.

Hannah whirled to find Jack glaring down at her from under beetling brows, his piercing blue eyes carrying reproach.

'No, you don't, what?' she tried, but her own eyes were smiling ruefully. When Jack had first noticed she'd given up cigarettes he'd declared himself her watchdog, he himself having only given up the dreaded vice a few months before. His vocal pride in her success so far had always stopped her sneaking one behind his back. Till tonight.

'Hannah, Hannah,' he sighed. 'I can read you like a book. You were coveting that fellow's cigarette over

there like a starving man covets a Big Mac. Admit it.
I caught you just in time.'

'Yes, boss,' she sighed back. 'I admit it. I was
about to become a fallen woman.'

He smiled a wry smile, showing big white teeth
within his wide, strong mouth. 'Not you, Hannah.'

'Yes, me,' she insisted, but laughingly.

'You two seem to be having a good time together,'
Felicia said as she snaked her arm through Jack's. 'Is
it a private joke, or can any old fiancée join in?'

'Hannah was about to have a cigarette,' Jack told
her in all seriousness.

'So? She's entitled to, isn't she? You're only her
boss, Jack, not her keeper.'

Was Hannah imagining things, or had she just seen
the first chink in Felicia's acting ability in front of
Jack? She could have sworn there had been a veneer
of acid coating the woman's supposedly light words.

'I know how hard it is to give up smoking,' Jack
said. 'Hannah needs someone to keep tabs on her.'

'What a sweetie you are, Jack,' Felicia said, reaching up to kiss him on the cheek. 'After we're married,
we'll *both* keep tabs on her!' This with a sly look
Hannah's way.

Hannah only just managed to stop herself from
pulling a face at Felicia in return. Why, oh, why
didn't men see through this type of female? It wasn't
as though Jack was naïve where women were concerned. Heck, no. There'd been a steady trail of girlfriends over the past year. Still, one had to concede

that a woman like Felicia didn't come along every day of the week.

Hannah endured the next hour of the party with great difficulty. Felicia spirited Jack out of her company in no time flat, leaving her to 'mingle' again, which wasn't all that easy. Really, this was a party of Felicia's friends, not Jack's. There was not a single employee present from Marshall Homes other than herself. She began to wonder why Jack had insisted she come. On top of that, everyone she spoke to and who spoke to her seemed to be smoking—several of them offering her cigarettes. In the end she couldn't bear it any longer, and accepted one.

Feeling guilty, and terrified that Jack would see her, she slipped out on to one of the two balconies the unit opened on to. Being midwinter, and with a cool breeze blowing at this height, none of the guests had availed themselves of either. Hannah had to huddle into an alcove to keep the cigarette alight, turning her back to the wind as she puffed away like mad. Oh, how soothing it felt! But how wickedly weak it made her feel!

Dwight's repeated criticism over her many failures to give up smoking permanently popped back into mind, making her drag even more deeply. To hell with you, she thought savagely. And to hell with that blonde bimbo you replaced me with!

When she heard the sound of a glass door sliding open, Hannah almost died. Fearing it was Jack, come to spring her, she quickly squashed the cigarette underfoot, then squatted down behind a leafy rubber tree. Not daring to breathe, she was waiting for her boss to discover her guilty quaking self when a low moan broke the cold night air.

Hannah froze as more telling sounds met her ears. Dear heavens, someone was kissing, or making love, or doing something decidedly sexual. How embarrassing if they found out she was there, listening to them!

Hannah almost groaned aloud when she heard the woman say 'darling' on a husky whisper. For it was Felicia. The thought of being a silent witness to Jack and that woman doing and saying intimate things made her skin crawl.

'You like that, darling?' she murmured.

'God, Felicia, what am I going to do without you?'

Hannah snapped to attention. For the man wasn't Jack!

'You'll survive, Gerald. You do have your new little mistress to keep you satisfied, after all.'

'She's not a patch on you in bed.'

'Such a flatterer, you are,' Felicia cooed. 'You're rather good yourself. I've never met a man with your style and imagination.'

'Then why the hell are you going to marry that big oaf? He's all brawn and no brains. I wish to hell I'd never introduced you to him. You can't possibly enjoy going to bed with him. I would imagine having Jack on top would be like being run over by a bulldozer. God, don't stop.'

Felicia laughed. 'In that case there must be something to be said for being run over by a bulldozer. Jack might not have your formal education, Gerald, but he's street-smart and not to be underestimated. And what he lacks in imagination he more than makes up for with a quite amazing stamina. I'm not that much a martyr that I would marry a man who couldn't satisfy me in bed.'

'I'd be quite happy to keep on satisfying you. Any time. Anywhere.'

'Yes, but you won't marry me.'

'That's because I'm already married. God, I'll pay you, if that's what you want.'

'Not enough, darling. Under that supposedly magnaminous façade you wear, you're the original Scrooge.'

'I didn't get rich by being stupid.'

'Neither will I. Modelling and acting hasn't brought me any real fame or fortune, and my looks won't last forever. I'm going to marry Jack Marshall, and there's nothing you can say or do to stop me. He's the ideal husband for me. A multi-millionaire. A self-confessed workaholic. And a man who doesn't want children. What more could I possibly hope for? Now, I really must go. Jack will be out of the bathroom by now.'

'But you can't leave me like this,' Gerald groaned.

When Felicia laughed, Gerald told her where she could go in decidedly obscene terminology. Felicia laughed again before opening the glass door and going back inside. Gerald must have quickly followed, because all of a sudden the balcony was very silent and very, very cold.

A shudder of revulsion ran through Hannah. Now the matter was settled. She could not let Jack marry that revolting woman. She wouldn't say anything tonight, but first thing tomorrow morning she would take Jack aside and tell him all she had overheard...

I would have, too, Hannah reminded herself valiantly now, as she glanced over at her sleeping boss again. If Jack had come straight downstairs into the office this morning. If he hadn't gone off instead to the site of the exhibition village Marshall Homes were building at Cherrybrook. And if that damned tile hadn't hit him on the head, knocking him unconscious and obliterating the last six weeks from his mind.

Lord, she could still see the shock on Jack's face when she'd announced their new relationship. If his head hadn't been aching so much, he might have sought to question her further. But his pain, plus his obsessive hatred of hospitals, had obviously kept all the questions she had seen in his eyes from finding voice at that time. His one and only objective had been getting out of there. Then, once in her car, the sedating painkiller the doctor had prescribed had taken over and he'd drifted off to sleep. He hadn't even woken when she'd made the stops required to complete her outrageous plan.

Now Hannah began to wonder just how long he was going to be out of it. Then she began to worry that it might not be the drugs keeping Jack asleep. Maybe it was a case of severe concussion? Maybe he was going to fall into a coma? Maybe he—

'Oh, hell!' she swore, slamming her foot down hard on the brake as the back of a mud-spattered semi-trailer suddenly materialised through the misty rain. Everyone and everything shot forward when the brakes gripped in the wet, the car slewing wildly. A collision was avoided by mere inches.

Jack was instantly but dazedly awake. 'What in blazes?' he growled, then shot a most disconcerting glance over at Hannah. It was part-pain, part-disorientation, part-disbelief. Gradually the fog seemed to clear from his eyes and he frowned at her. 'What in hell do you think you're doing, Hannah?'

Oh, my God, she thought. He's got his memory back.

CHAPTER TWO

'YOU'RE usually such a good driver,' he added, and Hannah tried not to shudder in relief.

She just wasn't ready for him to get his memory back yet. It was hard enough to cope with his being awake. She knew he'd been dying to ask questions back at the hospital about their supposed engagement. Now nothing was going to stop him.

'Sorry,' she mumbled. 'Didn't see the darned thing. This road's murder in the rain.' She slanted him a hopefully soothing smile. 'We'll be at the cottage soon. Only a few more miles.'

'What cottage is that?'

'Don't you remember? I told you about it back at the hospital, when the doctor insisted that if you were fool enough to discharge yourself then the least you could do was to go somewhere quiet and rest for a few days. When I mentioned the holiday cottage I owned in the Blue Mountains up near Leura, he said that would be perfect.'

'I can't really remember. I think at the time I was still too stunned by our engagement to take much in. Besides, I would have blindly agreed to anything to get out of that bloody hospital. So how did you come

23

to own this mysterious cottage? You've never mentioned it before.'

'Dwight bought it several years ago as a getaway. It was part of my divorce settlement.'

'I see. Well, that explains why I didn't know about it. You never talk about your marriage or your husband. Or you didn't before I lost my memory,' he muttered disgruntedly.

Which was pretty true, although Jack did know that Dwight was a doctor. And she *had* told him one day about the apartment she lived in, which was right in the middle of Parramatta's business district, and far beyond a secretary's salary. It was in a fairly new and prestigious building; the lower floors were devoted to shops and offices, and the upper floors housed exclusive executive apartments.

Dwight had bought one of these apartments only a couple of weeks before Hannah had left him. And had arrogantly—but stupidly, as it turned out—put it in her name for tax reasons. He hadn't even had time to put tenants in when she'd walked out on their marriage and laid legal claim to it. It had given her a small amount of satisfaction that there hadn't been a darned thing Dwight could do about it.

As it turned out, it was an ideal spot for her to live, despite Parramatta being a long way from the northern suburb of Mosman, where she'd lived all her married life. Her boys, of whom she had joint custody, were only a short distance away at Kings College, and it was only a ten-minute drive from Parramatta to Marshall Homes' head office at Castle Hill.

'Have you brought me up here before?' Jack asked abruptly, dark puzzlement in his voice.

Hannah tensed. 'No, I haven't,' she admitted.

Jack glanced at his wristwatch, his head snapping up and round in surprise. 'Good God, it's almost eight o'clock!'

'You've been asleep for hours. How are you feeling, by the way?'

'I've felt better.' His hand came up to touch the top of his head carefully.

'You don't feel nauseous, do you?' the doctor had asked her to watch for nausea and vomiting as a sign of a more serious concussion, making her promise to take Jack to a hospital if that happened.

'No,' he denied. 'Just headachy. It's not nearly as bad as it was, though.'

'Do you…er…still think it's May, and not July?'

''Fraid so. And I still can't believe you and I are engaged,' he added, shooting her a much sharper look. 'Hell, Hannah, how and when exactly did that happen?'

A wave of guilty heat filled her face, but she doubted he could see it. It was pitch-black outside, and the light inside the car was dim. 'Er…only this week, actually,' she said.

'Yeah, right, but *how* did it happen?'

Hannah decided that she had to take control before things got really sticky. 'Look, Jack, I realise our engagement has come as a big shock to you. Frankly, it came as a big shock to me too. One minute you were just my boss, then something happened, and suddenly I just…we just…'

Hannah wanted to groan her dismay. This was her taking *control*? Lord, why hadn't she thought out a believable story to tell him? There again, *was* there a believable story to tell him?

'We became physically involved with each other?' he prompted.

The lack of surprise in his voice sent her eyes jerking round to blink at him.

'That's not the part I can't believe, Hannah,' he said drily. 'I always did fancy you.'

Hannah swung her stunned eyes back on the road ahead, before she really ran into the truck in front of them.

'It was our getting engaged that shocked me,' Jack went on. 'Or, more to the point, your agreeing to marry me. You've told me more than once you'd never get married again. Frankly, I always believed you wanted nothing more to do with men—in that way or any way at all! So what happened to change that?'

She struggled to find her voice, but her mind was still reeling from Jack's bald announcement that he'd always fancied her. She found it hard to believe—but why would he lie?

This highly unexpected revelation gave a totally different meaning to the way he'd looked her over sometimes in the office. She'd always imagined he'd been mentally criticising her fashion sense—as Dwight had done *ad nauseam*. Now she saw him undressing her with his eyes, and suddenly she was all hot and bothered.

'Hannah?' Jack persisted. 'Tell me straight. How did this affair of ours start?'

'I…I don't know. I mean… Oh, God, I don't know what I mean.' She felt totally flustered now, yet she couldn't pull back. The die was cast and she had to roll with it. 'It…it happened the day my divorce papers came through,' she invented shakily. 'We… we…worked back late together that night. At one point I became upset. You comforted me and…and one thing just led to another…'

'Are you saying I seduced you at a weak moment?' he demanded disbelievingly. 'Hell, I didn't make you pregnant, did I? Is that why we're getting married? Because you're expecting my child?'

Her face flamed as she blurted out, 'No!' in a panicky voice. This was becoming awful!

Jack frowned across at her. 'I presume by that you mean, no, you're not pregnant.'

'No, I'm not pregnant. And, no, you didn't seduce me either. I…I wanted you to make love to me,' she insisted, appalled at herself for letting Jack think that he'd acted dishonourably, then more appalled at the corner she'd backed herself into.

'And once we went from friends to lovers, we actually fell in love?' he suggested. 'Is that what you're saying?'

'Not exactly.' God, this was going from bad to worse!

'Mmm. You mean it's more a matter of compatibility and convenience than runaway romance and passion?'

'I think it's more a matter of stupidity,' she muttered. 'Look, Jack, I think our engagement was rather a rash decision, and I won't hold you to any of it. We haven't even bought a ring yet, so our engagement's easily called off.'

'But I don't *want* to call it off,' he said, astounding her all the more. 'As I said before, I've always been attracted to you. And I like you more than any woman I've ever known. It was only *your* attitude to men and marriage that held me back from trying to deepen our relationship.'

Hannah gave him a startled look before wrenching her eyes back on to the road, her heart racing madly. Dear heaven, where would this all end? It was becoming more crazy by the moment!

'Frankly, my own attitude to marriage has been changing for quite a while,' he went on thoughtfully. 'I'd already come to the conclusion that one steady woman in my life would be much preferable to a series of semi-casual relationships. I don't really have the time to romance one woman after another, and the type who'll go to bed with you *without* romance was beginning to lose attraction for me.'

Hannah refrained from rolling her eyes, thinking to herself that she doubted Felicia had needed much romancing before she'd jumped into bed with Jack. Still, she must be super-dooper in bed, since he had not only asked her to marry him very quickly, but had even taken the whole of last weekend off work to be with her. Unheard of for Jack to do that!

'I must admit it *is* strange, though,' he added, frowning, 'not being able to remember anything about this new intimacy of ours. Damned annoying, actually. I wish I could remember our first time together. I feel I've missed out on something really special.'

Hannah could feel his eyes moving over her, and she blushed fiercely.

'Yes, I'm sure it was very special,' he said slowly, the 'very' seeming to slide down her spine, making her skin break out in goosebumps under her clothes.

Hannah was stunned. She had honestly never considered Jack thinking of her in a sexual context before, and the knowledge that he did was sending her into a spin. She hadn't thought of him in that context either, but suddenly she was very aware of him sitting in the car beside her. His size. His strength. His maleness.

She felt flustered and flattered at the same time.

It had been so long since any man had paid this kind of attention to her—so long since she'd thought of herself as a desirable woman. Dwight had eroded her confidence in her sexuality over the years. Whereas Jack, with his repeated assertions tonight about fancying her, and his hot gaze now roving over her, was very definitely revitalising her self-esteem in that regard.

A startling train of thought jumped into Hannah's mind and she sucked in a sharp breath. *Jack believes you're his fiancée. He believes you're already lovers. Maybe he'll expect you to go to bed with him tonight as a matter of course?*

Dear heavens, she hadn't thought of that!

There she'd been, imagining that she would only have to tuck him into bed, bring hot cocoa and generally play nursemaid till his memory came back. She had never contemplated having to fend off a very virile male who already believed he'd been to bed with her and was wanting to relive what he thought he'd missed.

Hannah had to nip this potential complication in the bud, so to speak, before it blossomed into a full-blown problem.

'If you don't mind, Jack,' she said awkwardly. 'Till you get your memory back, I'd prefer us to resume the relationship we used to have as just secretary and boss. I don't think I'd feel comfortable with anything else just now—what with your not remembering anything about our…er…new intimacy.'

'Really? Well, I guess I can understand that, but I sure hope I get my memory back soon,' he muttered testily.

Amen to that, Hannah prayed.

'The doctor said your memory could come back at any time,' she said soothingly.

'The sooner the better,' he grumbled.

A silence descended in the car, which suited Hannah. She was approaching the turn-off, and had to concentrate. Was it around this corner or the next? She wished it would stop raining. It was hard enough to spot in the daytime in fine weather.

The car rounded the corner and, yes, there was the turn-off. Relieved to have done with the highway, Hannah still had to slow appreciably as she turned on to the narrow and bumpy dirt track which led down to the cottage.

The headlights tunnelled through the sleety darkness, showing puddle-filled potholes plus the closeness of the encroaching bushland. They picked up a pair of glassy eyes up in a tree as the road turned. A possum, probably, Hannah thought. Not a koala. Koalas weren't at all nocturnal.

'What an isolated place,' Jack said.

'Actually, we do have several neighbours, but their homes are set back from the road and you just can't see them through the bush.'

'Is the cottage heated? If it isn't, we'll freeze to death.'

'It has two efficient combustion heaters built into the old fireplaces—one in the living-room and one in the kitchen. We'll be warm as toast once I get them going.'

'Won't the wood be wet?'

'I stacked plenty in the laundry when I was up here last weekend,' Hannah informed him without thinking.

'You came up here last weekend?' he immediately pounced, and she could have bitten her stupid tongue off. 'Alone?' he added on a puzzled note.

'Yes, you were busy working,' she said, marvelling at the speed with which she could lie. Not that it was all a lie. He had been busy. Busy having a dirty weekend with the treacherous Felicia, at a guest-house not all that far from here. Hannah had booked it for him herself. 'The place needed airing,' she went on quite truthfully. 'It hadn't been used for a while and I was thinking of bringing the boys up here next school-break.'

'The boys,' Jack repeated thoughtfully, and Hannah wanted to kick herself. Why, oh, why had she brought them up?

Jack swivelled to face her. 'Do Chris and Stuart know about us?'

'No, they don't,' Hannah replied frustratedly. Jack had met her sons during their last school-break, when they'd wanted to come and see where she worked. He had kindly taken them on a tour of the premises and attached exhibition homes, and they'd taken a real shine to him.

'Remember, we only got engaged this last week,' she added. 'Look, Jack, perhaps you should leave all those sorts of questions till after you get your memory back as well, then most of them won't be necessary. I think that would be less complicated and much less wearing all round.'

His sigh showed a very real weariness. 'You're right. I think I'm giving myself another headache trying to work everything out.' And he slumped down in the passenger seat, his head and shoulders drooping.

She slanted him an anxious look. 'Are you sure you feel all right?'

'I'll live.'

'You should be in bed, resting.'

'You could be right.' He began rubbing his temples.

'Won't be long now,' she said, throwing him a motherly smile. 'Here we are, in fact.'

The cottage was old and quaint, made of stone, with a pitched iron roof and two chimneys. It had a small enclosed front porch and front door with stained-glass windows on either side. Inside it had a central hall which opened into two bedrooms and one bathroom on the right, and one long living-room on the left. At the end of the hall was a large, comfy country kitchen, whose large pantry had been converted to a sleekly modern laundry, complete with dryer. Out at the back a wide and sunny veranda overlooked thick bushland, with mountain peaks in the distance.

Two paths led from this back veranda—one leading off on a bushwalk the boys called the Boomerang, because it brought one right back to its starting point, and the other going round the side of the house to a small stone shed which had once housed an old dunny and an equally ancient laundry, complete with copper and washboard. Now it was where the wood, the mower and other various tools were kept.

Hannah loved the place—its simplicity and its peace and quiet. The boys had always liked it too—especially the bushwalking. She'd come up here with them as often as she could after Dwight had bought it, mostly without her husband. He had always seemed to find some excuse not to come at the last minute. Hannah had suspected he was having affairs back then, but had turned a blind eye to it till the day had come when she had been forced to face her cowardice and make a stand.

Recalling her husband's infidelity renewed her resolve to do whatever she could to stop Jack from marrying that amoral woman. She would let Jack believe what he liked about their relationship provided he stayed up here with her, alone and away from Felicia's influence. Of course, that didn't include sleeping with him. That was carrying gratitude too far!

Gritting her teeth, Hannah pulled the car up next to the front steps and switched off the ignition.

'You go on inside,' she told Jack briskly.

'There's a big brass key in the geranium pot on the top step which opens the front door. Your bedroom will be the first on the right. I'll get your things.'

He frowned. 'When did you get my things?'

'While you were asleep. Come, now, no more questions, remember? Just accept I have everything in hand.'

'My ever-efficient Hannah,' he said, opening his door. 'How did I ever manage before you came along?'

Hannah knew what he was referring to. She often did little domestic chores for him, like delivering and picking up his dry-cleaning. She also took care of his personal bills, which he had a tendency to overlook when he was busy on a new project.

'At least now I'll never have to manage without you again,' he said, his smile disturbingly tender.

Hannah sat, transfixed, when he unexpectedly leant back over and took her mouth with his in an incredibly gentle kiss. The softly sensuous contact of his lips brushing hers sent little shivers of delight running up and down her spine. She stared at him as his head lifted, stared deep into those deep blue eyes, true panic welling up within her.

No, no, came the frantic thought. I can't allow this kind of thing to happen. It's not fair to him, or to me. I must speak now—tell him the truth before it's too late.

But then he kissed her again, not quite so gently, and immediately she lost the plot. Common sense kept telling her to keep her lips shut, but her lips didn't seem to be connected to her brain.

His tongue swept deep into her mouth, and she felt it all the way down to her toes. When she moaned, his hands cupped her face, holding it captive as his kiss grew more and more demanding. And more and more seductive. Hannah ached to surrender to its heat, and to its promise of more to come. It had been so long since she'd been kissed like this. *Too* long, obviously.

Guilt finally fought its way through Hannah's scrambled thought-processes, and she wrenched her mouth away from his, pulling back out of his grasp. 'No, stop!' she gasped. 'I can't let you do this.'

'Why not?' he returned thickly.

Because I don't love you, she could have said. Because you're not my fiancé. Because my response comes from nothing but years of frustration and neglect.

But Jack wasn't in a fit state for the truth tonight. And neither was she. Maybe in the morning.

'Your…your headache,' she said instead.

'What headache?'

'Jack, stop it. You promised. I…I can't handle this just now. And neither can you. The doctor said you had to rest. You might be suffering from concussion. The last activity you need is anything to get your blood pressure up. Surely this can wait till you're better?'

Jack let out a shuddering sigh. 'You're no doubt right. But damn it all, Hannah, I can't seem to stop thinking about you, and what it must be like between us. Hell, it must be incredible to have propelled us into a level of caring and commitment that didn't ex-

ist six weeks ago. Surely you can understand my curiosity…'

Everything inside Hannah tightened when Jack
reached out to lay a tender hand against her cheek.
His blue eyes, normally so cool and businesslike,
washed over her with a passionate warmth which had
a decidedly heating effect on her blood.

'Now that I've had a small taste of what's to come,'
he said, 'I have to admit my impatience to have you
in my arms. Besides, I rather like the idea of making
love to you while I can't remember. It would be like
experiencing our first time over again.'

'Jack, please don't make it hard for me to keep
saying no,' she pleaded, and meant it. For, astonishingly, she *was* tempted to go to bed with him.

It wasn't love, or even lust, she believed. To be
honest, Jack wasn't her physical type at all. She'd
always been attracted to fair-haired, smoothly elegant
men like Dwight. It had to be because she just wanted
to be wanted. Wanted to be needed. Wanted to be
stroked and kissed and told she was desirable and
beautiful.

Hannah was amazed—and rather shocked—at how
strongly she was tempted to take advantage of the
situation she'd created with her impulsive deception.
Only the realisation that Jack would eventually get
his memory back stopped her. As it was, she was still
probably going to lose her job over this. Things had
already got further out of hand than she'd ever anticipated.

'This weekend we're just good friends,' she stated stiffly. 'Nothing more.'

'We'll see, Hannah,' he muttered, his hand dropping away from her cheek. 'We'll see.'

'I mean it, Jack,' she said, her voice hardening further. 'Till you get your memory back, our relationship is strictly platonic.'

'And what if I said I've already got my memory back?' he tossed back, watching her face all the while.

Hannah was only shaken for a split-second. 'You'd be lying,' she said, quite confidently.

'How can you be sure?'

'I just can.'

'Hmm. Now, I wonder why that is, Hannah, love? What else has happened during the last six weeks to make you sure I'm still in the dark? No, don't tell me. I don't think I want to know. Not tonight. The morning will be soon enough to find out the awful truth. Tonight I think I'd best remain in blessed oblivion.'

CHAPTER THREE

BLESSED oblivion…

I could do with some of that, Hannah thought ruefully as she bent to put another log on the fire.

She stayed on her haunches, staring blankly into the flames, wishing she had never started any of this. It had been a crazy idea. She should have just told Jack the truth right away—all of it—and let him handle the situation with Felicia as he saw fit. He didn't need a mother to hold his hand. He was a grown man.

It had been a mistake in judgement to embark on this ridiculous deception—a silly, impulsive reaction which she hadn't thought through at all properly.

But it was not too late to tell Jack the truth. By morning it might be, however. By then he might well have regained his memory, and he would be furious with her. Not only furious, but suspicious of her motives in doing such a thing. He might even harbour doubts over her story about Felicia and Gerald Boynton, which was the last thing she wanted.

Hannah smothered an exasperated sigh. 'O what a tangled web we weave, When first we practise to deceive!'

'You make a good fire.'

Hannah flinched, then threw a rather stiff smile over her shoulder. Jack was sprawled along one of the two overstuffed sofas which flanked the living-room fireplace, his normally macho-clad frame distractingly clothed in the sleek navy silk pyjamas she'd found in his drawers. He was propped up on one elbow, his hands cupped around a mug of hot chocolate. His feet were bare but not his chin. It was sporting the beginnings of more than a five o'clock shadow.

This was hardly new for Jack. He often didn't shave, sometimes letting two or three days go by before he bothered. Clearly he hadn't bothered this morning. Hannah had always found such inattention to personal grooming unappealing. Dwight had been so meticulous in such matters.

Tonight, however, she found it disturbingly attractive. It seemed to highlight Jack's almost animal-like maleness, the silk pyjamas not really disguising a body more suited to caveman times than the nineties.

All thoughts of telling her boss the truth fled from her mind for a few moments, replaced by memories of how it had felt when he'd kissed her back in the car. She'd tried not to think about that in the hour since they'd arrived, during which time she'd busied herself with all sorts of household chores: lighting both fires, unpacking Jack's clothes, running him a hot bath, making them both some food and drink, showering and changing herself.

Now, all of a sudden, she couldn't stop thinking about her response to Jack's kisses, and what it might feel like to go to bed with him. The realisation that she was undressing him with her eyes and wondering if he was as well-built downstairs as he was everywhere else, really shocked her.

Wrenching her eyes away from him, she busied herself pushing the log right in, then closing and securing the glass door. 'I've had plenty of practice at firemaking,' she said, disguising her inner turmoil under a matter-of-fact voice. 'Not to mention wood-chopping and mowing. Dwight wasn't what you'd call the handyman type.'

Neither had he been a complimenter. It came to Hannah then that Jack was always praising her. She loved that about him.

But she didn't love him. The only man she'd ever loved was Dwight, her husband and the father of her children. No doubt, underneath her hurt and her anger, she was still in love with the rotter!

So why, dammit, couldn't she stop thinking about making love with Jack?

Hannah almost groaned in total exasperation at herself. There was no doubt about it now. She had to tell him the truth. And she had to tell him before things got any further out of hand.

But how? It wasn't going to be easy.

Frowning, she rose from her haunches, wiping her

hands down the legs of her jeans before pulling down her jumper from where it had ridden up over her hips.

'I like you dressed like that.'

Hannah's eyes snapped up, blinking her surprise and automatic scepticism. Around the time she had turned thirty Dwight had started saying that her *derrière* was too big to wear jeans, so she'd left all her jeans up here, to wear when Dwight wasn't with her. Admittedly she'd lost weight in the time she'd worked for Jack, but she still found it hard to believe that any man would genuinely fancy her in jeans.

It wasn't her *derrière* Jack was staring at, however, but the thrust of her full breasts against the soft wool of the pink jumper. They tingled beneath his scrutiny, swelling and peaking hard within her bra.

Her body's response both shamed and excited Hannah. God, but it was an eternity since such a thing had happened to her like that—so automatically, so wantonly.

'I like women in casual clothes,' Jack said. 'It makes them look approachable. You've no idea how much more approachable you look in those jeans than the tailored suits you usually wear to work. Mmm, I think I might make jeans your uniform,' he added, then chuckled drily. 'Perhaps not. I'd never get any work done.' Swinging his bare feet on to the floor, he sat up and patted the sofa next to him with his spare hand. 'Come over and sit down. You haven't stopped working since we arrived. It's time you put up your feet.'

Hannah's heart lurched. She stared at him for a few terrifyingly electric moments before panic at the feelings spiralling through her sent her scurrying towards the other sofa. 'I'll just sit over here, I think,' she babbled. 'There's not much room next to you and you might spill your drink.'

'No, I won't,' he said, sliding down to the far corner and depositing the mug on the side-table right next to his elbow. 'Now there's room,' he said, patting the sofa again, his blue eyes glittering with desire as they raked over her breasts once more.

Her panic flared anew. And she must have shown it.

His frown was swift and dark. 'What is it, Hannah?' he asked. 'What's troubling you?'

'Nothing,' she lied, sitting there with her knees clenched together and her hands nervously massaging her thighs. 'Nothing.'

'You can't honestly expect me to believe that. Your face is an open book, if one wants to take the time to read it. Something's definitely wrong,' he insisted, his penetrating blue eyes giving her no mercy.

He moved forward to perch on the edge of the sofa, his hands on his knees. 'Look, Hannah, I know I said I didn't want you to tell me any nasties till the morning, but I can see neither of us will sleep properly if the air isn't cleared. So out with it,' he commanded in his most effective 'boss' voice. 'What *else* has happened during the last six weeks which has you all tied up in knots?'

She grimaced, knowing that this was the chance she'd been looking for—the opportune moment to unburden her conscience. All she had to do was open her mouth and let the truth spill out.

But it just wasn't that easy. Not at all. Her head whirled and her tongue felt thick. She couldn't seem to find the right words. Or any words at all!

Her stricken expression brought an answering anxiety to his face.

'My God, it's not the business, is it?' he burst out, his head snapping up, his knuckles going white as his large hands gripped his knees. 'I haven't somehow stuffed it up, have I? I could bear just about anything, but not that. I've worked too long and too hard to start at the bottom of the heap again.'

Hannah's heart went out to him. She'd heard the stories about his childhood in a state institution for orphans, how he'd left to strike out on his own at fourteen, a boy with the body of a man, how he'd worked as a builder's labourer and learnt his trade by trial and error. He'd started small, buying a single block of land, building a house on it and selling it as a package, then using the profit to buy *two* blocks of land, repeating the process till he'd become one of the biggest home-builders in New South Wales.

Hannah could appreciate Jack's panic. In his shoes, she'd have felt exactly the same.

His obvious distress had the effect of her finding her voice. To a degree.

'Nothing bad's happened to the business, Jack,' she insisted fiercely. 'Truly. If you must know, I... I...' Once again her voice dried up, her courage failing her anew.

'What?' he demanded impatiently. 'For God's sakes *what*, Hannah?'

It was no use. She just couldn't tell him the truth. Not yet. Not tonight.

'I...I've failed, Jack,' she blurted out instead, jumping to her feet. 'At giving up smoking. I...I'm sorry but I just didn't make it. Now I simply *have* to have a cigarette!' Which was true. Anything to calm the nerves that were tap-dancing all through her body. 'I think I left a packet out in the kitchen,' she said, and promptly fled the room.

'And there I was, thinking something disastrous had happened,' he called after her, an amused chuckle betraying his relief.

Hannah groaned her dismay once she reached the kitchen, her trembling hands lifting to pick up several strands of hair which had come loose from their top-knot. She stuffed them back in, then rummaged through the drawers till she did indeed find a packet of cigarettes, plus some matches. Her excuse had quickly become a reality. A cigarette was definitely needed.

Putting one between her lips with shaking fingers, she finally lined the end up with an equally shaking match, then drew in deeply.

'You don't have to stay down there in Coventry,' Jack called out drily. 'I'm well and truly cured of that particular vice. You won't corrupt me if you smoke in my presence.'

Hannah shuddered. Maybe she wouldn't corrupt him, but being with him might well corrupt her. Once again she'd failed to tell Jack the truth, and she knew the reason why. She wanted him to go on wanting her, wanted him to keep looking at her as he just had, wanted to wallow a while longer in his admiration and desire.

It was wicked of her.

And downright dangerous.

Jack was not the sort of man to tolerate being teased for long. Hannah wasn't ignorant of the sort of female he'd dated, or the sort he'd finally proposed to. They were all overtly sexual creatures, who dressed provocatively and never bothered to hide the nature of their relationship with the boss of Marshall Homes.

Being Jack Marshall's girlfriend meant one thing and one thing only. Being his fiancée wasn't much different, from what she could see. Felicia had spelt it out to Gerald Boynton. Jack didn't want a family. He didn't want the love of a lifetime. He wanted a bed-partner. Permanent, as opposed to casual. Sooner or later, if she kept up this pretence, he would expect her to sleep with him.

And she wasn't sure she could find the strength to resist him. That was why to go on pretending to be Jack's fiancée was so dangerous.

Hannah drew deeply on the cigarette, knowing what she *should* do, but perversely unable to do it. All she could promise herself was that *she* would not initiate anything. She would stop undressing him with her eyes, keep her distance, and work hard at maintaining the platonic relationship she had asserted they should stick to till Jack's memory returned.

'I…er…I think I'll still stay out here for a while,' she called back, knowing she needed a few minutes' grace to gather herself and recapture some composure.

Two cigarettes and several self-lectures later, Hannah made a brief visit to the main bedroom then returned to the lounge, where she walked over to stand with her back to the fire, determined to act with her usual cool efficiency.

'I've switched your electric blanket down to one,' she told Jack, who was finishing up his hot chocolate. 'I think perhaps it's time you went to bed, don't you? The doctor said you were to rest.'

'I'm resting right here,' he returned, putting the empty mug back on the table. 'In fact, I...I—'

He broke off abruptly with a sharply sucked in breath, both his hands flying up to his temples.

'What is it?' Hannah asked, alarmed. 'Are you in pain?' When he didn't say anything, his eyes squeezing tight as his face screwed up, Hannah flew to sit beside him, her hands fluttering as she didn't know where to put them.

'Can you hear me, Jack? Talk to me, for pity's sake!' she cried.

Slowly his face unravelled, his hands dropping back to his lap as his eyes opened to blink blankly at her. 'That...that was the strangest experience,' he said at last, shaking his head as if to clear it. 'A series of flashes—like images up on a screen. Weird...'

'Images of what?'

'I'm not sure. There were lots of people in a big room. All dressed up. I didn't recognise most of them. Or the place. There was this blonde...dressed in blue. I felt I knew her, but now I can't seem to put a name to the face. Oh, and Gerald was there. Gerald Boynton.'

Hannah gulped. The party. He was remembering the party.

'Have I been socialising with Gerald lately?' Jack asked, still puzzled.

'Not over-much. He did throw you...er...us, I mean, an engagement party the other night. His wife's a blonde,' she said in desperation, aware that she was once again bypassing a chance to tell Jack the truth. 'Maybe that's who you were seeing?'

'Could be. I've never met his wife. Not that I recall, that is. When was this party? And why were we all wearing dinner suits, if it was just a party?'

'It was last night, actually. Thursday. Gerald insisted it be formal.'

Jack snorted. 'Typical Gerald. He's an out and out show-off.'

'Mmm.'

Jack darted her a sharp look. 'You don't like him, do you?'

'Can't say I do. He's what we women call a sleaze-bag.'

Jack frowned. 'He hasn't been making a nuisance of himself, has he?'

'No. I just don't like the way he looks at me.'

Jack laughed. 'Come now, Hannah, you can't blame a guy for looking. You must be used to men looking at you.'

Not really, Hannah thought, still astonished at how much Jack genuinely fancied her. Maybe she was better looking than she'd thought. Or maybe Jack had gone half-blind with that bump on his head.

'Have I agreed to that proposition of his yet?' Jack resumed abruptly. 'You know the one I mean.'

'Yes, I know the one you mean. And no, you haven't. *Yet.*'

'From the sound of your voice, I gather you'd prefer I didn't.'

'I wouldn't presume to tell you what to do, Jack. You're the boss.'

'Not even now that you're the boss's fiancée?' he asked smilingly.

Hannah flushed under Jack's warm and highly seductive tone. As much as she couldn't bring herself to tell him about Felicia, she felt she had to say something which her conscience could cling to, and which would give her some kind of defence later on, after his memory returned. 'As I said earlier, Jack, our… er…engagement was rather a spur-of-the-moment decision. Maybe you'll want to rethink things at some future date?'

'Don't be ridiculous,' he muttered, with a measure of exasperation, reaching out to draw her into his arms before she could escape. 'You're perfect for me in every way, Hannah. We get along. We work well together. You've already had children, so you won't pine for more, and obviously we're sexually compatible. I'm just glad I finally found a way to win you over to the male race again, even if I can't remember it.

'If I'd known you wanted me in that way I'd have seduced you earlier. Oh, yes, I know you said I didn't seduce you, but I have a feeling you're lying about that. I must have, for my Hannah is not a bold woman. She's rather shy in such matters, which pleases me all the more. I've had my fill of bold women.'

Hannah stared at him, appreciating the irony of that statement. If only he knew who he was really engaged to!

'You're such a classy lady,' he went on warmly. 'I can hardly believe that you're attracted to someone like me.'

Hannah's eyes widened when he started to bend his head, obviously intending to kiss her. She couldn't help stiffening in his arms, terrified of where this would end. She hadn't been this flattered or this complimented in years!

Or this excited either.

He stopped, his eyes clouding as they jerked up to frown down at her.

Hannah's stomach turned over. Was he reacting to her reaction, or had he remembered something more?

His hands dropped away from her as he straightened, a wariness entering his frowning eyes.

'Am I being thick here, Hannah?' he asked brusquely. 'Have you been trying to tell me that it's *you* who regrets our engagement? That you're having second thoughts? That you've decided I'm not good enough for you?'

'No!' Hannah exclaimed, her hands lifting to cradle his face before she could think better of it. 'No,' she repeated in a raw whisper as the hurt in his eyes moved her to reassure him.

'I'm not an educated man,' he grated out. 'Nothing like your doctor husband.'

No, he wasn't at all like Dwight, came the rather enlightening realisation. He wasn't arrogant like Dwight, or cruel, or critical. What did an education count for if all it produced was a self-centred, self-important ego, which left no room for anyone's wishes or feelings but their own?

And it wasn't as though Jack wasn't smart. He was. *Very* smart, as even Felicia had pointed out to Gerald Boynton.

'You're nothing like my husband, Jack,' she said, her voice shaking with emotion. 'And I'm glad you're not. You're twice the man he is, or ever could be,' she insisted. And astonishingly, she meant it.

They stared deep into each other's eyes, and gradually she became aware of the stubble beneath her fingers. Her thumbs moved to caress it, to feel the primitive maleness sprouting forth, hard and sharp against the softness of her touch. Something equally primitive began to rise within her. She ached for him to rub his chin against her cheek, to feel its roughness against her breasts and the soft inner flesh of her thighs.

In her mind's eye she saw him do all those things, and everything inside her kicked over. So intense was the feeling this imagined scenario produced that she jerked her hands away from him, but he caught them

in his, dragging her heated face back close, forcing
her eyes back to his.

'And you, my darling Hannah,' he rasped, 'are
more woman than any woman I ever hoped to call
my own.'

Hannah tried to feel guilt at his words. Instead her
only reaction was a wide-eyed soul-stirring wonder
that Jack could feel like that about her. She could
hardly believe it.

Tears pricked her eyes.

'Now, what's all this about?' he said gently, kissing
the moisture from her eyes and cheeks. 'Were you
worried that I might not feel the same way about you
just because I'd lost a few miserable weeks of my
memory? Did you think I wouldn't still want you?'

A sob caught in her throat as she nodded dumbly,
knowing that everything was now totally out of her
control. What would be, would be. She was incapable
of stopping the flood of feeling washing through her.
Dwight might not find her desirable any more, but
Jack obviously did. If he wanted her, she would not—
could not—stop him.

'Silly Hannah,' he murmured, and, tipping them
both back against the sofa, closed the space between
their mouths.

'We *are* good together, aren't we?' he whispered
thickly after he came up for air. 'Very good.'

Hannah shivered with sensual delight when he held
her close and his cheek grazed hers. Her hands slid

up over his silk-covered chest, lifting to splay into his glossy black hair, revelling in every sensual moment.

Till she contacted the huge scab on his crown.

When Jack flinched violently she sprang back from him, appalled that she had so quickly forgotten the accident he'd suffered that very morning, plus the doctors' warnings that he should be doing nothing but resting.

'Oh, Jack!' she cried. 'Your poor head. Oh Lord, I forgot! We…we have to stop this,' she said, jumping to her feet. 'You're…you're not well enough for this kind of thing.'

He gave a dismissive shrug. 'My head doesn't hurt that much if you don't touch it. And we were only kissing, Hannah. Still,' he went on a touch wearily, rising to his feet as well, 'perhaps you're right. As much as I'd love to take you to bed right now, I don't think I'd do it justice. I'm sure by tomorrow night I'll be in far better shape.'

'No, Jack,' she derided, finding some common sense now that she was out of his arms. Heavens, but he did have a way with that mouth of his, totally seducing her with just a couple of kisses. Lord, he'd even made her forget that to go to bed with a man one actually had to take off one's clothes!

If she wavered again, she would just have to keep remembering that harrowing and potentially humiliating fact. Once Jack saw her in the nude, he might be as turned off by her imperfections as Dwight had been.

'There won't be any bed together tomorrow night either,' she said, her resolve well and truly strengthened by this last thought. 'We agreed that till your memory comes back we'd keep our relationship platonic.'

'No, Hannah. We didn't *agree* on that at all,' Jack argued back.

'Well that's the way it's going to be!' she insisted. 'Look, for all we know you might have a serious concussion,' she went on, appealing to Jack's common sense. 'I'm not going to risk doing anything that might be dangerous to your health, Jack.'

His sigh was irritable. 'I see you've put your "mother" hat back on, and I know how hard that is to shift. Hell, Hannah, if I ever get the chance to be reincarnated, I think I'll come back as your third son!'

So saying, he stepped forward, took her by the shoulders and landed a very chaste kiss on her forehead. 'Goodnight, Mum. See you in the morning. Who knows? By then, I might even think it's July!'

CHAPTER FOUR

THE morning dawned crisp and clear and cold, a typical winter's day in the Blue Mountains.

Hannah woke with the arrival of watery sunlight through the window, blinking her bewilderment for a moment before she remembered where she was—in one of the boys' single beds, not in the big brass bed in the main bedroom.

It was the first time she'd slept in a single bed since she'd married Dwight over sixteen years ago. The flat she now lived in had come with a queen-sized bed already installed in the main bedroom. For ages Hannah had stuffed pillows down the empty side, till she'd got used to the space and the emptiness of sleeping alone in a large bed. Now she was well used to sprawling over the whole mattress and found a single bed rather confining, though cosy enough on a cold morning.

She toyed with the idea of getting up, but a glance through the window showed a thick frost on the ground, the below-zero temperature confirmed when she put one hand out to check the time and promptly almost shivered to death. Dropping the watch posthaste, she snatched her chilled hand back under the quilt and snuggled down.

So what if it was after seven? So what if she was normally up and about by now?

I'm not getting up, she vowed defiantly. I'm staying here till lunchtime, if need be.

Hannah snuggled down further, pretending to herself that the main reason she wanted to hide in bed was the cold, and not because she didn't want to face Jack. But it wasn't long before her thoughts turned to what had happened the day—and the night—before.

Stupid, she decided. She was stupid! First for pretending she was Jack's fiancée, then for not coming out with the truth once things had started getting sticky. In fact, 'stupid' did not adequately describe her actions. She would have to find a better word.

Dwight would have been able to come up with several, she decided bitterly. Over the years she'd been called illogical, over-emotional, ridiculous, foolish, dumb, even *non compos mentis* on occasions.

Dwight had had no patience with her sometimes sentimental impulses, such as the time she'd picked up a starving but obviously pregnant cat from the street and brought it home. He'd insisted she take the poor frightened animal to the RSPCA. If Hannah remembered correctly, he'd called her tears 'irrational'. So what if the mangy thing was put down? he'd argued irritably. It was probably diseased, and, even if not, Sydney already had too many cats.

Irrational...

That was exactly what he would have called what she had done yesterday. Irrational.

Still, Hannah thought there were *some* excuses for what she'd done. Everything had happened so fast, and her intentions had been good. Surely she wasn't entirely to blame for not seeing that it would all go wrong? How could she have anticipated Jack jumping on the bandwagon of their engagement so enthusiastically? She'd expected him to stay shocked for days, not become smugly pleased. She'd expected him to keep his distance, not be all over her like a rash. She certainly hadn't expected to *like* his being all over her like a rash.

One part of her said that the sensible course of action, for her own sake and the survival of her job, would be to tell him the truth first thing this morning. But the more emotional and decidedly female part of Hannah still didn't fancy risking Jack in Felicia's clutches again, not without his memory intact. The woman was a snake—a poisonous, venomous snake!

She was also an accomplished actress, who could lie her teeth out quite brilliantly without batting an eyelash. She might even succeed in making Hannah look the liar! The vicious bitch would probably accuse her of taking advantage of the situation because she wanted Jack for herself!

No, she could not tell him the truth. Not yet. On Monday, maybe, if he still hadn't got his memory back, because by then she would be forced to.

But that was two whole days away—two whole days of keeping up this pretence which was getting more difficult with each passing moment.

A least she'd put a temporary tin hat on Jack trying to make love to her. But she wondered how long that would last. There was no doubt he genuinely seemed to fancy her, which she still found amazing. Jack had not dated a female less than stunning or over thirty in all the time she'd known him. Frankly, before Felicia, they'd all been closer to twenty than thirty, and all very outgoing, sexy little pieces.

It was to be thanked for, in a way, that she did not possess such sexual confidence. Otherwise she just might have surrendered to Jack's advances last night.

And where would that have led? She shuddered to think.

'Hannah! Where are you? Hannah! Are you there?'

Jack's panicky cries propelled her out of the bed like a shot. Oblivious of the cold, or her bare feet, she raced from the room, down the hallway, past the bathroom towards the main bedroom. Her nightie, thank the Lord, was a roomy neck-to-ankle flannelette number—white with pink flowers on it and a sweet Peter Pan collar with lace edging—which didn't hinder her haste.

Hannah slid down the carpet runner into the open doorway like a hitter into first base, scrambling to keep upright by grabbing the doorframe. 'What is it?' she asked breathlessly, staring at Jack, who was sitting bolt-upright in the middle of the big brass bed, looking rather wild with his black wavy hair falling all over his face and his chin now dark with a two-day growth. 'Are you ill? Have you got your memory back? What? What?'

He scooped his dishevelled hair back with both hands, his mouth splitting into a wide smile of relief. 'Thank God. For a moment there I thought I was in the middle of a nightmare, or a Stephen King novel. I woke up not knowing where the hell I was. Then everything that happened yesterday came flooding back, and for a few appalling seconds I began to wonder if any of *that* was really real, or just a dream. You're not a dream, though, are you, Hannah? You're quite real.'

'I should think so,' she said, her teeth chattering as she stood there, hugging herself. 'Only real people freeze to death. So you haven't remembered any more of the last six weeks?'

'Not another second, I'm afraid. Damned annoying, isn't it? Maybe I'll never get those six weeks back. Maybe they're gone forever.'

Hannah had never even considered such a possibility, and she didn't like the idea one bit. 'The doctors seemed quite sure you would, Jack,' she said, praying they had been right. 'They said it was just a matter of time—that once the bruising on your brain went away you'd be back to normal.'

'What would they know?' he grumbled. 'You don't

honestly think they have amnesia victims wheeled in every day of the week, do you?'

'No, but if you weren't going to get your memory back at all, you wouldn't have even had those flashes last night. Try to be patient and stop worrying. Look, I'll just go and get my dressing-gown on. I'm freezing to death here.'

'Be my guest,' he muttered. 'That's the sort of nightie which a dressing-gown could only improve.'

It was the first critical thing Jack had ever said to her about her appearance and she bristled. 'It happens to be a very nice nightie,' she defended archly. 'And very practical.'

'Oh, I fully agree with you, Hannah. If ever there was a practical nightie, that one's it. It also has ''platonic'' written all over it!'

'Good,' she snapped. 'Because that's exactly the sort of relationship we're having this weekend.'

'Only till I get my memory back,' he countered, his blue eyes hard as nails. 'That *is* the agreement, isn't it?'

'Absolutely.'

'Well, when that happens—and it can't be too damned soon for my liking—I'm going to use that ghastly bloody nightie to light the fire!'

Hannah almost laughed. The only fire Jack was likely to light after he got his memory back was the fire of his own temper. He wasn't going to be at all happy with her for this pretence. Her boss had as much of an ego as any other man—and as much of a temper, as he was displaying at this very moment. If he thought she'd played him for a fool in any way, he would really hit the roof!

'Don't forget what the doctor said about your blood pressure,' she reminded him sweetly. 'How about I pop along and get us both some coffee? You're like me, Jack. You're never yourself in the mornings till you've had at least three cups.'

It had become something of a joke in the office, the amount of coffee the boss and his secretary consumed.

'I won't be long,' she said, and scurried off, happy to escape his grumpy company.

Hannah grimaced as she dragged on her pink chenille dressing-gown, sashing it loosely around her waist. Although lovely and warm, it was as maidenly as her nightie, as were her fluffy pink lambswool-lined slippers. Hannah hadn't liked Jack's comment about her nightie, or the way he'd looked at her in it. She'd much preferred the flattering way he'd stared at her in her jeans and jumper last night, and the compliments he's given her.

Still, she supposed it was wiser not to dress in any way which might revive his male urges. It was obvious by his bad mood and his pointed remarks that he was still feeling frustrated after last night. She suspected that Jack was one of those men who didn't like going without sex for too long.

Dwight wasn't really of that type—which was odd, since he'd been notoriously unfaithful. He could take it or leave it, especially when his mind and energy were occupied on more important things, such as money, power and success. Of course, Dwight liked challenges—and where was the challenge in bedding a wife? Those other little dolly-birds had been ego-boosts, not the result of an unquenchable thirst for sex.

Hannah wouldn't have been surprised if the girl he was now living with, and whom he planned to marry, had been not the object of passion but of ambition and pride. Dwight would get a real kick out of walking into a room with darling Delvene on his arm. For she was incredibly beautiful. Perfection, in fact.

She ought to be, Hannah thought with dry sarcasm. Dwight had operated on her often enough.

Hannah frowned, amazed that she could think of Dwight's betrayals this way, without feeling any real pain, without wanting to burst into tears. Who knew? Maybe she was getting over the hurt at long last.

It was certainly time she did—time to throw off old ghosts and go forward. If nothing else, last night had shown her that she was still a desirable woman with plenty to offer a man. Not everyone, she decided, with a burst of optimism and hope, wanted or expected physical perfection in their partner.

Hannah blinked with pleasant surprise, her new positive frame of mind suggesting to her that the small imperfections of her flesh were really just that. Very small. It was silly to keep being hung up about them because of Dwight's repeated and deliberately demeaning criticisms.

Her breasts didn't really sag all that much without a bra. Her hips were womanly, not wide. As for her stretchmarks... One would have to look darned hard to find them, since they were very low down and had faded over the years from purplish to pale pink.

Now Hannah frowned again. Such thinking might be good for her confidence and self-esteem, but it was downright dangerous to her resolves for this weekend. One of the only reasons she'd stopped Jack making love to her last night had been her negative feeling about her body. If she started thinking more confidently about herself in that way, she might find her boss's desires very hard to resist.

Hannah kept this thought to the forefront of her mind during a quick visit to the bathroom, where among other things she brushed out her hair, then knotted it severely at the nape of her neck. A brutally honest glance in the mirror told her that Jack wouldn't find her too desirable with her hair like that, her thirty-five-year-old face devoid of make-up and her eyes still slightly puffy from sleep.

She hurried out to the kitchen, which was still nicely warm from the combustion stove going most of the night. She was reviving it with a couple of fresh logs when a sensible thought crossed her mind and, after putting on the electric kettle, she marched back down the hall to the main bedroom.

Jack glanced up when she appeared in the doorway, his expression showing that the dressing-gown was as much out of favour as the nightie. 'And *that* little number will go in the charity bin,' he said testily. 'So where's the coffee?'

'Not ready yet. I was thinking, Jack,' she went on, steadfastly ignoring his disapproval in her appearance, 'it's much warmer in the kitchen than here in the bedroom. I couldn't find your dressing-gown when I looked yesterday, but there's an old one of Dwight's in the wardrobe. There's some slippers too, if you want. Why don't you put them on and come down to the kitchen for your morning coffee?'

Jack scowled down at her own slippers, shaking his head before looking up at her face. 'I get it,' he said, nodding wryly. 'This is your ''hands-off'' uniform. Waste of time, Hannah. I'm not a morning man, anyway. Besides, my head feels like it's full of cotton wool.'

'Perhaps you should take some of those tablets the doctor gave you yesterday.'

'Hell, no. They send me to sleep and make me feel worse. It's not a headache, exactly, just a thickness. It's probably part caffeine withdrawal. I'll get up, like you said, and consume a couple of gallons of coffee.'

'I'll see you shortly in the kitchen, then.'

Hannah couldn't help it. When he walked into the

kitchen she almost burst out laughing. Dwight's green checked dressing-gown was several sizes too small and he'd put some striped football socks on his feet in lieu of the slippers, which had undoubtedly proved too small for his big feet.

'If you dare laugh,' he snapped, glaring at her, 'you're fired!'

Hannah covered her mouth with both hands, but her eyes were dancing. Their eyes clashed, and suddenly he grinned at her. Soon, they were both laughing.

'So where *was* your dressing-gown?' she asked when she finally brought the mugs of steaming coffee over to the table, placing one in front of Jack, then carrying her own around to the opposite side of the table. 'I looked everywhere.'

'There *isn't* one,' he informed her, picking up the mug to sip appreciatively. After several mouthfuls, he sighed his satisfaction and put the mug down. 'Great coffee. I never wear a dressing-gown. I don't usually wear pyjamas either. These were a present from some female or other, but they've never been out of the drawer before. I only wore them in deference to your modesty and the cold. My place, as you know, is air-conditioned.'

'Oh,' she said, wishing his words didn't evoke such a vivid picture of him walking around his place in the nude. She fell uncomfortably silent, staring down into her coffee while she sipped.

'So what are we going to do all day?' he asked. 'You can't expect me to just lie around. I'm not a lying around sort of guy.'

Hannah had already thought of things they could do today, but suddenly her perverse mind added another way they could fill in the day. Feeling flustered for a moment, she took another sip of her coffee before putting down her mug and looking up, praying that there was no betraying heat in her cheeks. Jack's cool blue gaze across the table suggested that she was safe—for the moment.

'Well, after we're dressed and have had breakfast,' she suggested, 'I thought we might go on a long, slow bushwalk. That should help clear your head, and it's going to be a lovely day once the sun's well and truly up. Then, after lunch, I thought you might lie down in the sun on the veranda and either read or have a nap. There's a couch out there just made for napping. Then later, if you like, we could drive down to the shops at Leura, buy some take-away and pick up a couple of videos. Or, if you'd prefer, I could rustle up something here and we could just watch whatever's on TV.'

'Mmm. Can't remember the last Saturday I didn't work with Roger and co on-site somewhere. Which reminds me. Do you have a phone here? I'd like to ring Roger and have him fill me in on what's been going on during the past six weeks, building-wise.'

Hannah's stomach curled over. 'No,' she said curtly, panic making her sharp.

'No, what?'

'No, I don't have a phone here, and no, you're not going to ring Roger. The doctor ordered peace and quiet, and peace and quiet is what you're going to get! It's only two miserable days till Monday. Surely you can last two miserable days without Marshall Homes? Do you realise that people think you're a workaholic, Jack? There's more to life than work, you know.'

'I know that,' he growled. 'But the only other activity I enjoy in life has been temporarily banned!'

He glared at her, and she blushed furiously. 'I don't believe that's the only other thing you enjoy in life. If it is, that's a very narrow view, Jack. There are a lot of other things we could enjoy doing as a couple besides sex.'

'Are there, now? And what other things would you suggest I enjoy, Mrs Althorp? Going to the opera, perhaps? Visiting art galleries?'

'There's nothing wrong with enjoying art and music,' she defended hotly, while underneath recognising a degree of hypocrisy.

During her marriage to Dwight, he'd dragged her along to the opera and various trendy galleries all the time. Not because either of them had genuinely enjoyed or appreciated such activities, but because

Dwight had thought that that was the thing to do to rise in society.

Hannah had no doubt widened her mental horizons by going, and had learnt a good deal about that kind of music and art. But in all truth, she preferred listening to k d Lang rather than Joan Sutherland, and most modern art left her cold. She much preferred the old masters, or photographic prints, but when she'd said as much to Dwight he'd called her a Philistine of the first order.

But Jack didn't know any of that, and his sarcasm had sounded too much like criticism for her liking. It was the second time he'd criticised her this morning, and it was beginning to upset her.

'You're being very picky this morning,' she snapped. 'And in case you've forgotten, I stopped being Mrs Althorp some time back.'

'Did you? I don't think so, Hannah. I don't think so at all. He's left his mark on you, that bastard. One day you're going to tell me all about that wretched marriage of yours!'

'What makes you think I haven't already?' she flung at him.

Jack was taken aback for a second, sitting back in the chair, blue eyes wide. But then he moved back forward again, his hands cupping his mug, his expression quietly confident. 'Because I just know you haven't,' he said. 'Don't ask me how I know that, but I do.'

'Is that so?' she muttered.

'Yes, that's so. So why don't you tell me now? We've nothing much else to do today, so we might as well talk, don't you think?'

Hannah shrugged, her seeming indifference hiding instant tension. To talk about her marriage would be to hold herself and her inadequacies up to a mirror, which had never made her feel good.

'There's nothing much to tell,' she said brusquely. 'It's an old story. Brilliant working-class boy marries pretty, but not so brilliant working-class girl. He quickly goes up in the world and just as quickly leaves her behind. But by then she's had two children, and so, because he does have some affection for his sons, he tries to make over his unsuitable wife to a more suitable model, befitting his new successful life-style.

'Failure is inevitable, because of her unwillingness to co-operate fully, and eventually he starts looking round for someone else—which, of course, requires a lot of sampling before he makes up his mind. Finally he finds a near-perfect specimen, who's only too happy to have her slight imperfections corrected.'

'What imperfections?' Jack intervened, frowning. 'And in what way do you mean…corrected?'

'Didn't I ever tell you Dwight is a plastic surgeon?' Hannah tossed back, her own smile very plastic. 'A brilliant one, of course. He could have made me look twenty-five forever, if I'd have agreed, but stupid me didn't fancy going under the knife to win back his love. Stupid me wanted to be loved for myself.

'Clearly, dear Delvene doesn't have such scruples. Although she was already quite stunning, and only twenty-six, she's had her nose reshaped, her boobs enlarged, plus some negligible fat in her buttocks sucked out. Dwight was closely inspecting this last piece of handiwork in his surgery one day,' Hannah bit out, 'when his stupid wife walked in.

'When he had the gall to bawl me out for interrupting him during the examination of a patient, I pointed out to him—with superb indifference, I thought—that his fly was open. Then I walked out— of the office and of the marriage.'

She gulped down the lump which had filled her throat during this bitter version of her marriage, then glared at Jack's openly sympathetic expression, hating the pity in his blue eyes as they roved over her face. 'If you say, Poor Hannah, or anything like that,' she snapped, 'I'll scream.'

'All right, I won't,' he said, any lingering sympathy in his face so swiftly replaced by a matter-of-fact manner that she was startled out of her self-pitying state.

When he stood up abruptly, Hannah gaped up at him. 'Where are you going?'

'To have a shower and then get dressed. Oh, and don't make my bed for me, thank you. I'm quite capable of doing that for myself. I'm not an invalid. I

will let you cook me some breakfast, though. It's hard
to cook in someone else's kitchen. Whatever you've
got will do fine. I'm not fussy. Then, after breakfast,
I think we'll set out on that bushwalk you mentioned.
That sounds like just the thing.'

'Just the thing for what?' she asked, feeling both
rattled and instantly wary.

'Just the thing for getting some peace and quiet,'
he returned blandly. 'What else?'

CHAPTER FIVE

'THIS is some view,' Jack said. 'But you'd want to have steady feet.'

Hannah followed Jack's gaze into the valley below, where a mist was still rising from the depths of the forest-thick gorge. They were standing on the edge of a rocky outcrop, where the bush track turned sharply before winding its slow route downwards. Less than a metre ahead was a sheer drop, highlighting the dangers of such an untamed terrain.

Hannah had worried about the boys following this track when they'd been younger, and had always accompanied them, pointing out the pitfalls. But, with the passing of years, familiarity had bred a certain amount of contempt. The last time the three of them had been up here for the weekend Chris and Stuart had gone off on their own, and she hadn't felt a moment's concern.

Still, they were sensible boys. Good boys. And not boys for much longer. Chris would be fifteen in November, Stuart fourteen the following January. Her heart turned over as she thought of them. Divorce was always hard on children. At least they had each other, and they genuinely seemed to like their school, which

was large on sport and physical activities. Both boys
were into sport in a big way.

'You know, I have a definite feeling of *déjà vu*,
standing here,' Jack said slowly. 'Yet I've never been
in the Blue Mountains, to my knowledge. It's not an
area I'd ever choose to build in. As you know, I like
fairly level land. Rocky hillsides mean a fortune in
site preparation or extra foundations. I've never been
up here on holiday either, from what I can recall. You
did say you hadn't brought me up here during the last
six weeks, didn't you?'

He turned to face her, his question forcing her to
look up at him, which was highly unfortunate. She'd
been trying not to look at him too much, ever since
he'd reappeared in the kitchen for breakfast, dressed
as she'd never seen him dressed before.

When she'd gone up to his apartment yesterday, to
pack some clothes for him, Hannah had just grabbed
an assortment of warm tops and jeans, plus a couple
of jackets, choosing neutral colours which wouldn't
clash. Cream, white, grey and black. She'd expected
Jack to do what he always did—mix and match his
clothes pretty haphazardly. She'd never imagined for
a moment that he would choose to wear all black.

But he had—probably without realising the effect
it would have, or the fantasies it would evoke in Hannah's mind.

When he had strolled back into the kitchen after
his shower, his wet hair looking even blacker and

longer than usual, his face still unshaven and his tall, macho frame encased entirely in black from head to foot, Hannah's hazel eyes had nearly fallen out of her head. Even the scar on his cheekbone had added to the image he had unconsciously been projecting.

He'd looked wild, and wicked. And she'd wanted him to make love to her. Wildly and wickedly.

The only comfortable thing about that hot memory was that Jack hadn't been looking at her as he'd come into the room, giving her a few seconds to pull herself together before she'd served him his bacon and eggs.

When she looked up at him now, her feelings hadn't changed. She still felt the sexual impact of his bad-boy appearance, but at least she was learning to control those responses, learning not to gape or blush or drool.

Her eyes still travelled over him, however, noting the way the short leather jacket hugged his hips, showing how slim they were compared to the breadth of his chest and shoulders. Her gaze dropped further, to take in the taut curve of his buttocks before travelling down the muscular length of his legs, clearly outlined in his tight black jeans. Swallowing, she swept her eyes back up to his, hoping that she wasn't betraying the way her heart was suddenly thudding heavily in her chest.

It wasn't much comfort to find Jack staring back down at her, though she didn't think it was because he was similarly entranced with her own appearance in faded blue jeans, an ancient red jumper and an equally old dark navy duffle-coat. Her only surrender to femininity had been some red lipstick. Unless one also counted her leaving her hair down—although she'd told herself that that was for warmth, not because she wanted to look younger for Jack.

'Hannah?' he prompted, somewhat brusquely. 'I asked you a question. Have you or have you not brought me up here before?'

'No,' she told him quite truthfully. 'I haven't.'

He frowned, then turned to scowl at the panoramic scene before him, his narrowed gaze scouting the horizon with its unusual bluish haze then sweeping downwards. 'That waterfall seems very familiar,' he said, indicating the small stream of water which was cascading down the cliff opposite before settling in cool grey pools in the rocky creekbed below. 'I'm sure I've seen it before,' he muttered.

Hannah knew exactly what he was remembering without realising it—his recent jaunt up here with Felicia. Hannah hated thinking about his having spent the whole of last weekend in bed with that bitch—though whether her feelings were jealousy or guilt over her own present lustful state, she wasn't sure. She only knew that she wanted Jack herself. It was as simple at that.

'You must have seen hundreds of documentaries about the Blue Mountains on telly over the years,' she attempted to explain, though agitatedly. 'That's what you're probably remembering.'

His sideways glance was sharp. 'No,' he denied, 'it's not, and you know damned well it's not. You're lying to me, Hannah.'

She gasped when he grabbed her nearest shoulder and spun her to face him properly, his other hand taking possession of her other shoulder so that she was virtually imprisoned within twin steely holds. His eyes were just as steely as they darted fury and frustration down at her. 'Tell me the truth, damn it! I *have* been up here before, haven't I? When? Where? Doing what?'

She blushed under the images that sprang to mind. 'Can't you guess?' she threw up at him, her own temper frayed by his touch and his nearness. 'Since it wasn't work which brought you up here, then it had to be the only other thing you enjoy. But you weren't *here*, Jack. You were at a nearby guest-house.'

He frowned, obviously bewildered by her words. 'Why do you keep saying *you*, and not *we*. My God, Hannah, are you saying I was up here with some other woman? Are you accusing me of cheating on you?'

Her silence was both mutinous and wretched. Now she'd done it!

'I don't believe you,' he snapped, letting her shoulders go with an angry twist, then making the mistake of taking a step backwards.

Hannah seemed to see it all happening as though

in slow motion, horror rising within her as Jack over-balanced, his arms flailing wildly as he began to fall backwards, into the abyss.

Afterwards she did not know how she'd managed to grab one of those flailing hands, or how she'd stopped Jack's weight from pulling her over that cliff as well. She'd just screamed, then acted impulsively, instinctively, fuelled by a fear-filled burst of adrenalin.

'Jack,' she sobbed, when they both collapsed back on the ground together, a couple of metres from the top of the cliff. 'Oh, Jack.' And she clung to him, weeping and trembling.

'Hush, Hannah. Hush. I'm fine. You're fine. You saved me. Don't cry, now.'

But she couldn't stop crying or trembling, not for ages. They lay there on the ground, arms around each other, their bodies pressed together, Hannah crying and Jack comforting. She didn't really hear the soothing words he said, not after a while. The only physical awareness through the haze of her turbulent emotions was the heat of his body and the beat of his heart against hers. Gradually her shoulders stopped shaking and the tears dried up, and it was then that Jack rolled her over on to her back and kissed her.

She kissed him back.

Dear heaven, how she kissed him back—all the desire which had been building up within her finding full expression in her mouth. Her lips fed on his with avid hunger, her tongue savouring his, first in her own mouth, then in his. Her head lifted from the ground as she strained to make their mouths more as one, a raw, naked moan of need echoing deep in her throat.

Jack's head jerked up; he wrenched his lips away on a ragged gasp.

'God, Hannah,' he moaned, his hands pressing her shoulders back against the cold, hard ground.

She stared up at him, eyes as wide as her wet quivering mouth.

'You can't expect me to stop if we keep this up.'

'I don't want you to stop.'

'You can't mean that. You can't mean me to make love to you here.'

'Why not?' she whispered huskily, her hands reaching up to spear into the hair at his temples, her splayed fingers setting up a slow, erotic massage. 'Don't you want to, Jack?'

'Hell, yes. But I would have thought the boot was on the other foot, if I've been two-timing you.'

'I never said you had. That other business was before we…before we became involved with each other. It doesn't bother me any more,' she lied.

'Yes, but—'

'Just shut up, Jack,' she groaned, 'and kiss me.'

He groaned too, with a type of frustration, but his mouth sank back down on to hers and Hannah shuddered with pleasure. One kiss became two, then three, till neither of them were aware of the hardness of the ground under them, or the coolness of the air around them. Neither of them seemed aware of anything but each other.

Hannah certainly wasn't. She welcomed and answered Jack's increasingly savage kisses with a frenzy of her own. When his marauding mouth slid from hers to graze a hot wet trail across her cheek then downwards, she blindly turned her head to one side, as though offering up more expanse of creamy throat for his ravishment.

And ravish it he did, as wildly and wickedly as she'd been wanting him to. His hands swept her hair aside while his teeth joined his lips in a series of vampirish lovebites which sent the blood pounding through Hannah's veins.

Dazed, she lay there, arms flopped wide on the ground, revelling in the feel of his rough skin scraping over the softness of her throat, gasping at the sharp little nips to her flesh, quivering with pleasure whenever he clamped his mouth down and sucked...hard. A feverish heat swept over her skin, bringing an exquisite sensitivity to the areas on her neck he'd already ravaged and was at that moment ravaging, making them throb with an almost delicious pain.

A shaft of sunlight suddenly landed in Hannah's eyes and she instinctively squeezed them shut against the glare, only to find herself plunged into a world not just of darkness but of blisteringly heightened awareness. To feel, yet not to see, seemed to sharpen her senses. She felt heat gathering between her thighs, felt the swelling of her breasts under her clothes, felt the growing urgency of desire as it roared along her veins to inflame every sexual cell she owned. She was ready to be made love to as she'd never been ready before.

Jack must have reached the same pitch of passion, for suddenly he rolled on top of her, forcing her legs apart with his, his heavy male pelvis settling into the gap between her thighs. When his aroused flesh started pulsing against the melting valley between her legs Hannah answered his urging, her own hips lifting from the ground to grind frantically against him.

Her eyes flew open with a raw gasp when he wrenched open the waistband of her jeans, then yanked the zip down. He was kneeling back on his haunches, dragging at her clothes, his blue eyes glazed and glittering wildly.

A totally uncontrollable male of Jack's strength and size was outside of her experience, and while it seemed frightening at first, to find herself being stripped so roughly, Hannah eventually recognised her dry-mouthed, heart-racing reaction as excitement, not fear. She actually liked seeing Jack out of control this way—his face flushed with passion, his hands shaking, his breath coming in harsh, ragged pants.

He swore when he had trouble getting her jeans and panties over her boots, and in the end he yanked the boots right off.

Soon, she was naked from the waist down.

By this point Hannah hadn't much control left either. She might have been shocked back to some awareness of cold hard reality if her bare buttocks had been in direct contact with the cold hard ground, but her thigh-length duffle-coat was like a thick blanket under her.

Hannah's only feeling was a fierce impatience to have Jack back on top of her and inside her. Shaking, she sat up to help him take his own jeans down, not waiting for him to do more than ease his clothes down to mid-thigh before she pulled him back down on to her.

'Oh,' she gasped when she felt his naked hardness rub against the swollen lips of her desire. She cried out when he surged inside, stunned by the intensity of pleasure she felt at just being penetrated. She could not wait to have him fill her completely, to feel him move. Grasping his tautly bunched buttocks, she urged him deeper, then deeper, rocking her lower body in a frenzied rhythm.

Hannah was stunned by the speed and strength of her climax. It exploded within her and around him, spasm after violent spasm, quickly propelling him to a climax just as fierce, just as cataclysmic. She gasped at the feel of his flesh pumping powerfully into her, before her lips fell apart on a long, low moan. He muffled that moan by taking savage repossession of her mouth with his, his tongue driving deep, its undulating movements an erotic echo of what was happening inside her.

The Hannah who had brought Jack up here, full of good intentions, was shocked—both by the primitive nature of their mating and the feelings it was evoking in her. She knew, even as the passion began to ebb away, even as Jack's mouth slipped from hers in a sighing exhaustion, that she would never be the same person again.

She'd crossed a line with this raw surrender—abandoning any thought of right and wrong, giving in to the lust which had been building in her overnight, uncaring about anything but Jack's body blended with hers. The remnants of her conscience kept telling her that she should feel guilt and shame.

But she could not. She was too caught up with what had just happened, and the mind-blowing pleasure it had brought her. Her only concern now was Jack getting his memory back. She no longer wanted him to— at least, not for the rest of this weekend. She wanted him to stay in the darkness—with her—to make love to her over and over, to show her some of that incredible stamina Felicia had boasted about.

Already Hannah wanted him again.

Already...

Her face flamed with the admission. She could hardly believe the thoughts that were going through her head. It was as though she'd become a different woman—a wild, wicked, wilful woman, who wanted to experience everything lovemaking had to offer.

Jack levered himself up on to his elbows and stared down at her, as though he too was seeing a different woman. 'Is it always like that with us?' he said, clearly as shaken by the experience as she had been. That thought gave her even more pleasure. In one fell swoop Jack had wiped out all those years of Dwight telling her she had a very low sex-drive, implying that she was somehow…abnormal.

'Not quite,' she said, hardly recognising her own voice. It was low and husky, sleepy and sexy.

'It was…incredible,' he murmured, still looking a little stunned. 'Incredible…'

She reached up to run a fingertip over his lips, and he sucked in a startled breath. 'Are they sore?' she asked dreamily.

'Not as sore as your neck, I'll warrant. Good God, Hannah, I don't know what came over me. You'll be black and blue for days.'

She didn't doubt that. It crossed her mind that she'd never seen any lovebites on Felicia's neck. Which shouldn't have made her feel smug, but did somehow. 'My hair will cover it. Don't worry.'

'Don't *worry*! I didn't even think to use protection, yet I keep some in my wallet all the time. I've never ever not practised safe sex before. It's a religion with me.'

She reached up to cup his anguished face, her smile

soothing. 'Jack, darling, I'm on the pill.' Which was just as well, she realised, for she hadn't given much of a thought to such matters either.

'I've been taking it for years,' she went on, 'and when I left Dwight I simply didn't stop. Believe me when I say there's no chance of your becoming a father this weekend. And believe me when I also say there won't be any other unfortunate consequences from our making love without using protection.'

When she lifted her head from the ground and delivered a light little teasing kiss to his mouth, his nostrils flared, his startled eyes showing that he could not get used to such a Hannah as the one he was encountering. Hannah herself wasn't used to this new self of hers either. But she was loving it.

She'd never felt so confident in herself before. Or so rampantly sexual. She just had to kiss him again. Had to *have* him again.

Her hands snaked around his neck and she pulled him down, down on to her mouth and into the darkness once more. He half resisted for a few seconds, but when his flesh started to stir within her he moaned his surrender.

She gathered him in, body and soul, keeping herself half outside the experience at first while she revelled in Jack's rapidly escalating passion, exulted in the power of his surges, thrilled to the tremors that shook him whenever she dug her nails into his buttocks. There was a dizzying intoxication in the knowledge that she could arouse him so, could make him once again lose control.

Inevitably, though, she too was sucked into the whirlpool of need which already had Jack in its tenacious grip. Her heart began to hammer, her head threshed from side to side and her mouth gasped wide, dragging in air to breathe. His name was punched from her lungs, over and over, and when she finally splintered apart under him it was Jack who was ultimately triumphant, Jack who held her sobbing body in his arms afterwards, Jack who gently dressed her and began leading her home.

CHAPTER SIX

'ARE you all right?' he asked softly. 'You haven't said a word since we started back.'

'I'm fine,' she said, though a little shakily. What on earth had happened to her back there? Why had she cried so much afterwards? Why had she felt so shattered when Jack had held her close and comforted her?

'It happens that way sometimes,' Jack said, as though reading her mind and the worries whirling within it. 'We shouldn't have done it again so quickly. Though, damn it all,' he added, a wicked little smile twisting his lips as he looked down at her, 'it was bloody good, wasn't it? When do you think you could manage a third?'

She stared up at him, her mouth going dry at the prospect.

'Come now, Hannah,' Jack reprimanded her softly, taking her in his arms and pulling her hard against his body. 'There's no going backwards now. I always thought your idea of a platonic relationship till I got my memory back pretty silly anyway. We're engaged, woman. We're going to be married. We have every right to make love whenever we want to. Come on, I think a hot shower is called for, and some fresh clothes, then we'll light that living-room fire and snuggle up for the afternoon with some food and each other. What do you say?'

She should have said that no, they weren't engaged. No, they weren't going to be married. No, they had no right to make love whenever they wanted.

But Hannah didn't say any of those things. She was already melting with desire at that last thought, plus the scenario Jack had suggested.

She continued to stare up at him with brightly glistening eyes and slightly parted lips. He groaned, bending to kiss those lips, his arms tightening around her when their tonguetips met.

'God,' he muttered after a minute or two, his hands restless on her back. 'To think I wasted a whole year before I got to know the real you. Let's hurry, darling.'

He took her hand and practically dragged her back up the bush path, eager in his renewed passion. She went with him quite willingly, dazzled by his calling her 'darling', her conscience pushed steadfastly aside.

They had just rounded the last corner which would bring them into the back-yard of the cottage when Jack suddenly ground to a halt.

'What's that?' he asked, pulling Hannah over to one side of the path to stare down at a small brown bundle of fur lying in the long dry grass.

'I don't know,' Hannah said. 'But whatever it is, I don't think it's alive.'

Jack let go Hannah's hand to reach down and touch, moving the bundle carefully. As soon as Hannah saw the tail uncurl she knew what they were looking at. So did Jack.

'It's a ring-tailed possum,' he said.

'Dead?' Hannah asked, her heart turning over. Nothing moved her so much as the sight of a suffering animal. Better it were dead, she supposed, than mangled.

''Fraid so. She must have fallen out of the tree.'

Hannah glanced up into the branches of the huge overhanging eucalyptus, then back down at the poor dead possum. A branch lay on the ground nearby, one end sprouting forth with freshly jagged splinters, suggesting a recent break.

'Yes,' Jack said, seeing the direction of Hannah's eyes. 'I think she must have been on that branch when it broke.'

'How do you know it's a she?'

'Because there's a baby in her pouch,' he said, and drew out a tiny squirming ball of fur.

'Oh, the poor little darling!' Hannah exclaimed when it began to make frightened little noises, though it quickly quietened after Jack held it under his jacket, clearly finding some comfort in the warmth and darkness. When its head popped back out for a second, Hannah's heart squeezed tight. For it had the cutest little face, with velvety brown eyes, a tiny pink nose and small pointed ears.

'What a sweet little darling it is,' she said, with a wistful sigh.

'Now, don't go thinking you can look after it, Hannah,' he warned. 'Caring for an orphan ring-tailed possum is not the same as bringing up two boys, or even taking a useless bachelor under your wing.'

She blinked up at him. His return expression was wry. 'You do realise you mother me around the office, don't you? You bring in hot muffins every morning, in case I haven't had breakfast. You see all my bills are paid on time. You send out my clothes to the laundry and you even remind me sometimes when I should get a haircut.'

She blushed furiously, feeling oddly hurt by his teasing remarks.

'No, I'm not making fun of you—or complaining, or criticising,' he insisted. 'I *love* being looked after. It's something I never had when I was growing up and I've been selfish enough this past year or so to take advantage of your maternal instinct—although I think you get some pleasure out of doing these things. You're a born mother, Hannah.'

'Do you think that's what I want to do with you?' she snapped, still hurting inside. 'Mother you? I assure you that's the last thing on my mind where you're concerned, Jack.'

'So I've found out this weekend,' came his drily

amused reply. 'To my ever eternal appreciation, I might add. And I aim to take full advantage of that in future, too.'

'Do you, now?'

'Yes, as soon as we can deposit little Possie here somewhere safe. Do you know where the closest vet is?'

'No, actually, I don't,' she returned, her voice still sharp. Though she suspected that the sharpness was directed more at herself than at Jack. She could always say no to his making love to her, couldn't she? She could also enlighten him about who was really his fiancée if she was genuinely concerned by the increasing complications of the situation. *That* would put a halt to any lovemaking for a while; that was for sure!

But she already knew that she wouldn't do any of those things. Not today. Today she would let him do whatever he liked with her, whenever he liked, so fierce was her desire for him.

Hannah scooped in then let go a shuddering sigh of total surrender. She neither had the strength nor the will to fight the feelings he kept evoking within her. How could she, when they were all so new and so very, very exciting? She could not remember the last time she'd had a climax while making love, let alone anything like the ones she'd just experienced.

'I do know where we *could* take the possum,' she

suggested. 'Probably better than a veterinary hospital, too.'

'Then speak up. Where?'

'There's a lady lives just across the way who often raises orphaned baby animals—especially protected ones like this little fellow. She knows exactly what to feed them and how to look after them. I could take it over myself, if you'd prefer not to come.'

'Why would I do that?' He eyed her warily, no doubt having heard her sigh a moment ago.

She glanced down at his clothes, which were scuffed and dirty from rolling around on the ground. Hers weren't as bad, not being black, nothing a brush-down wouldn't fix. 'You're a bit of a mess,' she said simply.

'You're not much better, Hannah,' he countered drily. 'You might also want to put something around your neck before you go anywhere public. There's one spot which even your hair can't cover. Look, it won't take us a couple of minutes to shower and change. I don't think Possie here will expire in that time, do you?'

Hannah stood in front of the bathroom mirror after her shower, inspecting the damage. It was hard not to feel perturbed with the evidence of their primitive encounter starkly in front of her. Jack had been so right. There was one large purplish bruise at the base of her throat which was impossible to disguise, even with make-up.

She fingered it lightly, wincing and wondering if Jack bore the marks of her nails on his buttocks. The thought excited her. She stared into her own glittering eyes and vowed she would see for herself before this day was out—see and feel and kiss every single spot she'd branded with her passion out on that clifftop.

For the first time in ages she also looked objectively at her naked body, trying to see it with positive eyes and not through Dwight's warped view.

She was surprised and pleased to note that she *had* lost quite a few pounds since leaving Dwight—more than she'd realised. Not that she weighed herself any more. Hannah cringed when she thought of the humiliating way Dwight had used to make her get on the bathroom scales once a week, his comments scathing if she'd put on even half a kilo since the last weighing, his attitude still scornful if she'd only succeeded in maintaining her weight.

It also seemed that going to work had toned her up more than all those aerobic classes Dwight had insisted she attend.

Not that she had always gone. Sometimes she had slipped away to a movie, just to escape into another world for a while. And naturally one couldn't go to the movies without buying a large cup of popcorn plus a chocolate-coated ice-cream, all washed down sweetly with a huge Coke. Later, of course, Hannah had been consumed with guilt, and those had always been the weeks when the scales had told the tale—when Dwight had invariably pinched the beginning of a roll on her hips, his contempt obvious in his face.

She turned sideways and inspected her hips and bottom in the mirror, surprised to encounter not a hint of real flab or cellulite. Her hips *did* flare out from her waist, and her buttocks *were* well-rounded—nothing would ever change her natural body-shape—but enticingly, she thought, if a man liked womanly curves.

Turning back, she was satisfied to note that her stomach was fairly flat as well—only a small swell under her waist, which she didn't think unattractive. She had a nice navel, she thought. A neat little circle, dipping in.

Hannah's eyes lifted from her navel to above her waist, and she frowned. No way would her cup C breasts ever stand out high and perky as they had when she was nineteen. After nursing both her sons they'd settled in lower, heavier curves on her chest. In a push-up bra her bust was still very impressive, with a smashing cleavage if she ever chose to display it, but once the bra was removed the full globes did drop to a more natural outline.

Dwight had castigated her for breast-feeding the boys, saying it had ruined her figure. But she didn't really agree. Surely it was a matter of individual perception and taste? She thought the lusher look suited her womanly body. Nursing had certainly improved the shape and size of her nipples, which had been almost inverted before. Now they were well formed, pointy and highly sensitive. They'd also darkened from a pale rosy colour to a duskier shade of pink.

A banging on the bathroom door brought a gasp from her lips.

'What in hell are you doing in there, Hannah?' Jack called out. 'Get some clothes on and let's go.'

'OK. Won't be a sec. I'm just getting dressed now.'

Flushing, Hannah dived into the clothes she'd picked out for herself while Jack had showered and changed. Rather sexy black underwear, a pair of stone-washed grey jeans, a red polo-neck, which more than adequately covered her neck, and a stylish navy blue blazer-style cardigan with brass buttons.

She slipped her feet into navy loafers, then snatched up her hairbrush.

Despite her heart racing, she took some time to do her hair, parting it carefully and smoothing it down to her shoulders, where she used the circular brush to tease and turn the natural curl under, then spraying it to keep it in place. Full make-up was out of the question, but she stroked a little mascara on her lashes then applied some red lipstick, finishing up with a small spray of Sunflowers perfume. Hannah suspected that she would not get another opportunity for feminine titivating before Jack made love to her again, and she wanted to be at her best for him.

Thinking about Jack making love to her certainly brought colour to her cheeks, so there wasn't any need for blusher. Hannah took one last glance at herself, decided she looked pretty good, swallowed nervously, then exited the bathroom—only to find Jack pacing up and down the hall, talking to the baby possum in his hands and looking absolutely gorgeous in tight faded blue jeans and a huge cream cable-knit sweater.

He ground to a halt at her reappearance, glaring at her as a Viking might have glared at some maiden he was about to ravish.

'Damn, you look good enough to eat,' he muttered, his eyes sweeping over her, then fastening on her scarlet mouth. 'What a time to have to play Florence Nightingale to a possum! Still, I dare say we couldn't relax and enjoy ourselves while this poor little thing went to the big eucalyptus tree in the sky. So, where exactly is this lady's place?' he asked, tucking Possie under his jumper.

'Only about a hundred metres away, actually. We go back up the track I drove down last night for a short distance, then turn right along a small path through thick bush which opens out into a clearing. Marion's house stands right on the back edge of that clearing, overlooking the valley.'

'Is that her name? Marion?'

'Yes. Marion Cooper. She's married and her husband's name is Edward. Oh, and Jack, let's not mention your amnesia.'

'Why in hell would I mention it? We're just going to leave the possum and come straight back, aren't we?'

'Well…er…yes, I suppose so.'

'Let's go, then. The sooner we get there, the sooner we'll get back.'

Hannah hurried after him out of the house, stopping only long enough to lock up and stuff the key back in the geranium pot. She suspected that they might not get back as quickly as Jack anticipated, for Marion was not the sort of woman you dumped a possum on, then swiftly left. Neither was her husband given to letting a visitor get away, however unexpected. In a way, it was going to be interesting to see how Jack handled them both.

CHAPTER SEVEN

'HANNAH!' Marion cried with obvious and abundant pleasure when she opened the front door.

In her mid-fifties, Marion was a very big woman, tall as well as wide, given to wearing voluminous caftans in vivid Hawaiian patterns, regardless of the season. Today, her ankle-length dress had a white background with a red hibiscus print—the same outrageous red as her red frizzy hair.

'How nice of you to come and visit us,' she gushed, bright blue eyes twinkling. 'Edward!' she called back into the house. 'Hannah's here. And she's brought a friend. Light the barbecue, darling, and get out some wine.'

She turned back to face an already flustered Hannah. 'Well, aren't you going to introduce me to this gorgeous man?' she said, staring past Hannah straight at Jack.

Hannah cast a worried glance over her shoulder at Jack, met his drily amused eyes, and relaxed. 'This is Jack Marshall, Marion. My...er...um...'

'Fiancé,' Jack put in solidly before she could decide what to call him.

'*Fiancé*!' Marion exclaimed, looking from Hannah

to Jack to Hannah again. 'But you said nothing last weekend about being engaged when we ran into each other down at the shops.' Marion managed to sound mildly aggrieved and absolutely intrigued at the same time.

'It…er…it only happened this last week.'

'Oh, how lovely! I'm so happy for you, dear. I was worried that you might not want to get married again after putting up with that frightful husband of yours for years. But I'm so pleased you are. Life is far too lonely without a partner to share it with. I'd be lost without my Edward.'

She gave Jack the once-over, her expression admiring. 'And haven't you done well for yourself this time! Now, this one is a *real* man, if looks are anything to go by—which of course they aren't, but it's a nice start. Marshall, did you say your surname was?' she rattled on, frowning first at Jack then back at Hannah. 'You work for Marshall Homes nowadays, don't you, dear?

'Yes.' Hannah felt a guilty blush gathering.

Marion's pencilled eyebrows lifted, her blue eyes twinkling some more. 'But how romantic! Now, do come along inside, both of you. It's rather fresh out. Much warmer in the family-room.'

A sideways glance at Jack reassured Hannah that he was resigned to at least a short visit. Marion did rather overwhelm one, but she was such a generous soul underneath that Hannah didn't like to say no to her impromptu invitations.

Hannah had met her soon after Dwight had bought the cottage, succumbing to an on-the-spot invitation to dinner when they'd met down at the local video store. Dwight, however, had never hidden his contempt for a woman who looked and dressed as Marion did, though he had tolerated her company occasionally, in order to drink some of her husband's rare red wines.

'Actually, Marion, we didn't come over to impose ourselves on you,' Hannah elaborated swiftly as they were ushered inside. 'We found a dead ring-tailed possum in the bush this morning, and it had a baby still alive in its pouch. I told Jack you were just the person to look after it.'

'A baby ring-tail!' she cried, clapping her plump hands together in a gesture of prayerful gratitude. 'Oh, I just *adore* baby ring-tails! Where is the poor little darling? You have brought it with you, haven't you?'

Jack lifted his jumper and extracted his furry passenger, Marion's face just melting as he put the curled up ball into her motherly arms. 'We've called him Possie,' he said, surprising Hannah with the catch in his voice. It seemed that the little possum's plight had managed to spark an emotional response in the macho man by her side, evoking his protective instinct—or perhaps even his paternal instinct?

'Don't you worry, pet,' Marion reassured him—the 'pet' aimed at a startled Jack, not the possum. 'I'll look after your Possie. Ah, there you are, Edward. Take our guests down to the family-room, will you? And get them a drink. I'll whisk this little sweetie out into the kitchen and fix him up with a bed and a bottle. Yes, it *is* a him,' she added after a quick look. 'Oh, and by the way, Edward,' she threw over her shoulder as she waddled off, 'Hannah and Jack are engaged. He's Jack Marshall of Marshall Homes. Hannah's boss. Don't you think that's romantic?'

Edward said that it was, shaking his head as his wife went off, clucking and cooing over her new baby.

In his early sixties, he was as lean as Marion was wide. A very tall, aesthetically elegant man, he had silver-grey hair, a stylish silver beard, and a strong Roman nose separating intelligent grey eyes. Dressed in dark grey trousers, a polo-necked blue pullover and a tweedy jacket with leather patches on the elbows, he looked like a country squire or the conductor of a symphony orchestra. He was, in fact, a retired public servant who had a passion for all things fine—music, books, wine. And his wife.

He was Marion's second husband, her first having divorced her when she was twenty-five after they'd found out she couldn't have children. Crushed, she'd turned to food for comfort over the next twenty years, and had been a staggering two hundred kilos when she'd met Edward in a doctor's waiting-room. He had been a widower at the time, with a grown family.

They'd clicked immediately, and under Edward's encouragement Marion had trimmed down to a much healthier one hundred kilos, at which point he'd told her that he liked her as she was, and that if she didn't want to diet any further it was all right by him. Ten years after their marriage they were still inseparable, living up here in their mountain hideaway.

'You do realise that I'm going to be seriously neglected for at least a week,' Edward said drily as he led them into the gloriously spacious family-room which Hannah had always admired.

It stretched across the back of the house, floor-to-ceiling windows giving an unimpeded view of the mountains in the distance and sliding glass doors leading out on to a wide wooden deck which overlooked the valley below. Facing north, the room was pleasantly warmed by the winter sun—Edward only having to light the open stone fireplace on overcast days.

A long benchlike table stretched under the middle window, bathed in sunlight but littered with books and magazines of all sorts. Edward scooped up the magazines and dumped them in the nearest corner, just missing a large Persian cat which was stretched out, sleeping in a pool of sunlight. It didn't even flinch, showing that it was used to Edward's haphazard method of tidying up.

'Choose a chair,' he directed. 'If you can find an empty one.' In truth, most were occupied by other feline creatures of various breeds—all of them reluctant to give up their favourite spots. Jack managed to find a free seat, but Hannah ended up sharing hers with an overweight Abyssinian.

'You've more cats than ever, Edward,' Hannah remarked.

'True,' Edward said resignedly. 'Marion can't resist them. She likes having animals around her, but after all the demands her native orphans put on her she needs her own pets to be of the independent type. When she finally comes in here to relax, she doesn't want any animal needing anything more from her than one feed a day and the odd stroke.'

'Why does she do it?' Jack asked. 'Raise native orphans, that is.'

'It satisfies her maternal instinct,' Edward said. 'Marion can't have children, you see. Didn't Hannah tell you?'

'Er…no, she didn't.'

'Sad thing, not being able to have children.'

'I wouldn't know,' Jack said rather stiffly. 'I've never wanted to have any myself.'

'Really? Why's that?'

Jack shrugged, but underneath the seemingly nonchalant gesture Hannah detected a degree of discomfort. This was clearly something he didn't like talking about. 'I guess I don't see myself as good father material at this late stage,' he muttered. 'I'll be thirty-five next birthday.'

'Positively ancient,' Edward chuckled drily. 'So what shall I get for us to drink, Hannah? A nice Hunter Hermitage to go with our steaks, I think. And some tawny port for afterwards. Have you any preferences, Jack?'

When Jack hesitated before answering Edward looked perplexed. 'You *are* staying for lunch, aren't you? I've already started up the gas barbecue outside.'

'Of course they're staying,' Marion said as she bustled in, carrying Possie in what looked like a tiny Christmas stocking made out of a satin-edged blanket. His little mouth was clamped on to a miniature bottle, sucking madly, and his tiny paws clasped around it much like any other baby. 'A nice Hermitage will be perfect! Here, Jack, you finish giving Possie his bottle while Hannah helps me make some salad.'

'*Me!*' Jack sat bolt-upright, looking aghast.

'Why not? You'll want to get your hand in at feeding babies if you're going to marry Hannah. If I know her, she'll want some more sons—or maybe even a daughter.'

Edward cleared his throat. 'Er…Marion, love, Jack says he doesn't want children.'

Marion flashed Jack a look which one would have given to an escaped serial killer. But then she laughed. 'Don't be ridiculous, Edward. Everyone *wants* children. If Jack says he doesn't it's probably because there's something wrong with him. Maybe he has some sort of congenital defect which he doesn't want to pass on—isn't that right, Jack?'

Hannah's heart turned over with sympathy for Marion. The woman's deep pain at not being able to have children had never been more obvious. She simply could not accept that anyone would choose not to have them.

Hannah caught Jack's eye across the table, silently pleading with him to be gentle with the obviously distraught woman. He nodded almost imperceptibly, then looked up at their tensely waiting hostess. 'You're quite right, Marion,' he said gently. 'I do have a problem which I would not want to pass on to any children of mine. How very astute of you to realise that.'

He sent Hannah an odd look, and it crossed her mind that maybe he wasn't lying. Maybe he *did* have something wrong with him. He certainly was very emphatic about not having children. She stared thoughtfully back at him, but before she could glean the truth from his face he turned his eyes back to Marion, who was now bathing him in the full force of her own sympathy.

'Oh, dear. You poor man. But we must not dwell on what we cannot change, must we? We simply have to get on with our lives and do what we can. Which includes looking after poor little mites like this fellow, who can't look after himself. So here...' She thrust the bundle and bottle into Jack's startled arms. 'Have a taste of second-hand fatherhood! You might find you like it.'

Hannah watched, totally intrigued, while Jack's face went from frightened to fascinated to downright infatuated within no time at all. He couldn't seem to take his eyes off the baby possum as it gleefully sucked on the bottle, at the same time appearing to stare adoringly up into the man's face above. I know you, those soft brown eyes seemed to say. You saved me. You're my hero. I love you.

Tears welled up into Hannah's eyes and she had to turn away, a choking emotion filling her heart and her throat. It was a silly, typically feminine reaction to sentimental thoughts, but she could not help it, and it embarrassed her. Hoping no one was noticing, she looked down and blinked madly, surreptitiously wiping the corners of her eyes and not looking up again till she felt in better control.

But when she did, Marion was staring straight at her with a puzzled expression. Hannah somehow found what she hoped was a disarming smile and stood up. 'You did say you wanted me to help you with some salad, didn't you, Marion?'

'I certainly did. And you, Edward,' she ordered, 'down to the wine cellar!'

Hannah thought she'd successfully sidetracked Marion from any awkward questions, but no sooner had she begun cutting up the assortment of vegetables

Marion placed on the chopping-board than the inquisition began—and it was an inquisition, despite it being couched in more tactful terminology then earlier on.

'Jack's a very good-looking man,' she said carefully. 'And I'm sure he's a wonderful lover. But do you think marriage is a wise course, Hannah? Your divorce has only just come through, hasn't it?'

Hannah swallowed, then decided not to take this conversation too seriously. It wasn't as though she was really going to marry Jack. 'Don't worry, I won't be rushing into the actual wedding, Marion. I'm aware this...er...relationship could be a bit of a rebound reaction. But it's very nice having a man treat you the way Jack treats me.'

'He's kind, is he?'

A warm feeling washed through Hannah. 'Oh, yes...he's very kind.'

'That's good. I hope you don't mind my saying so, but Dwight was an out and out pig of a man. The way he put you down in front of us used to make me seethe. If he hadn't stopped coming up here with you when he did, I would have stopped inviting you over—simply because I could not bear to see you so unhappy. I don't know how you stood it for so long.'

Hannah's sigh carried a wealth of remembered misery. 'I don't know how I did either. But he...he had such a domineering personality, Marion. When I first met him I thought he was wonderful. I actually admired his intelligence and ambition. Once I married him, though, I began to see his flaws. There was a meanness about his inbuilt arrogance—a desire to belittle others to make himself feel even better and smarter. I, being his wife, was the perfect target. I was his whipping boy, and, because I thought I loved him, I allowed myself to be whipped.'

'You're not saying he beat you, are you?'

'No. He was never abusive. Not physically. But there are all kinds of abuse, Marion. I've only recently come to realise that he abused me mentally and emotionally. His constant complaints and criticisms robbed me of all my self-respect and self-esteem, whittling away at it over the years till I really believed I was fat and stupid and undesirable.'

'Fat!' Marion's eyes bulged with shock. 'And stupid? And undesirable? *You*?'

'Yes, I know,' Hannah said with a sad sigh. 'That's how sick in the head he made me. Towards the end, I believed everything he told me.'

Marion was shaking her head. 'Dear heaven, that's terrible. And was he critical of the boys as well?'

'Would you believe me if I said no? They could do no wrong. But there again, he probably saw them as being in his own image and likeness. They do look very much like Dwight, you know, though actually they're not at all like him in nature. They're physical rather than intellectual boys. Thank the Lord they're pretty smart too, so he hasn't noticed yet.'

'You have joint custody, don't you?'

'Yes. To give Dwight credit, he hasn't been vindictive about the boys. Of course, by the time I left him he'd been about to leave me anyway, having found his perfect spouse.'

'Perfect in what way?'

'Oh, physically. And sexually too, I guess. Naturally I never did measure up in that department either. He was giving his new choice a final audition in his surgery one day when I walked in on them. Oddly enough, my reaction was a cold anger—not shock. Underneath, I'd known for ages he was having affairs. But seeing it for myself seemed to fill me with the courage to change my life. Luckily the boys were in school, so I moved out that day and a month later started working for Jack as his secretary. He…he—'

Hannah broke off, a prickle of awareness at the back of her neck making her turn her head and look over to the doorway which led back into the family room. Jack was standing there, staring at her. How long he'd been standing there or how much he'd overheard, she had no idea. His blue eyes gave nothing away, remaining cool and unreadable.

Marion looked around and saw Jack too. 'He's finished the bottle, has he?' she said, putting down her knife and walking over to him. 'How did it go?'

Jack's face broke into a smile. 'Great. He's a greedy little beggar. Didn't leave a drop.'

'That's good. I'll just take him out and hang him up in the laundry.'

Jack looked taken aback. 'Hang him up? What do you mean?'

'I have an assortment of pegs on the walls, where I hang all kinds of beds for all kinds of babies who are used to being in trees. They seem to like the arrangement. Come with me and I'll show you. Be back in a sec, Hannah. Just keep chopping.'

Hannah kept chopping, hoping that Jack hadn't heard too much. She didn't think that he had. Maybe just the last little bit, about her walking in on Dwight and Delvene. He already knew about that anyway. She'd told him herself. But her earlier very brief recounting of her marriage and its break-up had not revealed the depth of Dwight's domination over her person and personality.

It was one thing to tell Marion she'd allowed herself to be bullied and humiliated by her husband for years, quite another for Jack to know about her belittlement and abasement. The only way she wanted Jack to look at her was with admiration and desire—never pity or, dear God, disgust.

Still, it had felt good to tell a sympathetic ear what a swine her husband had been. Perhaps it was something she should have done months ago, but she'd been too ashamed, believing that she should not have put up with such degrading treatment for so long.

Hannah could see now that one of the reasons she

had was because she had had no family support, no one close she could go to for help and advice. She was an only child, and her mother had died many years before, when Hannah had been just fifteen. Her father had insisted she leave school shortly afterwards and do a secretarial course, so that she could earn money and help support his gambling habit. He had been a cold, unloving man, and she'd felt no guilt whatsoever over leaving the family home as soon as she'd secured a decent paying job which would support her.

When her father had turned up at her office one day and made a big scene, she'd been asked to leave, so Hannah had moved further, from Wollongong up to Sydney, getting a job at Sydney University as secretary to one of the professors at the Faculty of Medicine. She'd met Dwight there, when he had come to the university one day as a guest lecturer on plastic surgery. He'd been twenty-nine to her nineteen. He'd asked her out and been astounded when she wouldn't sleep with him on their first date. Or their second. Or their tenth.

He'd married her three months later—Hannah still a virgin.

Looking back, she could appreciate now that their wedding-night had proved a big disappointment to him—she'd cried all night from the pain of their first encounter, not letting him near her again. Things had improved the next night, but clearly she had never fulfilled the sexual fantasies that had propelled him into marrying a girl who'd obviously been too young and too shy for him.

In fact, she doubted that Dwight's sexual infatuation had lasted much longer than it had taken her to get pregnant. Since their first son, Chris, had been born exactly nine months and one week after their wedding-day, the writing had been on the wall from the word go.

Hannah's mulling over her marriage was interrupted by Jack and Marion returning, arm in arm, both commenting smugly over Possie's progress. Apparently, after Marion had attended to the animal's toiletry needs with some tissues, the little devil had curled up in his pretend pouch and gone straight to sleep.

'What a good baby he is,' Jack told Hannah proudly. 'A right little trouper!'

Marion chuckled. 'Give him a couple of hours and he'll be whingeing out there with the best of them. Still, that gives us time to feed our own faces and have a nice long chat. I wonder what *vin extraordinaire* Edward has selected for our delectation this afternoon?'

'Actually, Marion, I'm just a beer man myself,' Jack informed his hostess, and she laughed.

'Not for long, dear man. I don't know anyone Edward hasn't corrupted to the sort of grape he serves. But I'll make a deal with you. Have one glass, and if you don't like it I'll bring you some beer. Fair enough?'

Jack had more than one glass. He had more than one bottle! A grandfather clock was chiming five by the time they left Marion and Edward's place—Jack having insisted that they stay, not just for one but for two more possum-feeds.

'Come back and visit again tomorrow!' Marion offered as they left, to which Jack happily agreed.

'You really liked them, didn't you?' Hannah said as they made their way back down the bush track, the setting sun throwing deep shadows across their path. 'It's not just the possum.'

'Why so surprised, Hannah?' His arm stole around her shoulders and he pulled her close, reminding her forcibly of where they'd been before they'd found the baby possum and gone to the Coopers' place five hours earlier.

'Most people find Marion a little…er…pushy.'

'Most people, Hannah? Or just that unfeeling sadistic bastard you were married to?'

Hannah's eyes dropped to the ground. 'Oh…so you did overhear.'

He turned her to face him, but she kept her eyes lowered, feeling mortified.

'Look at me, Hannah.'

She did—slowly, unhappily. 'What?'

'I'm not going to ask you about him. Or your marriage. I heard quite enough. I'm just going to tell you that I find you beautiful, and clever, and quite, quite wonderful. I meant it the other night when I said you were more woman than any I would ever have thought to possess. I'm crazy about you, Hannah. When are you going to marry me?'

CHAPTER EIGHT

HANNAH'S hesitation frustrated him.

'Don't come out with that "wait till you get your memory back first" crap,' he growled. 'Can't you see I'll never get those six weeks back? They're gone, Hannah. Whoosh! And who cares? I can remember the most important part—my sexy secretary and hopefully soon-to-be wife.'

Hannah blinked up at him. 'You really find me sexy, Jack?'

'Distractingly. I always thought you extremely desirable, but I was deceived by your ladylike manner into thinking you were somehow above sex for sex's sake. I used to watch you at work and wonder if you ever looked at a man—yours truly included—and really fancied him in the most basic way.

'I used to fantasise about being alone with you in the office—late at night—and suddenly those lovely hazel eyes of yours would start looking me over with such a raw, naked need that I would be instantly hard. I won't tell you the rest of my fantasy or you'll think me very crude. Suffice it to say I can well imagine how I reacted at finding you in my arms that night in the office.'

'What night?' For a split-second Hannah had forgotten about the story she'd told Jack concerning the way they'd first become physically involved. 'Oh, yes. That…that…night. I…er…I don't like talking about that when you can't remember it.'

'Not to worry. I'm having fun making new memories of what we're like together. If this morning is anything to go by I can't wait for more. Still, I think a more leisurely session is called for, don't you?'

He snaked his hands around her waist under her cardigan, then down over her bejeaned buttocks, caressing and kneading them with strong, knowing fingers. When he pulled her close, moulding her stomach around his starkly aroused flesh, her heart kicked over violently and her eyes widened on his.

'I'm going to take you home, light that fire in the living-room and make love to you,' he said thickly. 'Every time you waver from the idea of being my wife I aim to make love to you. If necessary, I'll make love to you all night. You're going to say yes to me in ways you haven't even thought of yet,' he vowed darkly. 'And when morning comes, you're going to say yes to me in the only way that matters. You're going to say yes to our marriage, once and for all!'

Hannah stared up at him, totally speechless as he swung her up into his arms and started carrying her back towards the house. By the time he made it up the front steps on to the porch some small measure of conscience had kicked back into her brain, and she tried to say something. But it was then that he kissed her, firmly dispensing with any scruples.

'The door's locked,' she whispered when he lifted his mouth from hers to try the doorknob. 'Lean me down to that geranium pot and I'll get the key.'

'Bloody stupid place for a key,' he muttered.

'Yes,' she agreed dazedly. She would have agreed to anything at that moment. 'Shall I put it in for you?'

'Don't be provocative,' he growled, and she blushed fiercely. 'But, yes, you'd better. I've got my arms full.'

'You're very strong,' she said as he carried her inside and kicked the door shut behind them.

'Having a physical profession does have some pluses, I guess.'

Her hands slid over his chest, feeling its power beneath his jumper. 'You have a great body, Jack.' What she'd seen of it, that was. Presently she aimed to see a whole lot more. And touch a whole lot more.

'It's all yours, love,' he said as he angled her through the living-room doorway. 'Hell, but it's freezing in here. Do you think we should give this room a miss, put on the electric blanket and dive into bed?'

Hannah looked rather glazedly up into his glittering blue eyes, happy to go along with whatever he wanted.

'No,' he went on, before she could say a thing. 'I don't fancy that at all. Since I can't remember if I've brought my office fantasy about you to life, we're going to live out the one that played through my mind last night, on that sofa over there. Correction. On those *two* sofas over there. I take it you've no objections?' he asked, his mouth dropping to brush seductive lips over hers.

'Whatever you want, Jack,' she agreed huskily, the blood beginning to pound a sensuous beat in her temples.

'You shouldn't make such broad-sweeping promises,' he said, and lowered her back on to shaky feet. She swayed and he caught her to him, their eyes locking, their mutual passion pulsating through the air around them. 'I just might take you at your word.'

For several exquisitely tense moments she thought he was going to strip her and take her on the sofa then and there. But eventually he let out a ragged sigh and put her from him, a wry smile twisting his mouth. 'Patience, Jack,' he muttered to himself. 'All good things come to those who wait. Show me where to get the wood, Hannah. I have no intention of spoiling a whole evening of potential pleasure for a few seconds of instant gratification.'

The next half an hour was the most excruciating half-hour of Hannah's life. They both went about the task of making the house warm and comfy for the approaching night—collecting a good supply of wood then lighting and building up both fires, first in the living-room and then in the kitchen.

Neither looked at each other much, underlining the

sexual tension gripping both of them, but the delay—
plus Jack's obvious intention of making love for
hours in the living-room and not in a bed—had res-
urrected several of Hannah's old doubts about her fig-
ure-faults. She hoped he wouldn't be disappointed in
her body. She hoped he wouldn't be disappointed in
her.

This morning, out in the bush, had been entirely
different. They hadn't even taken off all their clothes,
their mating being more of the 'wham-bam thank you,
ma'am' variety.

Not that she'd minded. It had been what she'd
wanted. What they'd both wanted. Technique hadn't
come into it. It had all been raw, primitive passion,
with no thought of who should do what, where, or for
how long. What Jack called a more leisurely lovemaking session, however, evoked all sorts of misgivings and inadequacies in Hannah.

Dusk came while they were busy with the fire in
the kitchen.

When Hannah left Jack there to walk back down
the hall to check the living-room fire, she found the
room very dim, with only the glow from the now
roaring fire throwing off any light. She automatically
reached up to turn on the switch just inside the doorway, crying out with fright when Jack's hand suddenly covered her hand, removing it from the switch.
Her eyes flew to his, puzzled, reproachful of his
frightening her like that.

'That kind of light is not in my fantasy,' he explained softly, lifting her hand to his lips and sipping at each fingertip in turn.

Hannah stared at him, transfixed when he started sucking her middle finger into his mouth, only an inch at first, then deeper…deeper…

'I…I thought only women had fantasies,' she choked out.

He withdrew her finger, his chuckle like dark velvet. 'Don't you believe it. I suspect, however, that a man's fantasies are a little more starkly sexual than a woman's.'

'And don't *you* believe *that*,' she whispered, hazel eyes heavy as her finger moved to seek re-entry.

She saw the flare of surprise in his own eyes, but then they narrowed and darkened as he sucked her finger back into his mouth, watching her all the while.

Hannah was in a daze of desire, her heart thudding behind her ribs, her stomach curling over. God but she actually wanted to do that to him—and not just to his finger either. She wanted to do a whole lot of things she'd never wanted before.

Heat bloomed up into her face at this admission. Or was it a confession? Dwight had insisted she do all sorts of things she hadn't really wanted to do, and of course, because she'd loved her husband—or believed she had—she'd complied. But she hadn't been at all comfortable with a lot of his demands, her feelings ranging from embarrassment to revulsion to fear that she would not do them right.

She had always been afraid of any activities which she might not perform to Dwight's perfectionist standards—such as herself being on top. On the few occasions she'd done *that*, in the early years of their marriage, Hannah had felt humiliated by Dwight's instructing her all the time she'd been doing it—telling her which muscles to squeeze, how far to lift her body before lowering it, when to lean down so that he could suck her nipples at the same time.

It had been impossible to find pleasure with his lecturing and criticising her all the time. She'd also frozen during other positions which she'd felt Dwight had demanded in order to humiliate her, to make her feel subjective to him.

But now...

A tremor quivered through her as she began to see the whole spectrum of lovemaking very differently. Doing things right didn't seem to come into it. Neither did thoughts of humiliation, or of demeaning positions. She wanted to do them all—mindlessly, madly. Jack had been right in saying that she would say yes to him in ways she had never thought of yet.

She would.

Did he know that she would? came the shaky thought. Could he see the abandonment in her eyes, the wanton willingness?

Perhaps. Probably. She really didn't care. She

didn't care about anything any more, except Jack making love to her.

'Jack,' she murmured without thinking.

'Mmm?'

'Make love to me.'

His dark brows arched slightly before settling back into their normal beetling position, his hooded eyes the colour of the night in the dimly lit room. He took her finger from his mouth, slowly curling its wet length under, then enfolding her whole hand in his while he led her over in front of the fire.

'Stay there,' he said, placing her so that her back was towards the heat. 'There's something I have to do first.'

Hannah watched, intrigued, while he moved the nearby furniture with quick, decisive movements, lifting the coffee-table and side-tables out of the way, then pushing the matching sofas together to form a large bed with sides.

'Won't be a sec,' he said, striding from the room, only to return less than a minute later with the quilt and pillows from the brass bed. When he spread the quilt across the sofa-bed base, tucking in all the sides and smoothing it out, Hannah realised that he wasn't planning on bringing anything to cover them. They were to lie in there naked.

Once again, her confidence was momentarily undermined, till she glanced around the room and realised how flattering the light was. Her stretchmarks—

even the little ones on her breasts—would hardly be visible in the warm golden glow of the fire. Everything, in fact, would look softer and younger and better.

'There!' Jack announced smugly, straightening to stand at the far end of the sofa-bed, glancing around the room. 'Have I forgotten anything? Ah, yes, the door. Can't let any of this delicious heat out.' And he moved over to close it, turning afterwards to face her across the room, his back against the door.

He was well outside the circle of light which radiated from the fire, so she could not make out the expression on his face. Or his face at all, for that matter. But she saw his arms cross over to grip the bottom of his cream jumper, saw him tug the garment up over his head and toss it aside.

He stood there, naked to the waist but still in shadow. She could just make out the impressive proportions of his shoulders and torso, but not much else.

'Take off your cardigan,' he ordered from the darkness, his voice low and fuzzy.

She hesitated, then did as he asked, her hands shaking.

'Drop it on the floor.'

She did.

'Now the sweater.'

It fell in a red pile on top of the cardigan, leaving her standing there with only a skimpy black lace bra between herself and nudity from the waist up. Her heart was pounding in her chest, her mouth drying as she wondered whether he would ask her to remove that as well.

'The bra too,' he husked, and the breath hissed between her teeth.

'No!' he counter-commanded, when her hands stretched shakily up behind her to undo the clasp. 'No…'

He came towards her then, breaking into the light, revealing a chest as magnificent and primitive-looking as she'd imagined. The colour of teak, it was covered by a fine matting of dark hair which thickened into a rug of black curls at the centre of his powerful chest muscles. His arms bulged with equally powerful muscles, throwing into contrast his washboard stomach and slender waist. Hannah ached to run her hands over him, to splay her fingers into those curls, to trace over the steely curves of his arms, kissing the path of her fingers as she went.

'Let me,' he said thickly once he reached her.

Hannah shivered when his hands slid up her bare arms, sucking in a strangled breath when he slipped the bra straps off her shoulders, letting them dangle at her elbows. Without their support, her full breasts settled lower, and the lacy half-cups only just covered her nipples.

She swallowed when he started tracing a lazy fingertip down over the swell of one breast, dipping into the chasm of her cleavage before climbing the other curve, bypassing her throbbing nipple by a mere millimetre. She swallowed again when he returned to the straps and peeled them down further, holding her breath as the cups gave up their secrets, gasping when she felt her nipples spring naked and stunningly erect before his eyes.

She searched his face for any sign that he thought them in any way disappointing, but found nothing but an avid and passionate concentration. He began to touch them, making her tremble. When he bent to lick them her eyes closed on a quivering sigh of ecstasy.

Hannah was beyond minding when he finally removed her bra, knowing nothing but a rapidly escalating desire to lie totally naked with him, to have his mouth and hands on all those other places which were burning for him. As he tossed aside her bra she was already kicking off her shoes, her hands busy on the zipper of her jeans. He saw her haste and matched it with his own, stripping off the rest of his clothes just as quickly.

Within seconds they were both naked, both panting. Hannah's eyes swept over him and she couldn't help thinking that he certainly was twice the man Dwight was—in more ways than one.

'Don't look at me like that,' he growled. 'You're embarrassing me.'

Startled, she glanced up at him. She had never thought of a man like Jack as ever feeling embarrassed. 'But you're so beautiful,' she said earnestly.

'Some women don't like big men.'

'Then they're fools,' she whispered, placing both her hands on his chest and sliding them slowly downwards. She felt him tremble when she passed his ribs but she would not—could not—stop. She had to touch him, had to show him how beautiful she found him.

He shuddered under the caress of her hands, sucking in repeated ragged breaths when she continued to touch him with long, stroking, loving movements.

'Enough,' he barked at last, and swept her up into his arms. 'You can do as much of that as you like later,' he ground out. 'But for now this is *my* fantasy. *My* turn to do the touching. Agreed?'

'Yes, Jack,' she agreed. 'I want whatever you want.'

'You might live to regret those words.'

'I might live to regret a lot of things,' she said, knowing the truth of it. 'But never you, Jack, and never tonight. Tonight I am yours to command. Tonight I will do whatever you want.'

'You mean that?' he husked.

'Yes.'

'God, Hannah. God…'

She woke to find him lying on his side, facing her and watching her with heavy, sated eyes. Smiling sleepily, she rolled over towards him, tipping up her chin in search of his mouth. He bent his head slightly, sipping briefly at her lips, reminding her how sensitive they were.

Which was only to be expected, she thought, her stomach curling over as the memories flooded in. But not with shame. She would never feel shame with Jack. Everything they'd done together was beautiful and natural. Everything *she'd* done had been done with desire and affection and total willingness.

Never in her life had she ever felt so beautiful and sexy as she had tonight. Jack had not been able to get enough of her attentions, allowing her free rein over his magnificent body for as long as she wanted.

And Felicia had been so right, the bitch. He did have a quite incredible stamina—not only was he able to last a long time once he put his mind to it, but he was quick to arousal again, even after the most torrid climax. She gained the impression that he would have been quite happy to go all night, bringing to life every single fantasy a man could have, but it had been she who had finally succumbed to exhaustion, drifting into a deep and dreamless sleep.

'What time is it?' she asked, her voice sounding drugged.

'Does it matter?'

'Not really.'

'I put some more logs on the fire,' he said. 'It was going out.'

She levered herself up on to an elbow, pushing her hair out of her face at the same time. There was no self-consciousness about her nudity any longer. Jack loved her body. He'd told her so often and at such length that she finally believed him.

'Have you had any sleep?' she asked him.

'Some.'

'I need to go to the bathroom,' she said, and scrambled out over the back of the sofa nearest the fire.

'Don't be long.'

'I won't.' She leant back over the lower arm-rest end and dropped a light kiss on his mouth. 'Don't go away,' she whispered into his lips.

His large arms lifted up over her head, cupping the back of her head and pressing her mouth back down. His mouth opened wide under hers, inviting her to send her tongue down inside. She did, and his lips closed around it, sucking hard. Desire flooded back into her veins and she moaned softly. By the time he let her go, she almost stumbled from the room.

The bathroom mirror was cruel with its vivid reflection of her ravished state. The bruises on her throat had faded somewhat, but there were new ones on her breasts and her thighs. Hannah stared at them, fingered them lightly, but still could not feel shame.

She'd loved every minute. There was no point in denying it. She also loved the woman she'd become tonight, with Jack. No more feelings of inadequacy for her in bed. No more sick-making nerves. No more imagining herself sexually inferior to other women—women like Felicia.

Hannah flinched. She wished she'd stop thinking about *her*. It reminded her of the problems to come, when Jack got his memory back. Even if he didn't get his memory back there would still be problems. If she didn't tell him herself about his real fiancée, people at work would. No doubt, sooner or later, the wretched woman herself would turn up, demanding answers.

No, she would have to tell Jack herself.

Tomorrow. In the morning. Over breakfast.

But that was still several hours of darkness away— several hours in which she could lose herself in a world she'd only just discovered, a world full of bittersweet pleasures which she suspected only Jack could give her.

She picked up the hairbrush lying on the vanity unit and began to put some order into her tangled hair. Afterwards she cleaned her teeth, rubbed some soothing salve into her lips, sprayed some eau de cologne over her whole body and then, taking a deep gathering breath, whirled and left the room.

CHAPTER NINE

'THERE'S something I've been meaning to do,' Jack said as soon as she climbed back into the sofa-bed and lay down beside him.

Hannah's heart fluttered when he picked up her left hand; she was not sure what he was about to do.

'I don't want to see these on your hand again,' he muttered, wriggling her wedding and engagement rings off her finger and dropping them into her palm. 'That wasn't a marriage you had. That was torture. Give them away,' he said sharply. 'Or sell them. Or put them in a deep dark drawer, if you like. As long as I never have to see them on you again.'

Hannah blinked her amazement. Jack acting proprietorial about her was an even newer experience than having him as her lover. Lifting her eyebrows slightly, she knelt up, reached over the high curved back of the sofa, and dropped the rings carefully on to the carpet. She stayed kneeling there for a few seconds, leaning her elbows along the top, staring blankly into the glowing fire and trying to work out if Jack's attitude pleased or annoyed her. Finally she glanced over her shoulder at him, only to find him frowning at her as though he too was not happy with the way he'd just acted.

130

'You're not going to marry me, are you, Hannah?' he said, in a low, taut voice.

She could not bring herself to lie. 'No, Jack,' she replied evenly. 'I'm not. And please don't ask me why.'

An emotion she could not identify choked her throat then, and she looked away, feeling utterly bereft. It totally confused her, for it didn't seem to have anything to do with guilt, but despair. His materialising behind her, gentle hands on her shoulders, tender lips on her neck, only seemed to make it worse.

'Don't, Jack,' she choked out. 'That won't work. I'm not going to change my mind.'

'Hush, my darling,' he murmured. 'Hush.'

'No, don't,' she groaned when he started tracing her spine with kisses, his hands trailing down with him, brushing past the edges of her breasts, which were pressed flat against the sofa-back.

'You don't understand,' she cried softly, then shivered violently. His lips and hands had reached her buttocks and weren't stopping.

'It's all right,' he murmured between kisses. 'I understand. It's too soon...much too soon... We'll just be lovers for now...and not think about anything else.'

She moaned at these words, for indeed she couldn't think of anything else—not when he started easing her thighs apart.

I must not surrender to this again, came the whirling feverish thought. Must not. I'm losing control of my life again. Losing control…

He stopped. Just in time, she thought shakily.

But any respite was to be brief. She tensed when she felt his body slide into the valley between her legs. She ached for his possession, yet feared it at the same time. There would be no control for her then. None.

He delayed the inevitable, however, tormenting her by rubbing himself slowly back and forth over her desire-slick flesh, making her quiver whenever he contacted nerve-endings already sensitive from their earlier lovemaking. Her whole body tightened when his huge frame loomed up behind her, enveloping her totally.

His hair-roughened chest pressed against her back, the stubble on his chin grazing her soft skin as he rubbed it over her shoulder. It felt as if she was being covered by a wild animal in the jungle, the thought making her mouth go dry with excitement. She felt utterly helpless, pinioned as she was against the sofa, Jack's huge muscle-hard body wrapped around hers. Still, her very helplessness held a perverse pleasure— the pleasure of total abandonment and surrender to Jack's superior male strength and size.

A sob caught in her throat, for while she was incredibly turned on she did not want to feel like this, did not want to allow any man this type of dominion over her. She tried to push back away from the sofa, but he misinterpreted her movements as the urgency of passion.

'Soon, darling, soon,' he murmured thickly.

She whimpered with dismay when he pressed her back even harder against her sofa, raining rough kisses over her shoulders and neck. He stroked her hair aside with shaking hands, moving his lips up her throat to nibble at her earlobe.

'Beautiful Hannah,' he breathed into her ear, then ran his tonguetip around it. 'Beautiful sexy Hannah.'

Her buttocks clenched tight as a shiver of erotic delight ran down her spine. He stroked her hair back some more, winding it through his fingers then turning her face so that he could cup her chin and kiss her properly. Her pitch of excitement flared wildly when his tongue surged hungrily into her mouth. Quite unconsciously she began pulsing her lower abdomen back and forth against him.

He groaned and abandoned her mouth, moving one hand down to splay it wide against the soft swell of her stomach, then pressing her back so that her body arched into his. She felt herself being lifted, and whimpered at the desertion of his body from between her legs till she realised what he was going to do.

She tensed, gasped, then groaned. Slowly he lowered her back on to her knees, the action making his penetration complete. She shuddered violently, not wanting him to move, yet at the same time wanting it quite desperately.

'You are one incredible woman,' he rasped into her hair. 'Tell me you'll never stop being my lover. *Promise* me.'

'I promise,' she said, then shuddered again as he began to move.

'I'll never let you go back on that promise,' he warned darkly. 'Never.'

Hannah didn't care, for by then she had ceased to think at all.

'We have to talk, Jack,' Hannah said over morning coffee, although it was almost afternoon. The clock on the wall said twenty to twelve.

They were sitting on opposite sides of the kitchen table, both a little bleary-eyed, both looking as if they might have been at an orgy all night. Jack still hadn't bothered to shave, though he had showered and dragged on the jeans and jumper he'd discarded last night. Hannah had bathed at length, then felt too limp to dress, throwing her pink dressing-gown over her rosy-hued nakedness.

Jack glanced up from his coffee, his blue eyes hardening with an instant wariness. 'I don't see why. I thought we settled everything last night.'

'There...there are things you don't know,' she said tautly. 'Things that happened during those six weeks. Things I...I haven't told you, but should have.'

Jack lowered his mug slowly to the table, every muscle in his face tightening. 'What kind of things?'

Hannah's stomach began to churn. God, but this was difficult. Yet it had to be done. She'd already waited too long.

Her mind raced back to the night before and she shivered. Much much too long, she decided ruefully.

She could not blame Jack. He'd acted like any modern virile man would have with such a willing partner. But she should not have let things go as far as they had. Frankly, in the cold light of day it was hard to believe that the woman who'd inhabited Jack's fantasy bed last night had been herself. She'd had no idea she'd be capable of such wanton behaviour.

Still, she'd gone into everything with her eyes well and truly open. But Jack… Jack had been under a lot of false impressions. He would never have done what he had if he'd known about Felicia. As rotten as Hannah thought the woman was, she was his fiancée, and Jack clearly had felt enough for her to ask her to marry him.

'There *was* an engagement during those six weeks,' she went on, having to practically force the words from her throat. 'And it *was* yours. But it…it wasn't to me.'

A deep dismay swept through Hannah at the look on Jack's face. She had never seen him look so sickeningly shocked. 'Not to you,' he repeated blankly.

'No.' God, but she felt awful!

He simply stared at her, clearly unable to say another word.

'It…it was to a woman named Felicia. Felicia Fay. She's an actress. You only met her recently. It was rather a whirlwind courtship. She…she has blonde hair.'

'Blonde hair,' he repeated, frowning.

His blue eyes slowly widened with a dawning recognition. Clearly he was putting two and two together. The blonde in his flashes had been his real fiancée.

'That party you sort of remembered,' Hannah went on quickly. 'It was actually your engagement party to Felicia.'

'I see,' he said, so calmly that Hannah was startled. She stared at him, not at all sure how to take his reaction. Why wasn't he furious with her? Why wasn't he ranting and raving?

'Might I ask why you pretended to be my fiancée, Hannah?' he said, his eyes narrowed upon her. 'Why you connived to get me up here with you…alone? You must have had a reason.'

'I…I did it on the spur of the moment,' she admitted.

'That much is obvious,' came Jack's dry remark. 'But why?'

'I…I found out something about Felicia at your engagement party—something pretty damning. And I just couldn't bear… I mean, I just couldn't bear… I mean, I just couldn't stand by and see you married to such a woman.'

He stared at her long and hard for several seconds. 'And what was it you found out?'

Hannah frowned. Jack was acting rather oddly, she thought. Not nearly as shocked and rattled as he should be. Either that, or his male pride was forcing him to put on a good act. Well, his male pride was just about to get another serious blow.

'She…she was having an affair with Gerald Boynton. She was only marrying you because Gerald wouldn't and she wanted a rich husband.'

Jack's eyebrows lifted ceilingwards in an attitude of almost mocking boredom. 'Charming,' he said drily. 'And how, pray tell, did you discover these little titbits of information?'

'I'd snuck out on to the balcony for a cigarette during the party,' she explained. 'When I heard the glass doors slide open unexpectedly I thought it might be you, so I hid.'

'As well you might,' came his rueful remark. 'Smoking is a filthy habit. And it'll kill you in the end. Might I remind you, Hannah, that you haven't had a single cigarette this weekend since Friday night?'

Hannah's hazel eyes blinked wide. Had Jack gone mad? What kind of comments were those to make at a time like this?

'Go on,' he said, almost sounding smug.

Totally thrown, she took a few seconds to collect her thoughts. 'I... Well, it turned out to be Felicia and Gerald. At first I thought it was you, because of what they seemed to be doing, but then I re—'

'What, exactly, were they doing?' he interrupted, his tone amazingly bland. Still, she supposed it was difficult for him to feel upset about a fiancée he couldn't even remember.

'They were... Felicia was... I...I'm not sure what they doing, exactly,' she finished, her face flaming.

'Yes, you are. Tell me. There's no need to feel embarrassment, Hannah. There are no sexual inhibitions between us any more, are there?'

Hannah dropped her eyes, not wanting to see any mockery in his eyes. 'She was...touching him,' she said, reluctantly and unhappily.

'I presume you mean masturbating him. And what did she say, exactly? Tell me everything. And please, don't spare my feelings. I'll survive.'

Hannah's eyes slowly lifted, but there was nothing in Jack's face to hurt or humiliate her. 'She...she said she was only marrying you for your money. She...she said you were perfect for her because you were a workaholic and you didn't want children. She did also say that you satisfied her in bed and that you...you had incredible stamina.'

One of his dark brows arched sardonically. 'Damned by faint praise. So is that why you pretended to be my fiancée, Hannah, instead of just telling me the truth up front? Because you wanted to sample that stamina for yourself? Not that I'm complaining, mind. It's been a weekend I'll remember for a long, long time.'

She shot to her feet. 'How can you be so cruel?' she said, hot tears stinging her eyes. 'You know that's not true. I was afraid what lies that two-timing slut might tell you about me to make *me* seem the liar. I thought if I got you away alone somewhere, without her influence, I'd be able to make you see the truth. I thought you'd get your memory back within a day or two, but you didn't, and you just wouldn't leave me alone, damn you! I tried to resist. Tried damned hard. But in the end, I just…I just…'

'Just what?' he snapped.

She glared back at him, her lips pressed mutinously together. Surely he could appreciate what he'd done? Surely he had to take some of the blame?

'Go on, Hannah,' he prodded mercilessly. 'Tell me the truth for once. Tell me exactly why you couldn't resist me—why you were so stunningly co-operative last night. What's your excuse? Are you going to put it down to a build-up of frustration? Or have I been wrong about you all this time? Maybe you've become a right raver since you left your dear hubby. Maybe you've been bonking everything in trousers behind my back.'

'You know that's not true!' she cried, hurt beyond belief. 'I'd never been to bed with any man but my husband before you! I certainly had no plans for seduction when I brought you up here. All I wanted was to stop you making the same mistake I did in marrying the wrong sort of person. You took me totally by surprise when you kissed me last Friday night, then capped it all off by saying you'd always fancied me. My own feelings took me by surprise as well. I…I'd never thought of you like that before, but suddenly I couldn't seem to *stop* thinking about making love with you.'

'Is that so?' he drawled.

'Yes, that's so!' she lashed out. 'And it was all your fault. You wouldn't stop talking about it! And you wouldn't stop kissing me, damn you. And then…when it finally did happen, it was just so incredible. I'd never experienced anything like it before and I simply had to have more. That's the bitter truth of it! Believe me when I say that if you're surprised then I'm shocked to the core. But I'm not going to say I regret it. Neither am I going to say I don't still want you. Because I do. God help me…I do!'

Suddenly she slumped down into her chair, burying her face in her hands and bursting into noisy tears.

It was at that precise moment that there came a loud knocking at the front door, followed by a loud male voice. 'Open up, Hannah!' it demanded. 'We know you're in there. Your car's outside.'

CHAPTER TEN

HANNAH'S head jerked up off the table, her tears abruptly choked off by shock. Round eyes flew to Jack's equally startled face. 'Oh, my God!' she exclaimed. 'It's Dwight!'

'Yes, but who does he mean by "we"?' Jack scowled. 'Surely he hasn't brought the boys with him, has he?'

'I wouldn't think so,' she said, though shakily. 'This isn't one of the weekends they're allowed home. He must mean Delvene.'

'That bimbo he threw you over for?'

'Yes,' she said tautly. 'That's her name.'

'Good.' Jack's face set into a grimly determined expression. 'I'll enjoy having a word with those two.' And, spinning on the heels of his boots, he stalked off down the hallway.

Hannah scrambled up from the chair and raced after him, grabbing his arm just before he reached the door. 'Wait!' she said. 'Let me see who it is first. It might not be Delvene.' And she pressed her face up against one of the stained-glass panels by the door. A small border of clear glass gave one eye a narrow view. 'Oh, my God,' Hannah gasped, catapulting back as if she'd received an electric shock.

Simultaneously Dwight started banging on the door again. 'If you don't open this door in ten seconds, Hannah,' he snarled, 'we're coming in.'

Hannah threw Jack a stricken look. 'It's not Delvene. It's Felicia. But what on earth is she doing with Dwight? Oh, God, I should have guessed she wouldn't take that fax at face value,' she muttered agitatedly. 'I'll bet she went to the office. They must have told her about your accident, and then the hospital would have told her I said I was your fiancée.'

'What fax?' Jack asked, blue eyes piercing.

Hannah grimaced. There was little point in not confessing all now, but she did so hate the way he was looking at her—as though he would never have believed her capable of such duplicity and deception. She wasn't at all sure if he'd believed her heated outburst of a minute ago, with all its claims of totally innocent intentions. She wouldn't blame him if he didn't. She'd made a right mess of things.

'I…er…I sent Felicia a fax last Friday saying you were having second thoughts about your engagement and were going away for a few days to think it over. I…er…forged your name on it.'

'Hell, you thought of everything, didn't you?' He almost sounded admiring.

'Obviously not,' Hannah returned ruefully. 'I didn't anticipate Felicia seeking out Dwight and making him bring her here.'

'Let me see this Felicia person,' Jack said impatiently, and bent to peer through the glass panels.

Hannah's inner panic turned to instant jealousy. For she knew what he was seeing. Five feet ten of female perfection, dressed casually but eye-catchingly in black leggings, high-heeled black Granny boots and a thigh-length woollen tunic in vivid orange with a black woollen fringe around the bottom. Her long honey-blonde curls were tumbling all over her slender shoulders in sensual disarray.

Jack snapped upright, as though he too had received a shock, which of course he had. His forehead was creased in a dark frown for several interminable seconds. Hannah could guess what he was thinking.

I'm engaged to *that*? I've been going to bed with *that*? I'm supposed to throw *that* over because of one little indiscretion? Hell, what's an affair or two between friends? I only want sex from a woman after all...

Hannah could not believe the dismay she felt at this line of thinking. She could not bear to think of Jack ever touching that woman again. Or any other woman, for that matter. Which was a rather disturbing train of thought. Was her sexual infatuation with him deepening into something more? Or was she just protecting her newly discovered source of physical pleasure?

Whatever, she had to say something—anything to stop him from being swayed by that evil bitch.

'Jack,' she began, 'I know she's very beautiful, but truly she—'

'Don't say another word,' he snapped. 'Not a single solitary word.' And, taking her hand firmly in his, he wrenched open the door just as Dwight was about to knock again.

Hannah had never before seen her ex-husband look so much at a disadvantage. His hand remained frozen in mid-air for a second, his elegantly handsome face not quite so elegantly handsome with his mouth and eyes doing a good imitation of a goldfish. His disbelieving gaze swept first over Jack's rugged masculinity before moving down to Hannah, who could feel her cheeks going as pink as her dressing-gown and slippers.

'*See*?' Felicia squawked from beside him. 'What did I tell you? Your precious ex-wife has not only been pretending to be *my* fiancé's fiancée, but she's been living the part as well! Just look at her! If that isn't a woman who's wallowed in bed with a man for the last two days then I don't know what is! My God, I'll warrant she hasn't got a stitch on underneath that robe. If I know Jack, I'll bet she hasn't had a stitch on since they arrived.'

Hannah felt Dwight's stunned grey eyes travel over her again, slowly this time, taking in all the signs of the tempestuous weekend she'd spent with Jack. In vain, she clutched the lapels of the dressing-gown together. For *nothing* could hide the marks on her throat, or the bruised state of her lips.

'My God,' was all he could say, each word a shocked whisper.

Felicia schooled her face into an expression of earnest anguish, then took a step towards Jack, placing a tentative but caressing hand on his free arm.

'Jack, darling, don't you remember me? It's Felicia, honey, your *real* fiancée. We met at Gerald's place. You must remember Gerald.'

When Jack remained stonily silent, Felicia sent Dwight an anguished glance. 'You see? I told you he had no memory of me. I knew that fax wasn't from him. *She* sent it, that conniving bitch there, who always tries to look like butter wouldn't melt in her mouth.' She dropped her act for a second to let her natural viciousness blaze through, her mouth looking quite ugly under a nasty sneer till she rallied and re-grouped her skills for another tender assault on Jack.

'When you had your little accident and lost your memory of me, darling, that despicable woman there told the hospital *she* was engaged to you, but she's not. *I* am. You've been cruelly tricked, darling. Cruelly and maliciously. She always hated me and she always wanted you. I could tell from the first moment we met. She used to be nice to me in front of you, but when you were out of earshot she was sour and mean. God knows how she thought she could get away with it, though. The mind boggles!'

Hannah wanted to cry. Dear heaven, but she was convincing, even managing to squeeze a tear from those large limpid blue eyes of hers. As for her luscious coral-painted lips… They trembled with feigned emotion so beautifully that Hannah would not have blamed Jack if he'd believed her.

'God knows how *you* think you can get away with *this*, Felicia,' he said, each word so cold and biting it froze the blonde on the spot.

It rather froze Hannah as well. Good Lord, if she hadn't known better, it would have sounded as if he had his memory back!

But of course he hadn't, she quickly reasoned, so he had to be acting. Still, it seemed he'd decided whom he believed in this situation, and Hannah's heart swelled with emotion. She moved her fingers within Jack's hand and he squeezed them tight, the reassuring gesture almost bringing tears to her eyes.

'*Jack*!' Felicia finally recovered, to protest—the perfect picture of injured innocence. 'My God, whatever has she told you about me?' she cried brokenly before turning on Hannah. 'Oh, how could you be so wicked?'

It was surprisingly easy, Hannah thought, a small smile tugging at her mouth. And compared to you, darling, I'm a saint!

'If I wasn't seeing this with my own eyes,' Dwight said, shaking his head and combing his perfectly groomed fair hair back from his frowning forehead with perfectly manicured hands, 'then I wouldn't believe it.'

'Wouldn't believe *what*?' Jack ground out, his anger hitting Dwight like a physical blow, for he took a step backwards. 'That the beautiful woman you married and did your best to destroy would ever have the courage to seek comfort in another man's arms?'

Hannah's hazel eyes blinked wide up at Jack. She was thrilled by his words, and his defence of her actions—thrilled and flattered and quite overwhelmed.

'I can understand your not believing it, you unspeakable bastard,' Jack raged on, splendid in his championship. 'You did your best to crush her confidence in herself as a woman, to make her think she wasn't desirable any more. But I'm here to announce you failed!'

Hannah gazed adoringly at her lover, then with dignified contempt over at Dwight, who was looking grey and sick.

'Yes, Hannah and I have been making love,' Jack went on, his voice loud and proud. 'We've been making love all damned weekend. And it's been so bloody fantastic I know I won't ever *stop* wanting to make love to her!

'As for *you*...' he swung back to face Felicia, who was looking pretty ashen-faced herself. 'I asked you before, now I'm asking you again. How on earth did you think you were going to get away with this?'

'With what, Jack?'

'Coming up here and playing the devoted and wronged fiancée. The last time I saw you, on Thursday night, you were scrabbling in the gutter, trying to get your engagement ring out of the drain—the ring you threw at me after I told you the wedding was off!'

Felicia paled some more, if that was possible. Hannah found it hard even to think. So Jack *did* have his memory back. But since when? And what was he talking about? He'd actually called his engagement off, back on the night of the party?

'You…you've got your memory back,' Felicia said, obviously shaken to the core.

'Yes. I remembered everything soon after Hannah walked into my hospital room.'

Now it was Hannah who was shaken to the core, till Jack's tightening fingers made her see that he was lying. He *had* regained his memory, but not when he was saying he had. It had probably happened some time after Felicia and Dwight's arrival.

'It was *my* idea for Hannah to say she was my fiancée,' he continued curtly, 'simply to facilitate getting out of that damned hospital. Some fool had mistakenly mentioned I had one, and I didn't want to explain anything to the doctors and nurses. I just wanted to get out of there. The doctors insisted I go somewhere quiet for a few days because they were worried about concussion. I remembered Hannah's cottage up here and asked her if she would bring me here for the weekend.'

Hannah swallowed, and tried not to look guilty. Lord, but he could lie well. Almost as well as she had found she could this weekend.

'Hannah hasn't been pretending to be my fiancée since we left the hospital,' came his next clanger. 'If you think she tricked me in some way to seduce me then you're quite wrong. If there's been any seduction around here this weekend it has been all on my part.'

Well, that bit was pretty right, Hannah thought wryly.

'I've always been attracted to Hannah, and once I had her alone, and away from the office, I decided to act on that attraction.'

'But...but what about that fax I received?' Felicia argued desperately. 'If it was really you who sent it— and it must have been if you had your memory back last Friday—then you said you were reconsidering our engagement...'

Hannah's stomach contracted. Who would have believed that what she'd thought was an outrageous lie could have been interpreted this way—that Jack had been thinking about reinstating his engagement, not breaking it!

'Jack,' Felicia said softly, in the most engagingly pleading tone. 'Look, I know you were upset on Thursday night about me and Gerald, but our affair really *was* over by then—believe me. I hadn't been with Gerald since meeting you. We weren't doing anything in the bathroom together, truly. I was simply telling Gerald it was over.'

Hannah was beginning to get the picture. Later that evening—no doubt after she'd left to go home—Jack had caught Gerald and Felicia in some kind of compromising position together, and had successfully put one and one together to make a disgusting pair!

Jack was arching a cynical eyebrow at his ex-fiancée. 'Somehow I doubt that, Felicia. I think perhaps you were finishing what you started out on the balcony earlier that evening. Don't bother to deny it. There was a witness out there who has subsequently told me what you and Gerald were up to. So you can forget about that fax. Our engagement is definitely off, believe me.'

'What witness?' she demanded to know, her face all red and blotchy with anger. 'Oh, I see. It was Mama Bear here again, this time sneaking around and spying on me, then lying her head off to make me look bad.'

Jack's laugh was harsh. 'No one has to make you look bad, Felicia. You *are* bad. In fact, you're rotten through and through, and so is Gerald. Now, get out of here, and when you get back to Sydney don't forget to ring your sleazebag lover and let him know what he can do with his deals. I don't want to ever see either of you again!'

That was the straw that broke Felicia's back. She

went white. For a split-second she looked as if she might collapse, but, true to her true nature, she soon recovered, all pretence gone from her face. Her blue eyes were vicious as they raked over Jack and then Hannah.

'So you've won, bitch,' she snarled. 'I hope you're happy with your prize. He's not such a catch, you know. Oh, he has plenty of money, and a certain macho appeal, but I have a feeling that won't be enough for you, Mama Bear. You'll always want the whole romantic deal, won't you? Plus the patter of little feet. He'll never give you that, honey. Never!'

Whirling away, she walked with cold arrogance back down the steps, head held high as she strode over to get into the passenger side of Dwight's new BMW. A blue one this time, Hannah thought blankly, trying not to let Felicia's barbs hurt her.

But they did hurt. Horribly. She hardly dared look at why too closely. She kept telling herself valiantly that she didn't want any of those things from Jack anyway. She'd only just divorced Dwight. The last thing she wanted was another marriage and more babies.

As for Jack's love... She'd long known that Jack wasn't the type of man to fall in love. Oh, yes, he could like, admire and desire a woman. But love? He hadn't been given any as a child, and she didn't think he knew what it entailed.

'Why don't you go too?' Jack suggested caustically

to Dwight, once Felicia had slammed the car door. 'Take the woman back to where I last saw her. It's where she belongs.'

Dwight, who had recovered some composure by this point in time, gave Jack a hard look, then turned slightly softer eyes to Hannah. 'I know you won't believe me when I say I'm sorry,' he said, in an astonishingly regretful tone, 'but I am. I had no idea. I guess I never have had much idea about other people's feelings. Dad's always telling me Mum spoilt me rotten—giving me far too much attention, filling me with all sorts of notions about what I could become and what I deserved out of life.'

Hannah could appreciate that. She'd never got along with her mother-in-law, who had made it perfectly plain from the word go that she thought Hannah not good enough for her one and only son. Oddly enough, however, she liked Delvene even less. Maybe Dwight would never pick a woman his mother would approve of.

'I told myself I was trying to help you, but I can see now how much I must have hurt you...'

Hannah was stunned by his seemingly sincere words.

'I hope you'll find it in your heart to forgive me. I love our boys, and I think they would like their parents to be friends. What do you say?'

When he extended his hand she simply stared at it, unable to think or to move. Dwight apologising was far too alien to her concept of his personality. She kept looking for the hidden put-down, waiting for the emotional slap in the face.

'The man's been man enough to say sorry, Hannah,' Jack said softly by her side. 'Be woman enough to at least accept his apology.'

When she remained frozen to the spot, Jack took her lifeless right hand and placed it in her ex-husband's. She stared down at his fingers closing around hers and thought of the time when they'd first met, and something as simple as his holding her hand had made her heart sing.

But her heart stayed silent this time. Silent and sad.

It was over, she realised. Over.

The hurt and the humiliation were gone—forever.

Now her heart did move, and her eyes began to swim. She looked through blurring lashes, first into her ex-husband's face and then up into Jack's, wanting to tell him that he'd been responsible for the cure but unable to find the words.

'I think you should go,' Jack told Dwight curtly. 'She's been through enough for one day.'

Dwight nodded slowly. Letting Hannah's hand go, he stretched out a hand to Jack. After an initial hesitation, Jack took it.

'Look after her,' Dwight said.

'I will.'

'She's a fine woman.'

'The finest.'

'You don't know what you've damned well got till you've lost it,' he muttered.

'Worse after you've driven it away,' Jack reminded him.

'Yes.' Dwight scooped in then let out a shuddering sigh. 'But there's no going back. I'm still the same man anyway. I can't change.'

'We can all change,' Jack told him. 'It's never too late.'

Dwight flashed Hannah a thoughtful look, and she wondered if he was thinking how changed *she* was.

And she was.

She would never again let a man make her decisions for her—never let anyone else convince her that she was less than she was. She might not be perfect, but she was as good as anyone else and better than most.

'Goodbye,' Dwight said with a weary sigh.

When he moved to turn away, something propelled Hannah forward. She clasped his arm and reached up to give him a kiss on the cheek. His returning look was so bleak that her eyes filled with tears again.

'Does that mean you forgive me?' he rasped.

She couldn't say so out loud; she just gave him another kiss on the cheek and ran inside. She was leaning against the wall sobbing when Jack came in and took her in his arms. He held her head against the wall of his chest, stroking her hair with one hand and her back with the other.

'You really loved him, didn't you?' he murmured.

'I...I suppose so,' she choked out. 'But I was... only a child...when I married him....'

He sighed, the action filling his huge lungs before expelling the air slowly. 'Well, you're not a child any longer, Hannah. You're an adult woman. So dry your eyes and tell me what you want of me.'

His abrupt question had the effect of definitely drying up her tears, her hands reaching up to dash them from her cheeks as she looked up at him. 'What... what do you mean?'

'I mean, Hannah, do you want to make your pretence a reality?'

'You mean, you...you still want to marry me?'

'Yes, I do.'

'But we don't love each other,' she protested, despite feeling a small twinge of guilt at this statement. Maybe she did love him. Maybe she was simply hoping to urge him into saying he loved her. She was certainly holding her breath to hear his answer.

But his reply wasn't what she wanted to hear at all.

'You were in love with Dwight,' he growled, 'and where did that get you?'

'It wasn't my loving Dwight that was at fault, Jack. It was the fact that he didn't love me back. You need to both love each other.'

He glared at her, his face grim, his eyes frustrated. 'So your answer is no.'

'It has to be, Jack.' God, but why did she feel so

wretched? She was doing the right thing, using her head for once. Because of course she wasn't in love with him. She hadn't been last Friday, and what had happened to change that? It was the sex confusing her. She'd gone a little sex-mad for the moment.

'I hope you don't think we can go back to things as they were before,' he said brusquely. 'I couldn't bear to work with you without having you as my lover as well. You must know that.'

'Yes, I know that,' she admitted, knowing it all too well. She knew she couldn't go back either. 'I want you as much as you want me, Jack.'

He pulled her to him, his arms steely with suppressed anger. 'I suppose I should have known you wouldn't fall in love with a man like me,' he bit out.

'Jack, I—'

'Shut up, Hannah,' he snapped. 'Just shut up.'

And he kissed her—furiously, hungrily.

When he started dragging the dressing-gown off her shoulders Hannah placed her palms on his chest and pushed back, wrenching her mouth away from his.

'Have…have you forgotten we promised to visit Possie today?' she said shakily, fearing that she was only seconds away from being successfully seduced again. She just couldn't let Jack ride rough-shod over her body all the time, or Lord knew where things would end up

'Is this your way of telling me you don't want to make love right now?' he sighed.

'Not really. I'm merely delaying things—that's all. We have all the time in the world, Jack. You…you could stay the night at my place tonight, if you like.'

'You mean, we're not staying here?'

'Not if you want us to get to work on time in the morning. I also hate driving down the mountains in the dark, so I thought we'd leave around four.'

'But it's already after one!'

'Then we'd better hurry along and see your little possum friend, don't you think?'

Fifteen minutes later they were locking the front door, Hannah having pulled on the jeans and pink jumper she'd worn on the Friday night then done a quick make-up and hairdo, twisting her hair into a loose knot on top of her head. They had just set off up the bush track, walking hand in hand, when a sudden thought crossed Hannah's mind and she turned to face Jack.

'Oh, I forgot to ask you. When *did* you get your memory back? I know it wasn't last Friday, like you said. If you say it was before last night I'm going to kill you.'

He looked down at her with a wry smile on his face. 'The truth is, Hannah…I haven't.'

CHAPTER ELEVEN

HANNAH'S mouth flapped open. 'You *haven't*?'

'Nope.'

'But…but…'

'I had a couple of those flashes, that's all. Remember when I peeped through the front door at Felicia? That's when it happened.'

Yes, she remembered. She'd thought he'd been shocked by her beauty, and had been thinking how desirable Felicia was, making Hannah herself feel awful.

'In one flash she was taking a ring off her finger and throwing it at me,' he went on. 'Then I saw her down on her hands and knees in the gutter, looking for it. That's all I remembered. I simply improvised. I said what I knew, hoping she'd hang herself. And she did.'

'Then you still can't really remember her? Either your meeting or your romance?' Hannah didn't want to admit how thrilled she was that he didn't. He couldn't very well compare them in bed if he didn't even remember the woman.

'I can't see myself having a *real* romance with a woman like that. Oh, she's good-looking enough—

and, brother, can she put on a good act. I dare say she got me in with an abundant supply of sex and flattery. I've always been a bit of a sucker for that from a beautiful woman, I must admit.'

'The sex or the flattery?' Hannah said drily.

'Both.' He wound steely arms around her waist and curved her body to his. 'Like to try some on me, beautiful lady?' he murmured.

'Don't be silly,' she said, but a little too breathlessly to be convincing. He'd just delivered some flattery of his own, calling her a beautiful lady. Hannah knew that she was equally susceptible to flattery—maybe even more so. And she was very susceptible to Jack holding her.

'I hope you're not going to carry on like this in public,' she warned.

'Like what?'

'You know. Grabbing me all the time. There's no need to, you know. You've already got me where you want me.'

'And where's that?' he asked, his blue eyes intense as they moved over her face before settling on her mouth.

Wanting you all the time, she thought, with a measure of self-exasperation.

But Hannah could hardly say that, so she searched for a suitably flip retort to defuse the sexual tension again building within her. 'In your private and personal office, of course,' she quipped.

He scowled, her answer obviously not pleasing him. 'Oh, I aim to have you there, Hannah. And any other place I can corner you. I told you I'd never let you go as my lover and I meant that.'

He glared at her, his jaw squaring stubbornly, his eyes a steely blue. Hannah began to worry that she'd merely exchanged one ruthless man for another.

Thank God she hadn't allowed him to bulldoze her into a hasty marriage. She had a suspicion, however, that he hadn't given up on the idea.

'I think we should get along to Marion's, don't you?' she said, proud of her firm tone. She certainly wasn't the same weak ninny who'd married Dwight. She would cling to that thought every time Jack put the hard word on her, in more ways than one. 'Time marches on.'

'*Dead*?' Jack repeated, his face and voice suggesting that he wasn't familiar with the word. 'Possie's *dead*?'

They were standing in Marion's kitchen, both of them stunned by Marion's bad news.

Jack's shock quickly gave way to a frustrated anger. 'But he *can't* be dead!' he raged. 'He was just fine yesterday. You said so yourself.'

Marion's kind round face showed true sympathy. 'I know,' she murmured. 'But it happens like that sometimes. No matter what you do, during the first twenty-four hours they sometimes start to pine for their mother and they just die. When he stopped drinking during the night I knew he was in big trouble. He was very young, you know.'

'You should have come and got me,' Jack said accusingly. 'He seemed to like me. I might have been able to do something!'

Hannah saw the hurt in Marion's eyes and placed a soothing yet warning hand on Jack's arm. 'It wouldn't have made any difference, Jack,' she said gently. 'Marion's obviously seen this happen many times. She did her best. You did *your* best. You have to let it go. It's nature's way. Possie's mother died when he was too young to survive.'

He fell silent then—painfully, broodingly silent. But finally he rallied, a deep shuddering sigh racking his big frame. 'Yes, of course. You're right,' he said bleakly. 'I'm sorry, Marion. I shouldn't have taken it out on you. He was just such a cute little beggar.'

'Babies have that effect on you,' Marion said, her eyes teary.

Her sadness moved Hannah, and she stepped forward and gave her a big comforting hug. 'There'll be plenty more baby possums for you to look after, Marion. And others. You do a grand job looking after them. Now, where's Edward? Jack and I have to go back to Sydney soon, but I don't like to leave you like this, if you're all alone.'

'No, he's here somewhere. Down the back, I think, looking after his herb garden. You mean, you can't stay a while?' she gave Hannah such a pleading look that Hannah knew she couldn't refuse.

'Perhaps for a cup of coffee.'

'Oh, that's lovely. Edward will be so pleased. He was looking forward to seeing you again today, Jack. He did so enjoy your company yesterday. I'll put the kettle on and go and find him.'

Hannah turned to face Jack rather reluctantly once Marion had bustled off. He was as silent and grim as she'd feared, but there wasn't any criticism over her agreeing to stay for coffee. He didn't even seem to see her staring at him, his mind off in another world.

'Jack? Are you all right?'

Visibly shaking himself, he focused on her and smiled. But it was not a happy smile. It was just a surface politeness, or maybe even a cover for some deep inner pain. She had a feeling he'd been thinking about something that went way back—maybe something from his childhood. But she knew he wasn't about to tell her, even if she asked him.

Men like Jack never talked about themselves—not on any deeply personal level. They thought such confidences weakened them, or made them look less than the strong macho image they presented to the world.

Hannah found such an attitude sad, for it meant that basically they remained lonely souls, never confiding their innermost feelings to each other.

Not that Hannah could judge him too harshly. She'd never been one of those women who could tell another woman anything and everything. Maybe this was the result of her mother dying young, or having no brothers and sisters. She wasn't sure, but she'd kept herself to herself on the whole. She'd never had a best girlfriend—not even in her schooldays.

How many times had she overheard the girls who worked in the various offices at Marshall Homes telling each other their life stories over a cup of tea, envying their openness, plus their ability to laugh at themselves and their relationships?

She decided then and there to be a little more open herself in future—not to hug her hurts to herself. No doubt such insular behaviour only made one's problems seem worse than they perhaps were. She wondered even now if she'd exaggerated the things Dwight had done in her mind, getting some of them way out of all proportion. Maybe he hadn't been deliberately cruel, merely totally insensitive.

Difficult, however, to become an instant communicator when Jack was standing there, arms aggressively folded, obviously in the grip of a black depression.

'I could do with a cigarette,' she announced, hoping that might snap him out of his mood.

'What? Not bloody likely!' he growled. 'And if you think you're going to smoke while you've got me captive in that car during the drive back to Sydney, then you can think again!'

'I can see you've put your ''boss'' hat back on,'

she quipped, sliding an arm through the crook of Jack's elbow and dazzling him with a saucy smile. 'Or is this your ''protective lover'' hat?'

He frowned down at her. 'What are you up to?'

'Up to?' She feigned innocence—almost as well as Felicia, she thought. For with her touching Jack she was already projecting ahead to tonight, the thought of having him with her in bed all night making her quiver inside. How exciting to be able to roll over at any time during the night and fondle his incredible body, arouse it with her hands or her mouth...

She coloured a little when she found Jack's narrowed eyes on her face, knowing that her thoughts had betrayed her.

'What on earth are you thinking about, woman?'

She knew she was blushing, but she refused to feel ashamed. 'You want the truth, or a white lie?'

'Which one will get me what I want?'

'Are we still talking about marriage, or sex?'

'Oh, I've given up the idea of marriage,' he practically snarled. 'A man has to appreciate when he's hitting his head up against a brick wall. I'll settle for the sex, Hannah. The kind that had you blushing a moment ago.'

Hannah blushed some more, a type of shame now joining a perverse hurt over Jack's no longer wanting to marry her. She should have been relieved. Instead she felt upset, and rather confused. She no longer knew what she wanted any more.

'I…I wasn't thinking about sex,' she lied, her eyes dropping from his.

'Yeah, right,' he drawled. 'So if I told you I wouldn't be staying with you tonight, what would you say?'

Her eyes snapped up, her bewilderment laced with anger. 'Is this your way of punishing me for not marrying you?'

'Not exactly. What if I suggested you come to my place tonight instead?'

'No,' she refused.

'Why not?'

'For one thing I don't want any of the staff catching me coming downstairs from your apartment in the morning,' she said, quite truthfully.

'You think it'll look better my arriving in the passenger seat of your car?'

'Probably not, but there are other things to consider.'

'Such as what?'

'My place in Parramatta is closer.'

His glance was startled. Hannah herself was startled at how much satisfaction she'd gained from the strong stance she'd just taken with Jack. During her marriage she'd always deferred meekly to Dwight. It was no wonder, perhaps, that he hadn't respected her. She would have Jack's respect, if it killed her.

'Let's make this a short visit,' he said, his glare having changed from surprised to smouldering.

Hannah, however, had no intention of rushing things, finding the feeling of anticipation about the night ahead acutely pleasurable.

'I wouldn't dream of offending Marion by racing away,' she said, eyes gleaming with suppressed desire. 'Besides,' she added on a husky breath, 'I don't want you having the time or the opportunity to make love to me again up here. I want to wait till I have you at home…in my bed.'

His blue eyes blazed, his own desire clearly unabated. 'I'll be ready to explode by then.'

'Mmm.'

'Witch,' he whispered under his breath as both of them heard Marion returning.

'You sure you've got that word right?' she whispered back, reaching up on tiptoe to give him a lightly teasing kiss.

His face said it all as Marion swept back into the room.

CHAPTER TWELVE

THE clock on the dashboard of Hannah's car showed ten past eight. It would probably be eight-thirty by the time they made it into the Marshall Homes car park—the same time most of the staff arrived. Hannah wished now that they'd started out earlier.

They were in the midst of heavy Monday morning traffic, just north of Parramatta, and a fine rain was falling, which always seemed to make the traffic worse. Hannah could never understand why it was that when it rained the number of cars on the road seemed to double. Maybe people who normally took public transport just couldn't face it in the rain.

She sighed when they slowed once again to a crawl.

'You've been very quiet this morning,' Jack said abruptly. 'Anything wrong?'

'I'm a little tired,' she said, which was true, but only half the story.

'You have only yourself to blame,' he said drily.

'I suppose so.' Her decision not to feel guilty about wanting Jack seemed to have given her an endless supply of energy last night, as well as a desire to explore further ways of making love, further ways of extending and heightening their pleasure in each other. She'd revelled in taking her time, and in making Jack take his, discovering the sweet delights of a much slower surrender to the passion they engendered in each other. It had been after two in the morning by the time they'd fallen asleep in each other's arms.

Hannah supposed that it wasn't any wonder she felt a little under the weather this morning. Five hours' sleep really wasn't enough.

But it wasn't the physical fatigue making her quiet. It was the change in her feelings about what she was doing. Maybe it was the cold light of morning, or the rain, or the fact that they would soon be at work, under the scrutiny of her colleagues.

Hannah wasn't sure how she would handle the situation if the people at Marshall Homes clued on to the fact that the boss and his secretary had become lovers. Jack was already exhibiting a proprietorial and possessive attitude towards her which she was sure would not go unnoticed. That, combined with the fact that he'd broken his engagement to Felicia, would soon set tongues wagging. It was impossible to keep such news a secret.

She recalled what had happened when their last sales manager—a married man—had started having an affair with *his* secretary. Amazingly this had seemed to give the man in question an added status in some people's eyes. Ladies' men, for some reason, were admired in certain quarters. Lord knew why!

The girl, however—who had been only nineteen years old and very naïve—had been labelled a fool and a slut. Hannah imagined that *she'd* be given some similar tags if her affair with Jack became common knowledge—with a few more thrown in, given her age and divorced status. It made her feel sick just thinking about it.

'Jack…'

'What?'

'I…er…don't want people in the office to know. You know…about us…'

They had just turned into the street which housed the Marshall Homes head office, the two-storeyed brick and glass complex just visible on the hill in the far distance.

Jack slanted her a savage glance. 'I suppose I can understand your wanting to keep our involvement a secret, Hannah. But, damn it all, I don't like the way it makes me feel. I've never had a woman ashamed of my being her lover. To give Felicia credit, she knew how to make me feel great all the time. Maybe there's something to be said for getting mixed up with gold-diggers. At least they always say what you want to hear.

'Do try not to run off the road,' he snapped. 'Yes, you don't have to say anything. I've got my memory back. All of it.'

Hannah's hands clenched on the steering-wheel. 'When did this happen?' she asked, hating the way this news was affecting her. She knew in her heart that Jack would never go back to that woman, but she still detested being compared with her in any way.

'When I woke this morning everything was as clear as a bell,' he drawled, his tone implying that he was leaving a lot of things left unsaid.

'And?' she prompted.

'And pull over here,' he grated out. 'I'll walk the rest of the way. That way no one will see us together. I wouldn't want to embarrass you. And don't worry, when I walk in I won't grab you. I won't do a damned thing to raise anyone's suspicions that my poor put-upon secretary is providing her boss with more services than usual. I'll even wait till everyone else's gone home before I let my disgusting lust off the leash.'

Hannah's face flamed as she wrenched the car over to the kerb. She couldn't trust herself to say a word as he slammed out of the car and took off up the street with furious strides. She didn't turn her head as she drove past him. She didn't speak to him when he marched through her office into his. She was too busy hating him with all her heart.

When he stormed back out of the office ten minutes later, snapping that he wouldn't be back all day, she slumped down at her desk and burst into tears.

By ten she had the most excruciating headache behind her eyebrows. By eleven her throat felt as if it was lined with sandpaper. By noon she was running a temperature. She would have gone home if she'd had the energy. No doubt it was the flu. Most of the office had come down with it that winter at some time or other. It seemed it was her turn.

She swallowed some aspirin and stayed clammily at her desk, doing little but answer the telephone and take messages. The boys rang, as was their habit at lunchtime on a Monday, and she had to make a real effort to sound cheery. Nevertheless, she was relieved to hear that they hadn't heard from their father—either yesterday or as yet that day.

Not that she thought Dwight would say anything about their mother having a dirty weekend with her boss. His relationship with his sons didn't include telling them anything which was awkward or of an intimate nature. Hannah had done her best to explain the birds and the bees to them when they'd approached puberty, only to find that they already knew more than she did!

They had been less than impressed with their father having an affair—Hannah had managed to keep all his other affairs from their knowledge. She imagined that they wouldn't be thrilled with their mother doing the same, even if she *was* a divorcee. Sex, it seemed, was for other people. *Young* people, not parents. And certainly not mothers!

Still, just in case Dwight was tempted to say something, she rang him at his surgery and asked him not to tell the boys about her involvement with Jack, impressing on her ex-husband that she wasn't about to marry Jack. That it was merely an affair. Oddly enough, he laughed.

'Just an affair?' he mocked. '*You*, Hannah? Don't be ridiculous. You've fallen in love with the man. Anyone with even the tiniest brain in their heads could see that. From what Felicia told me, you've been in love with him for ages!'

Hannah protested and finally hung up, even while the truth blasted into her feverish and maybe tiny brain. She *did* love Jack. She just hadn't recognised it, for it had been the love of a mature woman for a man—not the silly adolescent infatuation she'd once felt for Dwight and mistakenly called love. It was firmly based on all those emotions she'd already admitted to—liking and respect and, yes, gratitude. Jack had always been good to her—and kind, and decent.

His bringing to the surface her long-buried sexuality had confused to issue, that was all. She'd mistaken her obsessive desire for the man as something more superficial than a natural extension of a very real and deep affection, calling it lust, not love.

Yet it *was* love. *True* love.

After she had hung up, she sat there for ages, mulling over her astonishing realisation, shock gradually changing to a confused dismay. What should she do now? Tell Jack she'd changed her mind about marrying him? Tell him she loved him? Or tell him nothing?

Hannah still believed in her heart that marriage needed both partners to be in love with each other to be successful. But, given the situation she found herself in, she would rather marry Jack than go on being his secret lover. Respect was important to her, and what she was doing would inevitably erode Jack's respect for her, plus her respect for herself. On the other hand Jack had changed his mind about marriage yesterday. Then this morning he'd been none too pleased with her. Maybe she'd left it too late all round.

God, she couldn't think with her head throbbing away as it was. It was impossible.

Four-thirty slowly rolled around—the time the general office closed for the day. It wasn't uncommon for Hannah to work late, so no one commented when her light remained on, and her car stayed in the car park.

What the rest of the staff didn't know was that by this time Hannah felt too ill to drive home. She was lying down on the couch in Jack's well-appointed office, contemplating calling a taxi, when the man himself walked in, a sarcastic expression flitting across flinty eyes when he saw her.

'If your position is some kind of invitation,' he snarled, 'then I'm sorry, but I must decline. I'm too damned tired and not bloody interested! Nothing turns me off a woman more quickly than her being ashamed of being seen with me.'

Hannah squeezed her eyes tightly shut for a few seconds, Jack's derision having hit her hard. Yet she was beyond defending herself to him at that moment—beyond even reacting to his nasty outburst. She was beyond everything.

With a weary sigh she levered her feet over the side of the couch and stood up. Too quickly, as it turned out, her head spinning and her knees suddenly wobbly. She swayed, her right hand shooting out to grip the arm-rest of the couch for support, her left fluttering up in a vain attempt to dash the black spots away from her eyes.

She didn't actually faint. But she almost did; only Jack grabbing her and lowering her quickly back down on to the couch stopped its inevitability.

'Why didn't you tell me you were sick?' he groaned, stroking her hair gently back from her fevered brow. 'What is it? The flu? You're awfully hot.'

'I think so. I've been feeling rotten all day.'

He groaned again. 'I wish you'd told me. I wouldn't have been such a bastard if I'd known.'

She just looked at him, then turned her face away, a couple of tears sliding down her cheek.

'Geez, Hannah, don't make me feel more of a heel than I already do. Come on, let me take you upstairs. You're sleeping there for the night.' He bent and scooped her up into his arms as if she was a feather.

'And don't bother arguing with me,' he said as she stiffened and went to open her mouth. 'You're not fit to drive home. I'm going to get you into bed and then I'm going to call the doctor. This is no time for stupid displays of pride. You need looking after and I'm going to look after you.'

'I...I don't want to put you to any trouble,' she said weakly. 'Looking after sick people can be very tiresome. I might not be better for days, and I know you're busy, trying to finish the display village before spring.'

'If there's one thing last weekend taught me it's that the business won't fall apart if I take some time off. I've got good people working for me, Hannah. Marshall Homes will still be there next week.'

Hannah really had no energy to object to anything, so she lay back in Jack's arms and allowed him to carry her upstairs without further ado. She remained mute when he took her into the sleekly modern apartment, through the white and blue living-room and down the hallway into the master bedroom. When he sat her gently down on his big blue-quilted bed and began sliding the jacket of her tailored black suit from her shoulders, she sighed total acquiescence to his will.

His undressing her was oddly asexual, however, his touch not in any way seductive, merely gentle and concerned, his face similarly so. 'You're burning up, do you know that?' he said, once she was down to her black silk underwear. 'I think you should have a cooling shower. Are you strong enough? Good. I'll get you a clean T-shirt to wear to bed. Meanwhile I'm going to ring a doctor friend of mine to come and have a look at you. I don't think it's anything worse than flu, but I'm not taking any chances.'

Hannah was happy to follow his suggestions meekly, although she did faintly suggest that it might be better if she occupied the bed in the guest-room. Jack would have none of it, saying that his bed was king-sized and he wanted to be nearby in the night if she needed him.

She smiled wanly as her hot, aching head hit the pillow, hoping that the aspirin he'd given her would work quickly. Her eyes were beginning to water and her nose felt all stuffed up, with a vicious pain in her sinuses.

She wasn't feeling much better when Jack's doctor friend bustled in an hour later, apologising for not being able to come straight away. Marshall Homes had built his new home at Dural, Jack had told her while they were awaiting his arrival, in record time and to his demanding wife's satisfaction. It seemed the man felt somewhat in Jack's debt.

'So how is she?' Jack asked anxiously, once the doctor had completed his examination. 'It's just the flu, isn't it?'

'A particularly nasty case, but, yes, I think it's only flu.'

'I don't want you to just *think* so,' Jack snapped. 'I want you to be sure. My mother was diagnosed with the flu by a doctor and died two nights later from meningitis.'

'Hannah hasn't got meningitis, Jack. Sometimes the symptoms she's presenting can be a bad case of hay fever, combined with a simple cold. Did you perhaps spend some time on the weekend outdoors, Hannah?'

'Er…we did go for a bushwalk up in the Blue Mountains on Saturday,' she admitted, trying not to blush at the memories *that* evoked. 'But I've never had hay fever before.'

'There's always a first time. Are you a smoker?'

'Not any more, she isn't,' Jack muttered.

'I've not long given them up,' Hannah admitted.

'Well, don't go back on them if you can help it. Certainly not while you've got this virus. I'll prescribe you some antibiotics for your sinuses, plus some capsules combining antihistamines and painkillers. Really that's all that can be done at this stage.

'Stay in bed for at least two days,' he went on while he scribbled on a prescription pad, 'and drink plenty of fluids. And no going to work for the rest of the week. I would say by the weekend you'll be over the worst, and by next Monday you should be fighting fit again.'

'If she's not,' Jack said, in a darkly menacing tone, 'I know where you live.'

The doctor gave a rather nervous laugh as he

looked up and handed him the two prescriptions. 'Very funny, Jack.'

'I don't have a sense of humour,' came the dry reply. 'Ask Hannah. She knows me better than anyone.'

'Only in the biblical sense,' Hannah muttered to herself while Jack ushered the harassed-looking doctor to the door.

'You weren't very nice to that poor man,' she reproved with a weary sigh when he returned. 'It was good of him to come as quickly as he did. Not many doctors make house-visits at all these days.'

'Maybe I'm just not feeling kind to doctors these days,' he grumbled. 'Look, I'll just dash out and get these scripts filled. The sooner we get some medicine into you, the better.'

He wasn't gone long, yet by the time he returned Hannah was on the verge of panic. Her head was killing her. She hoped she *didn't* have anything more serious than flu.

Jack frowned down at her. 'You look terrible. Here, get some of these into you.' He tipped out three capsules into the palm of her hand, then picked up the glass of water which he'd placed earlier on the bedside chest, holding it gently to her lips while she swallowed each pill. 'I'll go get some ice in a cloth,' he said, 'and cool your face down a bit.'

Hannah hated him leaving her alone, keeping her eyes glued to the doorway till he reappeared. Her gaze followed him as he strode back across the thick grey carpet. When he sat down on the bed and held the improvised ice-pack to her forehead, she sighed her satisfaction and closed her eyes. 'That feels wonderful,' she murmured.

'Don't talk,' he said, and began wiping the cool cloth over her forehead and head in a gently stroking fashion. 'Just rest. Go to sleep if you can.'

'Mmm.'

She did as she was told, but although she gradually began to feel a lot better, sleep eluded her. Finally she opened her eyes and gazed up into Jack's face. Knowing that she loved him seem to make him appear even more handsome to her now, his kind concern for her lending a softness to his hard-edged features.

'You must be tired of doing that,' she murmured.

'Not at all.'

'It feels lovely. I'm feeling much better. Thank you.'

'My pleasure.' And he smiled down at her.

Hannah's heart turned right over at that smile, for it was so sweet, and so utterly giving. She recalled how Dwight had always reacted with impatience to her ever being sick. He'd never stayed at home to look after her. Never showed her this kind of attention or caring.

There again, Dwight hadn't loved her...

'Oh!' She gasped as the implications of what she'd just thought blasted into her brain.

Jack's hand immediately whipped the cloth from her head, his eyes anxious upon her. 'What is it?' he demanded to know. 'Are you in pain? Hannah, darling, what is it?'

'You…you love me,' she said in a shocked whisper. 'I mean…you *really* love me.'

His expression became one of rueful tenderness. 'You've only just realised that, have you? Why do you think I asked you to marry me? Oh, yes, I know what you're probably going to say. A little over a week ago I asked Felicia to marry me, and I certainly didn't love *her*!'

He dropped the cloth next to her glass of water and returned to stroke her damp hair back from her face with his hand, his feathery touch infinitely tender and loving. 'I think I've been falling in love with you since the first day I interviewed you, Hannah, only I didn't realise it. Or maybe I did,' he revised. 'Subconsciously. But I didn't think I had a chance in hell with you.

'I guess my own personal survival instinct kept a firm hand on my private desires where you were concerned, so that I didn't make a fool of myself. Yet I still made a fool of myself—letting Felicia sway me with her flattery and her lies.

'Losing my memory the way I did was the best thing that could have happened to me. With that lying manipulative bitch out of my head, and you suddenly being receptive to me in a sexual sense, my true feelings for you began to surface with a vengeance.

'I've never wanted a woman before as I wanted you this weekend, believe me. But it was more than sex, Hannah. It was a compulsion—an obsessive need to stamp my possession on you as my woman. And I succeeded in some small way, didn't I? I know you don't love me the same way I love you, but I think you—'

'But I *do*!' she broke in, grabbing his hand and pulling herself up into a sitting position. 'I love you so much I've been in the depths of despair all day!'

He seemed even more shocked than when she'd told him last Friday that she was his fiancée.

'I…I refused to marry you because I didn't think you really loved me,' she hastened to explain, not wanting to tell him that she hadn't realised her own feelings till lunchtime today, or that it had been Dwight who'd finally made her see the truth. Jack deserved better than that. 'Oh, darling,' she said, cupping his face and gazing adoringly into his eyes. 'I'd kiss you if I wasn't afraid I'd give you germs.'

'God, Hannah. I can't tell you how happy you've just made me.' And he hugged her fiercely, almost squeezing all the breath out of her. 'I'm never going to let you go, my darling. Never.'

'If you don't,' she whispered weakly, 'I might just expire from suffocation.'

He swiftly let her go, then fussed over her some more, lying her back on the pillows and apologising profusely. For her part Hannah no longer cared about her flu, or whatever it was she had. Happiness seemed to be a wonderful and almost instant cure. Or was it love? Love, she decided dazedly, could cure anything—most of all the hurts of the past.

'We're going to be so happy together,' Jack vowed fiercely. 'I'm going to build us a fantastic house to live in down here, and another one up in the mountains. That cold, mouldy old cottage just has to go!'

'The houses that Jack built?' she said, teasing lights gleaming in her eyes.

'Trust you to say that, Miss Smarty-pants,' he growled. 'You'd better watch it, madam, or I won't give you any of those little *bambinos* everyone says you'll want.'

She sat bolt-upright again. 'But I thought you didn't want children!'

'Where on earth did you get such a stupid idea?'

'From you!'

'Yeah, well, I was wrong, wasn't I? I realised how wrong I was the moment I held that cute little possum in my arms. I reckon I'd make a good father after all.'

Hannah's eyes began to water even more than they already had been. 'You'd make a great father, Jack.' Which was true. He'd been fantastic with Chris and Stuart during their last holidays, the boys having taken to him straight away. Hannah had no doubt that her sons would really like Jack as their stepfather.

'I guess my own father dumping my mother when he found out she was pregnant rather jaundiced my idea of fatherhood,' Jack explained. 'That, combined with all those lonely years I spent in the orphanage after my mother died, turned me into a bit of a loner.

'I trained myself into not needing or loving anyone. I guess it got to be a habit till I hired a certain secretary and she began to show me what a woman's love could mean. It sent me off looking for the wrong kind of love for a while, but she eventually got me back on track.'

'I shudder to think what would have happened if that tile hadn't fallen on you,' Hannah said, shaking her head. 'We might never have known how much we loved each other.'

'Oh, yes, we would,' Jack pronounced firmly. 'I didn't call off my engagement to Felicia just because of her apparent involvement with Gerald Boynton. I didn't like the way she treated you at the party that night. Don't think I didn't notice. I couldn't help comparing the two women in my life and knowing instinctively which one I preferred. I'd already decided by the time that night ended to start pushing the issue with you. I was going to start slowly, because I knew you'd been hurt in your first marriage, but then that tile fell on my head, and things happened very quickly indeed.'

'Maybe too quickly,' Hannah murmured.

'Hell, no. The quicker the better at our age. If I can ever find that title I'm going to have it bronzed! Now, try to get some sleep, darling,' he said. 'I want you getting better as quickly as possible.'

'If I'm to stay here, you…you'll have to go over to my place in the morning and get me some things. Especially my pill.'

'Why don't you stop taking that?' he suggested softly.

'You mean that, Jack?'

'We're not getting any younger.'

'True.'

'Do you think Marion and Edward would like to be godparents to our first child?'

'They'd be ecstatic.'

'They'll make excellent babysitters when we need them, won't they?'

'More than excellent.'

'We can leave any little *bambinos* with them, and sneak off by ourselves occasionally.'

'Mmm. That sounds good.'

'Are you sure I'll get germs if I kiss you?' he asked thickly.

'Yes.'

'What if I don't kiss your mouth? What if I concentrate on other parts of you?'

'You're incorrigible.'

'Must you use such big words?'

Hannah smiled up at him.

'I think I'll go back to stroking your forehead,' Jack said wryly. 'I know if I start any of that nonsense I won't want to stop.'

'There's always tomorrow, Jack.'

'I suppose so.'

'And every other day for the rest of our lives.'

His face brightened appreciably. 'What a lovely thought.'

'It is, isn't it?'

'I still can't believe you love me,' he said, choking up. 'I don't deserve you.'

'You deserve the best, my darling.'

'I have the best,' he said, and dropped a kiss on her forehead.

'Oh, Jack…' She looked up at him, eyes swimming.

'Bugger the germs,' he growled, and his mouth began to descend.

*　*　*　*　*

A WOMAN
TO REMEMBER

by

Miranda Lee

PROLOGUE

SHE took the clothes from the case and laid them out on the hotel bed: a leopardskin-print halter-necked mini-dress, sexy gold sandals with outrageously high heels plus the obligatory ankle strap, and a cream stretch satin G-string which would give the illusion of nakedness underneath the oh, so tight dress.

Not another thing. No bra. No stockings. No petticoat.

A shudder rippled through her at the thought of what she would look like dressed in that garb, with her long tawny blonde hair wildly fluffed out around her face and shoulders, her full mouth made to look even fuller with carefully applied lip-liner and filled in with the sort of lipstick it would take paint-stripper to remove.

Hardly subtle.

Still, that was what she wanted to look like. There was no time for her usual ladylike image. No time for demure or coy. She had only this one night. A few bare hours.

Dismay swept in at the thought of what she was going to do, of how she would have to act to get what she wanted so quickly and so thoroughly. Dear God, what had happened to her this past year? What had she become?

For a split-second she almost backed away from the idea, but desperation and a fierce frustration brought renewed resolve. She had to go home in the morning—home to her dying husband, home to nothing but more weeks of disappointment and despair and loneliness such as she'd never known before.

She could not let this chance go by. She had to grab it. She simply had to!

Snatching up the folded newspaper lying on the pillow, she rechecked the address of the photographic exhibition—the only opening she could find on that particular Wednesday night. It was not a street or a gallery she recognised, but there again it had been some years since she'd lived and worked in Sydney.

She jotted down the address, hoping against hope that this type of function would be the same as they'd always been—full of highly sociable swinging singles. Admittedly, a percentage of the seemingly available men—and often the best-looking—would be gay, but there would always be a sprinkling of straight males with more machismo than morals.

And where are *your* morals, Rachel? came the taunting inner question.

'I left them at home,' she snapped aloud as she threw the newspaper into the wastepaper basket. 'Along with everything else I once held dear. Life is a different ball-game these days. A different ball-game,' she bit out, her heart hardening as she strode quickly into the bathroom, dragging off her wedding ring as she went.

There was no time for guilt tonight. Or conscience. Or, God forbid, shame. Shame was for normal wives in normal situations. It had no place in her life at that moment. No place at all!

CHAPTER ONE

'YOU'LL have to go to the dentist.'

Luke popped the two painkillers into his mouth and swigged them back with a large glass of water.

'I'll go when I get back to Los Angeles,' he said, turning from the kitchen sink to smile at his still frowning mother. 'It's not that bad.'

Grace wasn't about to be distracted from her maternal mission, although she recognised that her son's smile would have distracted most of the female gender. Distract, disarm and downright disorientate.

At thirty-two, Luke had become a lethal weapon where his looks were concerned. Age and life had finally put some interesting lines on his once too smoothly handsome face, especially around his eyes and mouth, giving him more sex appeal than ever.

His two elder brothers were good-looking men, but Luke was matinée idol material, having inherited the best of his parents' genes—his father's tall, well-proportioned body, clear olive skin and flashing dark eyes, and his mother's symmetrical features, high cheekbones and sensually carved mouth. All in all, a potent mix.

As a teenage boy Grace's youngest son had been a big hit with girls. No doubt nowadays he was an equally big hit with women. Pity he couldn't find one to settle down with, Grace thought wryly.

Not that he mixed with the type of woman she would have chosen as a daughter-in-law. Luke's life as private and personal photographer to the stars in Hollywood meant that his immediate circle of acquaintance was the entertainment and movie-world crowd. Hardly the sort of people renowned for long-term commitment and traditional values.

Motherly concern had Grace wishing that one of these days Luke would come home to Australia to live permanently, not just pop home to Sydney for the odd week every year or so. He was an Aussie at heart, and she felt sure he'd be happier at home.

He never looked very happy these days. There were always dark smudges under his eyes, and his mouth had taken on a cynical twist which made her feel quite sad. The young man who'd flown off to see the world and make his fortune ten years ago had not been a cynic.

The man who'd flown in yesterday definitely was, and had been for quite some time. He also hadn't been too happy for quite some time.

Not that it was easy to be bright and bushy-tailed with jet-lag and a nagging tooth. Knowing how difficult men could be when something physical was wrong with them, Grace had no intention of letting Luke procrastinate over getting his tooth fixed.

'You don't fly back to LA till Sunday week,' she pointed out firmly. 'That's two whole weeks away. You can't put up with a toothache for that long. Now,

don't be such a baby, Luke. Lord, I know you hated
the dentist when you were a boy, but you're a grown
man now.

'Fancy!' She tut-tutted, well aware that nothing
prodded a man into action more quickly than a jab at
his male ego. 'Thirty-two and still scared of the dentist.'

'I'm *not* scared of the dentist,' he shot back testily,
all smiles abandoned. 'I simply don't like being in that
damned chair. I detest how it makes you feel, sitting
there. Totally out of control and at someone else's
mercy!'

Grace glanced at the stubborn set of her youngest
son's jaw and thought, Yes, you'd hate that, wouldn't
you? You've always wanted to run your own race—
always resented being pushed into corners. No one
could ever make you do something you didn't want to
do, or dissuade you from doing something you *did*
want to do.

Still, Grace had to admit that she admired Luke's
tunnel vision and tenacity. He'd dared to do what others had only dreamt about. He'd followed his dreams
and made them come true. At least professionally
speaking. Privately, his life hadn't been so successful.
She wondered what had happened to that young actress he'd been living with a couple of years back.
Luke's letters had indicated that marriage was imminent, but then suddenly nothing.

Grace would never forget how grim he had looked
when he'd flown home a couple of months later. And
how bitter he'd become about women. He hadn't con-

fided in her, of course. Boys gave up confiding in their mothers at around the same time they discovered the opposite sex. With Luke that had been a good twenty years ago.

But his being his own man didn't stop her being his mother, and wanting to do mother-type things for him.

'Going to the dentist is not as bad as it used to be,' she argued reasonably. 'The new drills are practically painfree, and they have that gas which helps a lot if you're the tense type.'

'They still stuff sixty million wads of cotton wool in your mouth so that you can't speak properly,' Luke returned irritably. 'Then there's that damned hook thing, which makes the most appalling sucking noises—not to mention the way it drags the corner of your mouth down so that you look like some mutant from Mars.'

Grace chuckled. 'So that's the root of the problem. You simply don't want to look less than your gorgeous best for Dr Evans's pretty little dental nurse.'

Luke's left eyebrow lifted with a mildly sardonic interest. 'Does Dr Evans have a pretty little dental nurse?'

'He did the last time I went. Goodness, if I'd known I'd have mentioned her earlier. So you've still got a weakness for pretty women, have you?'

His glance was sharp, confirming Grace's opinion that some pretty woman had hurt her son once—hurt him badly. She wondered if it had been the actress.

'I've moved on from pretty to gorgeous these days,' he said drily.

'And is there one particular gorgeous girl in your life I should know about?' Grace asked.

'Nope.'

It was a bit like pulling teeth, Grace thought, trying to get information out of Luke. 'What happened to that Tracy girl you used to write me about?' she persisted. 'It sounded like you were going to marry her at one stage.'

'I was. But in the end she decided to embrace her acting career rather than yours truly,' came his coldly caustic remark.

'Why did she have to make a choice? I thought American girls tried to have it all. Marriage and children, *and* a career.'

Luke's laugh was hard. 'Don't go believing those sitcoms you see on television, Mum. That's fantasyland. Tracy didn't mind the marriage bit. She quite fancied being Mrs Luke St Clair. But she drew the line at babies, and at least she was honest enough to say so up front. I didn't see the point in marriage without children, so we called it quits.'

'And rightly so. Marriage without children for you would be a disaster. You'd make a great father.'

He seemed taken aback, throwing her a surprised look. 'What makes you say that?'

'Oh, Luke, don't be silly. I'm your mother. I know these things.'

'Aah. Feminine instinct, is it?'

'Maternal instinct. And paternal example. Your father was a great father. His sons take after him in that regard.'

'Well, that's too bad, because I'm afraid I don't see myself marrying now, let alone having kiddies.'

'You really loved Tracy that much?'

'Good God, no! I'm well and truly over that ambitious little bitch.'

'Then what is it, Luke?' she asked, genuinely confused. 'You're only thirty-two. You've still plenty of time to get married and have a family.'

An awkward silence descended on the kitchen while Luke rubbed his jaw and frowned darkly.

'Who is she?' Grace said abruptly. 'Another actress?'

Exasperation sent dangerous lights glittering in his deeply set black eyes. 'This is exactly why I don't tell you anything, Mum,' he bit out. 'Before I know it, I'm getting the third degree. Let's drop the subject of women all round, shall we? I've come home for a nice, relaxing holiday—not to face a modern version of the Spanish Inquisition!'

'I only have your best interests at heart,' Grace defended herself. 'I only want you to be happy—like Mark and Andy.'

Luke glared at her for a moment longer, before a rueful smile smoothed the frustration from his face. Walking over, he took his mother into his arms and gave her a big hug.

'I am not unhappy, Mum,' he said. 'Hell, what have I got to be unhappy about? Other than this damned tooth, of course,' he added, grimacing.

Grace could see that she wasn't going to get any more out of him about his love life. But she wasn't going to let him off the hook so easily where the dentist was concerned.

'In that case I'm not going to take any more nonsense from you,' she said staunchly. 'I'm going to ring up and make you an appointment at the dentist. If I say it's an emergency they're sure to fit you in some time this morning. I'll drive you down to the surgery myself. I've got some shopping to do and I can do it while you're in there.'

'Oh, all right,' Luke grumbled. 'I can see you're determined, and if there's one thing I know about my mother it's that she can't be swayed once she sets her mind on something. You're as stubborn as a mule!'

Takes one to know one, Grace thought wryly as she left the room and made her way to the telephone.

Ten o'clock found Luke in the passenger side of his mother's battered old blue sedan, feeling rather ambivalent about where they were going. He'd lied to his mother when he'd said that he wasn't afraid of the dentist. He was.

But thirty-two-year-old men couldn't admit to such failings. They couldn't admit to anything which other people might jump on and make fun of, which men might use against them or—worse—which women might look down upon.

Being a real man was a bloody lonely business sometimes, Luke conceded drily to himself. Real men didn't moan or groan. Or enter therapy. They certainly didn't cry on their mother's shoulders.

Hell, no! A real man looked life straight in the eye

and didn't blink an eyelid in the face of adversity. No matter what, he forged on—strong and silent and self-sufficient!

Damn, but he hated being a real man sometimes—especially when going to the rotten dentist!

'I have no idea why you won't let me buy you a new car,' he grumped as his mother backed out of the garage. 'Or a new house,' he added, scowling up into the sky as a jumbo jet roared overhead, the noise deafening.

'I like living in Monterey,' his mother returned, exasperation in her voice. 'I've lived here all my married life. Your father and I were very happy living in this house. I raised you and your two brothers in this house. Most of my friends live round here. Not only that, your father's buried not two miles down the road, and I—'

'All right, all right. I get the point,' Luke broke in frustratedly. 'I just wanted to do something for you, Mum, that's all.' He adored his mother. And admired her enormously.

She hadn't gone to pieces when a heart attack had left her a widow five years ago after nearly forty years of happy marriage—hadn't asked any of her sons to let her live with them. She'd picked herself up and gone on with her life, filling the lonely hours with lots of volunteer work and generally being a fantastic person.

But she could be a bit of a pain once she got her teeth into something.

'You *can* do something for me, Luke,' she piped up suddenly, and Luke shot her a wary glance.

'What?'

'Come back to Australia to live. I'm sure once you get home you'll find a nice girl who'll be more than happy to marry you and have all the children you want.'

Luke felt a deep, dark emotion well up inside him, but he dampened it down, hiding his feelings as best he could. Impossible to tell her that he *had* found a girl, here in Sydney, the last time he'd been home.

Unfortunately she hadn't been at all nice. Neither had she been the type to settle down and have children.

But, for all that, Luke had not been able to forget her afterwards. Not for a minute. She obsessed him every waking moment, haunted his dreams and was slowly destroying his peace of mind.

His mother talked of his seeming unhappy. How could he be happy when he didn't know who he was any more, or where he was going with his life? He'd been lost since he'd woken that morning eighteen months ago to find her gone. He'd searched and searched, but could find no trace. It was almost as though she'd never existed.

But she *had* existed. He only had to close his eyes and the memories would sweep in. Her face. Her passion. The all-consuming heat of her beautiful body.

God, if only she would let him go! If only he could stop remembering!

'Luke?' his mother prompted. 'Don't go giving me

the silent treatment. I can't stand it when one of my boys goes all quiet and brooding on me.'

Luke pulled himself together, finding a cool mask from somewhere to turn towards his far too intuitive mother.

'I would have thought Andy and Mark had more than adequately fulfilled your grandmothering needs, Mum,' he pointed out drily. 'They have five very nice children between them—three boys and two girls— plus two perfect daughters-in-law for wives. You really don't need me to add to the St Clair brood, or the St Clair wives. Two out of three ain't bad, you know. Don't become one of those meddling matchmaking mums, or I might be forced to stay in LA in future.'

Her hurt look made him feel instantly guilty, and he sighed his regret. 'Just kidding, Mum. You know you're my best girl. I could never stay away from you for too long.'

'Flatterer,' she said, but he could see that she was pleased.

His mother mollified, Luke sat back silently and tried to distract his wretched mind by focusing on the familiar but still beautiful surroundings. He stared out at the blue waters of Botany Bay on their right, then up at the clear blue sky. Nowhere in the world had he ever found skies such as in Australia. Their clearness and brightness was unique, but it made for harsh light—not the easiest background for good photography.

It took special skills and equipment to photograph Australian scenery really well—unless one captured the shots at dawn or dusk—skills which he had never honed, but which could present an interesting challenge, Luke decided unexpectedly.

His passion had always been photographing people, right from his boyhood days. He'd perfected portraiture, especially in black and white, and had made a small fortune out of it.

There'd been a time when he'd got a kick out of surprising people with his flattering photographs of them. Models and actresses with a portfolio by Luke St Clair had a definite edge in the cut-throat world of auditions in the US. He was sought-after and paid handsomely for his work. He could command huge fees.

But, quite frankly, it had all become somewhat of a bore.

Besides, he no longer needed to do things for money. An inspired investment in a small independent movie which had taken the world by storm a couple of years back had ensured he never had to work again if he didn't want to. So perhaps it was time to spread his photographic wings, so to speak. To find a new direction to satisfy his creative eye.

Maybe his mother was right, he began to muse. Maybe it was time to come home—if not to marry then to find a new life-path. He could not go on as he had this past year. It was slowly destroying him.

'I'll let you out here,' his mother suggested, pulling over to the kerb. 'The dentist is just in that small arcade over there. There's a narrow staircase which leads up to a corridor, and his surgery is the second door on the left upstairs. I'll meet you in that coffee-shop on the corner. Whichever one of us gets there first can wait for the other.'

Butterflies gathered in the pit of his stomach as he mounted the stairs and pushed open the glass door. A very attractive brunette looked up from behind the reception desk, saw the cut of the man standing there and smiled a smile as old as time itself.

'Yes, can I help you?' she asked hopefully.

Luke did his best to ignore the silent invitation in her pretty blue eyes, despite his own gaze automatically shifting to her left hand. He was almost relieved to see a diamond engagement ring twinkling there, for in all truth he'd become horribly addicted to picking up pretty women during the last year or so, taking them out, then home to bed, then never contacting them again.

He wasn't proud of his behaviour, but he understood it. He was punishing them for *her*.

He excused himself by saying that he only picked up the really eager ones—the ones who made it perfectly obvious what they wanted from him. Like *she* had. He always hoped to gain some darkly twisted satisfaction from being the one who did the seducing and the dumping. Instead he always felt like a rat in the morning, hating himself more and more with each episode.

The women involved didn't know it, but they were better off without him. He'd become a right bastard—sexually speaking—since that night, his only concession to his conscience being that he steered clear of married and engaged women. He took some small comfort from that, soothing his escalating qualms with the thought that he hadn't descended to being a complete scoundrel yet.

'My name's St Clair,' he announced, deliberately leaving off the Luke. 'I have an appointment for ten-thirty.'

'Oh, yes, Mr St Clair. I'm afraid Dr Evans is running a little late. Maybe fifteen minutes or so. Would you like some tea or coffee while you wait?'

Tea or coffee on his churning stomach? A whisky, perhaps, but he didn't think she'd offer him that. 'No thanks,' came his brusque reply. 'I'll just wait.'

'There are plenty of magazines,' she told him as he walked over to settle himself into one of the black leather two-seaters which lined the starkly white walls.

Luke did his best to relax, resting his right ankle on his left knee and spreading his arms along the back of the seat. But he soon found his fingers tapping impatiently on the leather. In the end he picked up one of the dog-eared women's weeklies lying on the table next to him, smiling wryly when he saw that it was dated four years previously.

He began idly flicking through it, just to pass the time, and might have missed her picture altogether if his attention hadn't been attracted by the headline above it: MODEL GIVES UP BLOSSOMING CAREER TO MARRY NOTED SCIENTIST.

It had been years since Luke had made his living doing fashion magazine layouts, but during that time many of his friends had been models—and some had been more than friends—so curiosity had him open the double page in his lap and look to see if this particular model was anyone he knew.

His eyes skimmed the kissing couple to see if he recognised them, but it was impossible with their faces obscured—though he noted that the bridegroom had greying hair. So he scanned the words beneath, looking for names.

No bells rang in his brain when he read that a twenty-two-year-old model named Rachel Manning had married noted geneticist Patrick Cleary at St Mary's Cathedral, Sydney, that Saturday afternoon four years previously. It was only when his gaze dropped further, to another smaller photograph of the bride alone, that he recognised her.

Had he gone as white as a sheet?

Luke fancied that he had.

His knuckles certainly went white as his fingers tightened around the pages, his eyes wide upon the photograph of the smiling bride—the gloriously golden-haired and exquisitely beautiful bride.

How innocent she looked in her white bridal gown, he thought savagely. The picture of perfect purity. The very essence of untouched womanhood.

A rage began to grow inside him as his shock gave way to anger. She'd been *married*! The bitch had been *married*!

My God, it explained so much. So damned much!

There had been so many elements of that night which had stayed to haunt him. So many unanswered questions.

Now he had the answers.

Or did he?

Just because she'd been married four years ago it didn't mean that she'd still been married eighteen months ago. There was such a thing as divorce, wasn't there? Maybe she wasn't an adulterous little tramp. Maybe there were other reasons why she'd acted the way she had that night—why she'd chosen to disappear while he was asleep, without leaving a trace of her true identity.

And maybe pigs might fly, came the blackly cynical thought.

'Dr Evans is ready for you now, Mr St Clair.'

Luke schooled his face into what he hoped was a normal expression, snapped the magazine shut and placed it back on the pile in the corner.

Forget her, common sense whispered. She's bad news.

He stood up and walked over to where the dental nurse was waiting for him in the now open doorway. Her petite prettiness didn't even register. He no longer felt nervous either. *She* dominated his mind again, turning his thoughts from the present.

Luke distractedly settled in the dental chair and closed his eyes, his mind whirling with memories. But how could he forget her now? Now that she had a name.

Rachel.

He hadn't known her name when she'd picked him up at the exhibition that night eighteen months ago.

Hadn't known it the next morning, when he'd woken to find her gone.

Rachel…

It didn't suit her, he decided viciously.

Oh, it suited the bride in the photograph, but not the sultry feline creature who had undulated into his sight that night. Rachel sounded like a lady—but it had been no lady who'd boldly approached him within seconds of spotting him leaning against a pillar, who'd stolen his drink from his hands and taken a deep swallow, who'd smiled seductively at him over the rim before uttering the most astonishingly forthright proposal he'd ever heard from a woman.

And he'd heard a good few in his time.

The dentist was talking to him as he worked, but Luke didn't hear a word. He was back at that exhibition, hearing her say those astonishing words again, reliving every moment of that unforgettable but ultimately soul-destroying night.

CHAPTER TWO

'I HAVE a hotel room nearby,' she said in a huskily sexy voice, her incredible green eyes locked to his all the while. 'If you're as bored as you look, perhaps you'd like to join me there.'

Luke straightened, glad that his drink now rested between those long, elegant fingers with the equally long bronze-tipped nails. Otherwise he would surely have spilt his drink down his front. Though perhaps that might not have been such a bad idea. Things were happening down there which could do with a spot of cooling down.

He stared deep into those exotic green pools, because it was safer than looking at the rest of her. Not that he hadn't already had a damned good look as she'd slowly sashayed towards him across the gallery floor.

She had a stunning face—exotic perfection framed by a wild tawny blonde mane—but an even more than stunning body. Tall and slender, with high, firm breasts, a riveting cleavage and long, long legs which ran right up to her tiny waist. Or so it seemed.

Dressed a touch obviously for his usual taste in women, her leopardskin-print mini left nothing to the imagination. Hell, if she was wearing anything underneath he couldn't spot it. The silky material clung like a second skin, the halter-necked style leaving her shoulders and arms bare, the short, short skirt showing an expanse of firm tanned thigh which would do a stripper proud.

This last thought made him wonder what she *did* do for a living. Though perhaps it was better if he didn't know.

Normally he was attracted to cool, classy types, sophisticated career women who exuded an understated and challenging sexuality which left it up to him to do the chasing. They sent out silent and very subtle messages for him to follow. They didn't openly invite, like this bold creature.

'Are you in the habit of propositioning perfect strangers?' he drawled, trying not to sound as shocked as he was feeling. Or as aroused.

He told himself that it was because he hadn't been with a woman since he'd broken up with Tracy a couple of months before. But underneath he knew this wasn't so. He'd wanted this she-cat the moment he'd set eyes on her.

A slight frown drew her perfectly arched eyebrows close together. 'You're American,' she said.

He could have enlightened her, but something... some indefinable tension which this mistaken conclusion was evoking in her, made him keep his Australian heritage to himself. He'd been told that he'd picked up an American accent, but he hadn't believed it till that moment.

'You don't like Americans?' he asked, taking the drink back from her suddenly still hands and draining it dry. He had a feeling he might need to be a little drunk to get through this evening.

'That depends,' she said, a touch warily. 'Are you holidaying here? Or staying indefinitely?'

'Holidaying,' he said, quite truthfully. But I might stay indefinitely, came the dark thought. If it means I can spend every night with you.

Already he could feel the blood rushing hotly to his loins. Already...

His flesh might have become a painful and obvious embarrassment if he hadn't been wearing a longer-line sports jacket loosely over casually fitted dark trousers which also had plenty of room. Luke could put up with the discomfort, if it was his alone to contemplate and suffer in private.

He had no intention of letting this feline huntress see that he was ready prey for her animal-like sexuality. As much as he was turned on by her amazingly forward approach and absolutely knock-out body, his male ego insisted that he play hard to get for a decent amount of time.

At least a minute, came the drily self-mocking thought.

'Does that disqualify me?' he said lazily.

'On the contrary,' she murmured, her husky voice rippling down his spine like a mink-gloved hand. 'I love tourists. Especially tall, dark, handsome ones with sexy black eyes. You are alone, aren't you? No little wife or girlfriend back at the hotel, or in the States?'

'I'm so alone,' he told her, trying to sound cool but feeling anything but, 'that it's positively indecent.'

'Nothing about you is indecent, handsome,' she murmured. 'You're positively gorgeous and positively perfect. Come with me...'

She pried the empty glass out of his suddenly frozen hand and bent to place it on the floor, giving him an uninterrupted view of her quite perfect breasts. Rising again, she smiled a siren's smile, slid her right hand into his still frozen left and began leading him away, across the upper gallery floor then down the wide white staircase.

The shredded remnants of Luke's common sense finally burst through his paralysed brain and he ground to a halt, momentarily resisting the hypnotic pull of the softly feminine fingers entwined through his.

'You're not a hooker, are you?' came his harsh-sounding question as they faced each other on the stairs.

He could not have mistaken the momentary shock which flared within those gorgeous green eyes, or his own inner shudder of relief. For what would he have done if she'd said that she was?

Still have gone with her, came the appalling admission.

'My mistake,' he muttered. 'Lead on, lover.' Obviously she was just a good-time girl, out on the tiles for the night. She wanted a one-night stand—without complications, without strings.

As much as that was not usually his style, Luke could see that it was going to be for tonight. It was no use pretending that he wasn't bowled over. *More* than bowled over. She seemed to have bewitched him with the primitive and alluring sexuality which emanated from every pore of her body. It wafted from her in waves, weaving a spell around his senses, teasing his flesh and his imagination, making him wonder what it would be like to spend the night with her.

She kept glancing over her shoulder at him as she drew him down the rest of the stairs and through the crowded foyer, her eyes sometimes smiling invitingly, sometimes seemingly checking that he was still there—as though she too could not believe he'd come with her so readily.

It was those glimpses of unexpected vulnerability which began intriguing Luke. The suspicion that this was not her usual style either began to form in his mind. She looked at him that way one time too many after they'd finally made it outside into the street, and he suddenly whipped her over into a darkened doorway, pulling her against him in a jolting embrace.

Her shocked gasp and almost frightened eyes confirmed his opinion that she was not used to playing such dangerous games. Either that, or she had never run into real trouble before.

'You little fool,' he snarled, infuriated by this last

thought. 'Don't you know the risks you run in going off with a stranger?'

Her chin whipped up, green eyes glinting an answering fury at him. 'I take it you've changed your mind—is that it?' she snapped. 'If so, then say so, damn you.' She began to struggle to free herself from his arms. 'I have no time for cowards tonight.'

'Cowards! Why, you little...' Red spots of fury went off in his brain like flashlights, and before he knew it he'd grasped a large clump of her hair and yanked it back so that her chin tipped up all the more.

Before she could do more than cry out through startled lips, his mouth clamped down over those lips and he was kissing her as he'd never kissed a woman before. With anger, not passion, with a desire to punish and hurt, not seduce.

But seduction was the final result.

His, not hers. For as his tongue drove repeatedly into the depths of her mouth she moaned a moan which moved him as no woman's moan had ever done before, making him want to protect her, not punish her. Hold, not hurt.

He found it impossible to keep kissing her with such ferocity. His tongue gentled to a series of sinuous slides against hers, his free hand finding the small of her back and pressing inwards. He thrilled to the feel of her sinking weakly against him, then to the sound of another longer, more sensual moan—this one signalling total surrender to his male domination over her body. It brought a dizzying sense of sexual power, and he simply could not wait to have her naked and trembling beneath him.

'This hotel room,' he muttered thickly against her mouth. 'Is it far?'

She shook her head in the negative, the movement brushing her lush lips to and fro across his.

He shuddered as a rush of blood almost had him doing what he hadn't done since he was fifteen. Gulping, he drew back from the raw heat of her body to stare down into wildly dilated green eyes. She looked...stunned, he realised. Stunned, and totally at his mercy. It was an exhilarating and intoxicating thought—a male fantasy come true. Impossible to resist.

'Then take me there,' he muttered. 'And take me there quickly...'

The drill contacting his tooth brought Luke back to the present—physically at least—but his mind continued to churn over his still vivid memories.

Had she deceived him with that air of vulnerability, with her seemingly mindless surrender? Had she been so diabolically clever, so skilled in seducing strangers that she had made it seem as if *he* had been master of what had happened that evening? Whereas in reality *she* had been the one pulling the strings and making all the moves?

He desperately wanted to believe that she hadn't been married at the time—although it seemed likely that she had. Given that assumption, he clung to the idea that it had been her first foray into adultery. Even so, he could not deny that she had come to that exhibition right and ready for a night of casual sex, dressed for the occasion and armed to the eye-teeth with the equipment necessary to reduce fools like him to instant mush.

Looking back, he could see that she'd also gone to great pains to protect her true identity—to cut down the risk of ever being caught out in her outrageous behaviour. She'd wanted a mad fling of some kind, but she hadn't wanted any evidence of that mad fling left behind. The only part of the puzzle which remained was why she'd taken that appalling risk during the middle of the night.

It couldn't have been deliberate, he decided, unless it had been part of some crazy fantasy she'd wanted to fulfil. He preferred to think that she'd simply been carried away—as *he* had been carried away.

It was one of the reasons why she haunted him. Because he'd never been carried away like that before. Or since…

'I don't even known your name,' he said when he finally closed the hotel room door, neither of them having said a word as she had led him swiftly down two blocks and into the foyer of a small but surprisingly elegant hotel. Not at all the sort of place for a cheap rendezvous.

The lift-ride up to the third floor had been tense, the presence of another man in the lift stifling any conversation or physical contact. Luke had hardly been aware of his surroundings as he'd eagerly followed her down the corridor. He had absorbed little but a brief impression of red-patterned carpet and black and white prints of ships on the walls.

'My name?' she repeated, almost as though she were in a fog.

He liked her disorientation, liked the way she gasped when he pulled her abruptly into his arms. 'Never mind,' he growled. 'No names for tonight. We'll exchange names in the morning.'

He kissed her again before the fog could lift.

God, but he liked the woman his kisses turned her into, liked the sounds she made under them, liked the feel of her lips melting along with her body. He'd never known a woman become so pliant in his arms before. Her sweet surrender to his mouth and hands filled him with the heady power to do as he pleased with her.

He pleased to take off all her clothes. What little there was of them.

He pleased to carry her over to the king-sized bed and stretch her, seemingly dazed, out on top of it.

He certainly pleased to sit beside her gloriously naked body and touch her all over…at will…and very, very thoroughly.

She didn't stop him, merely gazed up at him all the while with glazed green eyes, her lush lips gasping apart occasionally. Her pleasure was obvious, as was a bewildering amount of surprise. Hadn't she expected to enjoy his touch so much? Or was it that she wasn't used to a man giving her pleasure first this way?

She was getting close, he knew; her thighs were beginning to tremble. When her back began to arch from the bed he stopped abruptly, and she moaned her frustration.

It was only when Luke stood up that he realised his breathing was as hard and fast as hers. God, he hadn't been this excited in years, he realised. Or this enthralled with a woman. Stripped of those sluttish clothes, she had taken on a totally different persona. There was nothing cheap about her any more. She was all classical curves and sweetly fragrant beauty. She was even a genuine blonde!

He couldn't wait to bury himself in those softly golden curls, to have those lovely long legs wrapped tightly around him, to see those lush lips form a gasping O at the moment of her orgasm.

Funny, he had no conscious thought of his own satisfaction—which was a first for him. In the past, his priority when making love to a woman had always been what *he* would get out of it.

But not this time. This time he wanted to give even more than to receive.

Luke hardly recognised the man he'd become since entering this room. He felt all-powerful, yet that power was tempered with a strange tenderness. If he hadn't known better, he might have thought he'd finally really fallen in love. Even if not, it was certainly an experience outside his normal realm of experiences.

He could not even remember the first time he'd made love to Tracy, though he'd fancied himself in love with her back then. Yet already he knew he would never forget this night, not as long as he lived.

'You haven't done this before, have you?' he remarked as he began undressing himself, slipping out of his jacket and draping it over one of the bedposts.

She licked her lips, her eyes wide upon his. 'Why do you say that?' Her voice was husky, as though desire had dried her mouth and throat. But not the rest of her. The rest of her was far from dry, he recalled, with a lurching in his stomach.

'You seem too nervous.'

'I'm no virgin,' she protested, though shakily.

'I never said you were.' But her gaze was definitely close to virginal as it clung to his half-naked body.

Luke found her mixture of fascination and fear a real turn-on. He knew he had a good body, knew it was well equipped to satisfy most women's fantasies. So there was no hesitation when he finally stripped off his underwear. He actually saw the swallowing action in her throat, and revelled in her reaction.

'Where have you put the condoms?' he said as he joined her on the bed, running a gently caressing hand down her body as he did so.

She quivered uncontrollably and closed her eyes.

'Hey,' he prompted, quietly but firmly. 'The condoms?'

Long lashes fluttered open; the green eyes were

pained. 'Oh, God,' she groaned, shaking her head from side to side. 'I didn't think. I just didn't think.'

Her distress touched him, despite his flash of annoyance at her naïvety. He would have to make sure that she never did insane things like this again. There again, she wasn't going to have any lovers other than him after tonight. He was going to make sure of that. Come morning, there would be no more of this 'stranger' nonsense.

'It's all right,' he reassured her, trying not to sound irritated. 'I always keep one in my wallet.'

And that was what was annoying him. One. Only *one*! They would need more than one before this night was out. He tossed up between dressing now and finding a twenty-four-hour chemist or doing it later.

Later, his intense desire told him. *Much* later.

He could not wait another minute. Or even another moment.

'No!' she cried out when he swung his legs over onto the floor.

His glance over his shoulder carried impatience and puzzlement. 'No, what?'

'No, I can't,' she rasped. 'I can't...'

Luke had no intention of letting her change her mind at this point. It was beyond bearing just thinking about it.

'It's all right,' he murmured, turning back to cup her face with firm hands and stare deep into her anguished green eyes. 'I understand. You've only just realised what a very silly girl you've been tonight. But

I'm a good guy. Really. I won't hurt you, loveliness. I'm going to make beautiful love to you,' he promised, pressing her back against the pillow and kissing her.

He kept on kissing her till she began clinging to him and squirming with renewed desire. But he didn't dare leave her even then, reinforcing his temporary triumph by sliding down her body and kissing her all over till she was beyond stopping him, even when he had to abandon her for a short while.

She reached for him when he returned to the bed, pulling him down on top of her and not letting him indulge in any further foreplay. By this time Luke was ready to explode anyway, so when she opened to him, winding her legs high around his back, there really wasn't any option.

He drove deep into her hot, honeyed flesh, shuddering with pleasure at her exquisite tightness. He'd barely moved within her when her first fierce contraction seized his flesh, and it was all too much. He could not hold back another second, tremors racking his body as he climaxed uncontrollably, his spasms totally in tune with hers, going on and on for simply ages.

At last it was over, and he sank down upon her, feeling sated with pleasure. Yet even in the aftermath there was more pleasure, a sweet intimacy rising between them as her arms stole around him then squeezed, holding him tightly to her flattened breasts. His lips nuzzled her left ear and she sighed her satisfaction with him. He felt deliciously loved and loving,

every limb and muscle flooded with a warm and won-
drous peace.

He never wanted to leave her, but he had to in the
end, though he returned from the *en suite* bathroom as
quickly as possible. He began to see what the Bible
meant about man and woman cleaving together to
make one flesh. He felt only half a man away from
her, already addicted to the feelings she evoked in him.

She was lying on her side watching him as he came
back into the room, her position showing the delicious
female curve of waist, hip and leg. Her breasts looked
swollen, he noted, her nipples still hard, and her eyes
were heavy-lidded and incredibly sensuous as they
travelled slowly down his body.

His heart kicked over when her gaze drifted down
past his navel, having an immediate effect on his till
then flaccid flesh. The thought hit him immediately
then he should dress and go in search of that chemist
before another moment passed, but then she smiled
that siren's smile at him and stretched out a beckoning
hand. She drew him down onto the bed beside her and
began to caress him with that hand, bringing him to
full erection within an amazingly short time.

Transfixed by this sudden reversal of roles, Luke
simply lay there, stunned and speechless as she continued to kiss and caress every inch of his body. There
was nothing even remotely virginal about her now;
everything she did was designed to tantalise and torment him to the point of no return, yet without grant-
ing him release.

He knew the enveloping heat of her mouth, the flickering torture of her tongue, the teasing touch of fingers which knew exactly what to do to drive him mad then stop him in midstream.

He tried closing his eyes against the sensations growing within him, and it proved to be a disastrous mistake. For during those seconds of desperate darkness she moved to straddle his hips, taking the full length of his pained hardness deep within her. His eyes flung open on a raw cry of panic, but already she was riding him, green eyes glittering wildly.

'No,' he groaned. But weakly. Pathetically.

'Yes,' she hissed back. 'Yes…'

His hands found her hips, and he should have heaved her from his body. Instead he gripped her flesh and urged her on to a stronger, faster rhythm. His own hips began to rise and fall, and it felt incredible.

God, but she was so hot in there. So hot. He could feel his own blood heating even further, racing along his veins like molten lava. The volcano of his desire would not be contained this time. Or controlled. It surged higher and higher with each drumbeat of his madly pounding heart, and then it was erupting, flooding into the already spasming heart of her womanhood, dredging raw groans from his parched and panting lungs.

When the climax had passed, he reached up to bring her down so that he could kiss her, wanting to feel the heat of her mouth as well.

He was startled to encounter the wetness of tears

running into the corners. He didn't know what to say; could think of nothing but to cradle her close, to stroke her back and say whatever came to mind.

'Don't cry, darling. Please don't cry. God, but I can't bear it. Hush, sweetness. There's nothing to worry about. Nothing. As I said before, I'm a good guy. And I can see you're a good girl. We're good people. Hush, my loveliness. Hush. Go to sleep, there's a good girl. Yes, that's it. Go to sleep.'

They both went to sleep…eventually…though Luke took quite a while to come to terms with what had just happened. He hoped he was right. Hoped that she *was* a good girl. If not, he'd just done the stupidest damned thing he'd ever done in his whole life. Slept with a perfect stranger. *Without* protection. Then, to top it all off, he'd fallen in love with her…

'All finished, Mr St Clair.' The chair snapped upright and the nurse moved to unclip the paper bib around his neck.

Luke's black eyes blinked open to stare blankly into her smiling face. His gaze went to the clock on the wall. Eleven-fifteen. He'd been at the dentist over half an hour and he hadn't felt a thing! Unless one counted what had been going on within his head. And his heart.

An impotent rage simmered beneath the cool façade he presented to the dentist and his nurse as he thanked them and said goodbye, and then to the receptionist as he paid his bill. In cash.

'I hope you enjoy your stay here in Australia, Mr

St Clair,' she said, reminding him that he still sounded like an American.

'I'm sure I will,' he returned, trying to keep the grim satisfaction out of his voice. 'Enjoy' was probably not the right word, but he had no doubt that this visit was going to be memorable. At last he had a name to put to his obsession. A name and a past. He would leave no stone unturned till he came face to face with the woman who'd haunted him all these months.

And when he did?

God only knew what he was going to do. Because *he* didn't.

'Would you mind if I took one of those old magazines with me?' he asked the receptionist. 'It has a picture in it of an old friend of mine.'

'Take it, by all means.' And me too if you like, her eyes seemed to be telling him.

Unfaithful bitch, he thought as he strode over to the corner table. They were probably all unfaithful bitches, all the beautiful women in this world.

He snatched up the magazine in question, not giving the girl a second glance as he stuffed it under his arm and strode angrily from the room.

CHAPTER THREE

HIS mother was waiting for him in the coffee-lounge,
a cup of capuccino in front of her, a jam and cream
doughnut to her left, a newspaper to her right and a
plastic shopping bag at her feet. She shut the newspaper on Luke's approach and folded it, frowning up
at him as he scraped out the chair and sat down.

'What's wrong with you now?' she said. 'Couldn't
you get your tooth fixed?'

He resisted the urge to scowl. Five minutes he'd
give her, then he'd be off in a taxi to the nearby air-
port, where he would rent a decent car. He needed his
own wheels. And the privacy that went with them.

'There's nothing wrong with me,' he said. 'I'm fine.
My tooth's fine. The weather's fine. Life's fine.'

'Then why are you still in such a foul mood?'

'Lord, what is it with you? Do you have some special mother's antenna that can pick up my mood at
twenty paces? I've just walked in and sat down. How
could you possibly gauge my mood? I hadn't even
spoken when you made your instant judgement.'

'You were walking cranky,' came her simplistic but
accurate observation.

He couldn't help it. He had to laugh. There was no
hiding anything from his mother. Which reminded

him. He slipped the magazine from under his arm onto a spare chair and thought of something to say to distract her.

'Tell me, Mum. Were you ever unfaithful to Dad?'

'Heavens to Betsy! What a question!'

'That's no answer. That's an evasion.'

'I needed a moment to catch my breath. Might I ask what's brought such a question on?'

'Well, you're a good-looking woman. From photographs I've seen when Dad married you forty-five years ago you were pretty stunning. Stunning women have temptation put in their way, whether they're married or not.'

Grace wondered which stunning married woman her son had been getting mixed up with, but tactfully refrained from asking. *This* time.

'I won't say I didn't have my offers,' she answered truthfully. 'And I won't say I wasn't tempted, once or twice. But I managed to stay faithful to your father. Technically speaking, that is.'

Luke blinked his shock at her. 'Technically speaking?' he repeated rather dazedly. 'What do you mean…''*technically* speaking''?'

'Well, I did let a man kiss me once for a few seconds longer than I should have.'

'Oh, is that all?'

'I thought it was pretty terrible of me at the time. But he was awfully good-looking. And very charming. I was flattered to death that he fancied me. He was only in his early thirties and I was a silly forty-one at the time, thinking I was over the hill and desperate for some attention. He gave me some.'

'And would have given you a whole lot more if you'd let him,' Luke said drily. 'Who was he, this Casanova?'

'No one you ever met. He was Danish, visiting Sydney one summer. Your father met him down the local pub and was silly enough to invite him home for supper one night.'

'And you let him kiss you that very same night?' Luke could not contain his surprise.

A small blush of guilt stained his mother's normally pale cheeks. 'As I said,' she muttered, 'he was very charming.'

'So how did it happen? And where was Dad, damn him?'

'Watching TV, as usual. Eric offered to help me with the washing-up, and he sort of cornered me against the kitchen sink. At first I was shocked. But when he started kissing me, I have to admit I liked it. Oh, I stopped him before things went too far, but after he left I thought about him a lot. I knew which hotel he was staying at—since he'd made a point of telling me—and I actually rang his room one day. But when he answered I panicked and hung up.'

'I see…'

'Do you, Luke? I doubt it. I loved your father, and he was a good lover when he was younger. But time and familiarity can do dreadful things in the bedroom. Boredom sets in, and your father did work terribly hard. Most nights he was too tired. Our sex life had deteriorated to a quickie once or twice a month, and I was silly enough not to know what to do about it. So, of course, I was a ready victim for the likes of Eric, who really was a sleazebag of the first order.'

Luke frowned at his mother. 'You're not lying to me, are you, Mum? You didn't really go with him, did you?'

'Of course not! I went out and bought myself a sexy black nightie and started doing a few of those things I'd only ever read about in books before. Things really looked up after that.'

'Mum! I'm shocked,' he said, then grinned at her. 'You devil, you.'

She blushed some more, though she did look rather pleased with herself. He felt inordinately proud of her at that moment. She'd been handed temptation on a plate, when his dad had foolishly been neglecting her, but her essential goodness had come through in the end.

Luke's mouth thinned as he accepted that not all women were as strong, or as decent. Some were weak, self-centred creatures, who went out and took what they wanted, and to hell with the people they hurt in the process.

A waiter appeared by the table and asked Luke if he wanted to order. He declined, giving the excuse that his mouth still felt numb from the injection he'd had—which was true—but the real reason was that he could not stand to sit there any longer. He had places to go. Leads to follow. A woman to find.

'Would you mind if I loved you and left you, Mum?' he said as soon as the waiter had departed. 'While I was at the dentist's I remembered I'd promised Ray to look him up the next time I was home.'

'Ray? Ray who?'

'Ray Holland. He's a photographer.' Who I'm hoping and praying still lives and works in Sydney, he thought grimly.

'Never heard of him. There again, the only photographer friend of yours you ever talk about is Theo, and that's never very complimentary. I remember poor Theo had the hardest job talking you into going to the opening of his photographic exhibition last time you were home, and then the next morning he rang and complained that you'd disappeared ten minutes after you arrived!'

'Yeah, well, over the past few years poor Theo's work has gone from really good stuff down to the most pretentious crap. I thought if I stayed there any longer that night I might be tempted to tell the truth and offend him.'

'Where *did* you get to that night? You didn't come home, if I recall.'

'Come now, Mum! You don't really expect me to tell you, do you? I gave up reporting in when I turned eighteen.'

'Don't underestimate yourself, Luke. You were fifteen. The most difficult and rebellious boy God ever put breath into! I can see you haven't improved much either. You're still difficult.'

'What about rebellious?'

'"Rebellious" is not an adjective suited to a thirty-two-year-old bachelor. Let's just leave it at difficult.'

'Yes, let's,' Luke said, and stood up, sensing that his mother was about to deteriorate into emotional blackmail of some sort. She had that gleam in her eye which heralded that her female curiosity was far from satisfied.

Women could be quite ruthless when they really wanted to know something, he mused. If cool reason didn't work, they tried every trick in the book—from Chinese-water-torture-style demands, to sulky silences, to floods of tears.

Luke could bear just about all those methods except tears. They were the undoing of him every time.

'I must go, Mum. I have a lot to do today. And before you suggest it, no, I don't want you to drive me. I'm going to rent myself a car.'

'Will you be home for dinner this evening?' Grace asked archly.

'What are you cooking?'

She lifted her nose in a disdainful sniff. 'I have no intention of telling you if that's all that's bringing you home.'

'In that case you can surprise me. See you around seven, sweetie,' he said, distracting her with a peck on the cheek while he scooped the women's magazine up from the adjoining chair.

Grace watched her son stalk across the coffee-lounge, well aware of the hungry female eyes which turned to follow him. Her sigh held a weary resignation. That boy is up to no good, she thought, her own eyes zeroing in on the magazine curled up in his right hand.

And it's all to do with some woman, I'll warrant. A woman featured in that magazine he's been trying to hide. A married woman, no doubt, whom he met the last time he was home and whom he's off to meet again in secret.

Oh, Luke…Luke…

Grace shook her head unhappily. When was he going to learn that there was no future with a married woman? No future at all!

Luke paced up and down the living-room of Theo's apartment, impatiently waiting for his friend to come out of his darkroom.

He still could not believe his luck—or the ease with which he'd reached his objective! Within an hour of leaving his mother he'd been leaving the offices of the magazine with the address of Ray Holland in his hot little hands. Half an hour later Luke had been walking into the man's studio in Randwick, and once again his luck had been in—he'd caught the freelance photographer just before he had to leave. Luke had come to the point immediately.

A trendily dressed man in his early forties, Mr Holland had remembered the Cleary wedding very well, because he'd worked with the bride herself several times previously—her speciality having been modelling swimsuits and lingerie, both as a photographic and catwalk model.

He'd also heard on the grapevine that his 'darling Rachel'—Luke's teeth had ground when he'd called her that—had recently returned to modelling. Word around the photographic traps was that her scientist husband had died recently, and that financial difficulty had forced her to go back to work.

Luke had absorbed this last piece of news with ambivalent emotions. He hadn't been able to deny his momentary elation at finding out that the object of his obsession was now a widow, but the news that the husband had only died recently—meaning she'd still been well and truly married that night eighteen months ago—had revitalised his underlying bitterness towards her.

Unfaithful bitch, he'd raged inwardly while he'd taken down the name and address of the modelling agency she worked for.

The niggling suspicion that her much older husband might have been ailing at the time of her adultery had crossed his mind as he'd driven on to that agency. Such a circumstance might have mitigated her behaviour somewhat, if she'd gone about having her affair with some class and style, but there had been nothing of class or style in the way she'd been dressed that night—or the way she'd picked him up, or the way she'd slunk off afterwards while he'd been asleep.

That was one thing he would never forgive. Her running out on him the way she had—leaving him to worry and wonder, leaving him feeling a total fool and in torment for months, till a second blood test had assured him he wasn't about to die for his insanity in going to bed with such a creature.

He'd always wanted to meet her face to face, and see what it was about her that still haunted him so. But also to ask her why. Why she'd chosen him. Why she'd taken such a crazy risk. Why, why, why?

And now… Now he would have the opportunity to do just that…in two days' time. God, he could hardly wait!

'That's some smile, pal. It's sending shudders down my spine. What are you up to?'

Luke's dark eyes snapped up to find that Theo had emerged from the darkroom and was watching him closely. Theo had once been Luke's employer, in the early days. Now he was Luke's one remaining close friend in the Australian photographic world. Still a bachelor, he was an elegant-looking man in his late thirties who changed girlfriends as regularly as he did cameras and styles of photography.

Luke didn't like the way Theo slavishly followed the photographic fashion of the moment. He believed that that was not the road to success or personal satisfaction. But he liked the man, who was easy-going and great company. Unfortunately Theo could also sometimes be as intuitive as Luke's mother—something Luke had temporarily forgotten. His mind, after all, was rather preoccupied at that moment.

Luke casually wiped the darkly triumphant smile from his face, replacing it with an innocuously bland expression. 'I'm contemplating how you're going to react to my asking to borrow two of your cameras.'

Theo's blue eyes narrowed, suspicion in their intelligent depths. '*You* want to borrow *my* cameras?' he said, his voice sceptical in the extreme. 'That'd be a first.'

'True. But I've been thinking lately how bored to tears I am with photographing faces—especially in black and white. I've decided to try my hand at something different.'

'Such as what?' Theo walked across his living-room in the direction of his well-equipped kitchen. 'Care for a cup of coffee?'

Luke nodded, recognising the hunger pangs in his stomach for the first time that day. A glance at his watch showed him the reason why. Hell, it was after three, and he hadn't stopped for a bite to eat since breakfast!

It just showed what effect that witch could have on him, he thought blackly. She disturbed his equilibrium as no woman had ever done before. Splitting up with Tracy had left him feeling wretched and lonely for only a few short weeks. Not being able to find this Rachel, after spending one short night together, had shattered him for months, then haunted him for another year, spurring him on to indulge in a personal lifestyle which was basically abhorrent to him.

Neither was it working.

Being with other women didn't rid him of the memories of that night. It kept them alive by making him compare all the time. Yet no woman *could* compare— either with the physical feelings that that green-eyed alley-cat had initially evoked, or the emotional feelings she'd managed to engender later, once they had been alone together in that room.

'Penny for your thoughts,' Theo drawled as he slid a mug of coffee down the breakfast bar to where Luke had blindly propped himself up on a kitchen stool. Luke blinked a couple of times, then focused on his friend.

'They're worth a lot more than that,' he muttered, thinking of all the jobs he'd knocked back this last eighteen months. It was as well he'd become independently wealthy these past few years, or he'd have been stony broke by now.

'You're talking in riddles, man. Care to tell your old mate what's eating you up?'

'No. Not really.'

Theo nodded up and down, his expression accepting. 'Fair enough.'

Luke appreciated his friend's not pressing. Maybe he would tell him one day about this Rachel, depending on what happened on Wednesday. But there again…maybe not…

'So what cameras do you want to borrow?' Theo asked.

Luke shrugged, then grinned. 'Damned if I know. I'll have to put myself in your expert hands.'

Theo grinned back. 'Flattery will get you everywhere. Well, first things first, what are you going to photograph?'

'Lots of beaches and bikinis.'

Theo's eyebrows shot up. 'Are we talking art-shots here, or some sort of Australiana promotion?'

'That depends,' Luke returned non-committally.

Theo's blue eyes twinkled. 'Ahh. Methinks I'm beginning to see what lies behind this unexpected career-change. And there I was thinking you were the only other man I knew to have escaped the tender trap. So! Might I enquire her name?'

'Who?' Luke drawled.

'The model you'll be using, man. What do you take me for—a fool? Now, give. Who is she? Do I know her, and why are you going to so much trouble to be with her?'

Luke decided he had nothing to lose by telling Theo her name. Who knew? Theo didn't do much fashion work any more, but he might still know her.

'Rachel Manning,' he said.

The agency had confirmed that she was working under her maiden name. They'd also confirmed that she was still specialising in swimwear and was free of bookings that week.

Luke's stomach had twisted into knots while they

rang her on the spot and booked her for a shoot on the Wednesday and Thursday up on the Central Coast beaches, starting at Terrigal on the Wednesday, with an overnight stay at the Holiday Inn there that night.

Luke had known she wouldn't refuse—not if she needed money. He'd offered a top fee, feeling quite safe when he'd heard the agency inform her over the telephone that the photographer's name was Luke St Clair and that he was Australian, but had been working overseas.

'Don't recognise the name,' Theo muttered. 'There again, I never was good with names.'

'Not to worry,' Luke said, hating the way his heart was pounding just talking about her. He picked up his coffee-mug and sipped the now tepid drink.

Theo threw his friend a frustrated look. 'Well, aren't you going to tell me all about her?'

'Not at this stage.'

Theo's expressive eyebrows waggled up and down. 'Do I get to know all the sordid details afterwards?'

'For pity's sake, don't you have a sex life of your own?'

'Not for over a week now.'

Luke always laughed at Theo's crestfallen expression. 'A veritable drought,' he said drily.

'It is for me.'

'Maybe you should settle down, Theo. Find yourself a nice girl and get married.'

'Perish the thought.'

When Luke didn't say anything to this typical bachelor remark, Theo stared at him. Hard.

'You're not thinking of getting married, are you?' he said, almost accusingly. 'Damn it all, Luke, you haven't gone and fallen in love, have you?'

Luke didn't know what to say to either of those questions. Both distressed and confused him. His brain denied each in turn—the first as impossible, the second as highly improbable. Yet his heart leapt at both ideas.

Don't be a bloody fool, he told himself scathingly. The likelihood is that she's bad through and through. Bad and mad. You don't go giving your heart and your life to a woman like that!

'No,' he denied aloud. 'I'm not going to get married. And I haven't fallen in love.' What he *had* done, however, he rationalised brutally, was tumble headfirst into lust. A lust which hadn't had the opportunity to burn itself out. A lust which still simmered, waiting for the instigator to come back into his life.

Well, that instigator was going to come back this Wednesday, and Luke was going to do everything in his power to satisfy not only his curiosity about her, but everything else she'd managed to keep aroused in him for the past eighteen months.

CHAPTER FOUR

WEDNESDAY morning could not have dawned more perfect. At least weatherwise. A little crisp—since it was only the first week in September—but clear, with the promise of some real spring warmth later in the day.

The sun had crept over the ocean horizon at around six, quickly dispelling the grey pre-dawn light, its gleaming rays spearing through the Norfolk pines on the beachfront and hitting Luke's hotel room windows.

That had been nearly an hour ago, during which time he'd showered, shaved and dressed, before sitting down to eat the breakfast delivered to his room. Each mouthful had been accompanied by thoughts of *her*, already on her way up here, totally unaware of the true identity of Luke St Clair.

He had toyed with the idea of asking the agency to have her drive up the night before and stay here at the Holiday Inn with him, but he had dismissed it in the end as too dangerous. His intention was to catch her completely off guard, then sweep her into a day's supposed work before she could even think.

He had a plan of action which he hoped would work—a strategy which would put her in his secret power and possibly make her more open with him. It would work too, if she felt guilty about what she'd done eighteen months ago.

And he suspected that she might.

Seven o'clock arrived—the time Luke had given the agency for her to meet him in the foyer of the hotel. Her instructions were to have his room paged if he wasn't there. Which he had no intention of being. Luke expected that it would take her a few minutes at least to decide to do this, even if she was on time. No one liked to rush things these days, and punctuality was not the virtue it used to be.

While he waited for the telephone call he wandered out onto the balcony of his hotel room. Leaning against the railing, he stared down, first at the magnificent turquoise swimming pool below, then out across the road to the beach and the sparkling blue sea beyond.

He'd chosen Terrigal because it was away from Sydney and he knew it quite well, having camped up here often with friends when he was in his late teens. All the local beaches were picturesque, and he knew that he would have no trouble finding some magnificent shots to photograph.

Above everything, Miss Rachel Manning was not to suspect that this was anything but a proper, professional photographic shoot. If she did, then all would be lost. No one liked to be fooled, or manipulated.

No one, Luke thought with a black bitterness.

The seconds began ticking away with agonising

slowness. Five past seven came and went. Then ten past.

She was late.

A couple more minutes dragged by, but still no call came.

Luke was dismayed to find that he was beginning to feel more than a little agitated. He actually felt sick—sick with something like fear.

But fear of what?

Fear that she might not arrive at all? Or of finding out, when she did, that it had all been an illusion? What if he saw her again and felt...nothing? What if he found out that his obsession with her had all been a perverse fantasy of his mind?

The ring was shrill to his ears and he whirled around, staring back into the room and at the telephone sitting on the writing desk in the corner as if it were a cobra about to strike. Paralysed for a few moments, Luke listened to it ring and ring before lurching in onto the grey carpet and snatching the hated thing from its cradle.

'Yes?' he said sharply.

'Good morning, Mr St Clair,' the male desk-clerk said, in that smooth, unruffled voice which the best of hotel staff always possessed. 'Sorry to disturb you so early, sir, but there's a Miss Manning here who says her instructions were to have you paged when she arrived. She says she's sorry she's a little late, but there was an accident on the expressway.'

Luke's stomach churned some more. She was here…downstairs…waiting for him.

'Tell her I'll be down shortly,' he said in decidedly strangled tones.

'Very good, sir.'

Luke hung up, then dragged in several deep steadying breaths. This would never do. He couldn't let her frighten him. *She* was the one who was going to be frightened. At first. That was part of his revenge.

He checked his appearance in the long mirror hanging on the back of the bathroom door, approving of his choice of clothes. His tall, lean body looked well in jeans. Stonewashed grey this morning, matched to a simple white T-shirt and a lightweight charcoal-grey jacket which could be zipped up against the wind if necessary.

There was nothing about him to betray his wealth, except perhaps for his watch, which was a gold Rolex. Still, there were plenty of fake Rolexes in this world. Luke wasn't sure why he didn't want her to know how well-off he was, but he didn't. He almost regretted offering such an exorbitant fee, but without it she might not have come.

Steeling himself, he slipped the hotel room key into his pocket, smoothed his dark brown hair back from his face, covered his glittering black eyes with wrap-around sunglasses and left the room.

The lift carried him noiselessly down to the first floor, where he alighted, choosing to walk down the long sweeping staircase to the ground floor and give himself ample opportunity to survey the foyer and its occupants below as he did so.

She would not be expecting him to arrive that way. Neither would she be expecting *him*. Eighteen months ago she'd thought him an American, had believed he was only holidaying in Australia, unlikely to return and turn up in her life again.

But he *was* turning up, he thought with a grim satisfaction as he began a slow descent down the elegant staircase. And he had no intention of leaving again— not till he'd got what he wanted from her.

He walked slowly, his gaze searching the groupings of armchairs gathered in the centre of the foyer down below. They were all empty. His frown deepened as his eyes scanned first left and then right, towards the reception desk.

He didn't recognise her at first, for her back was to him and her hair was longer and straighter, and blonder. Almost white-blonde, in fact, hanging straight down her back. She was wearing black leggings and a black blazer-style jacket, with a canvas satchel slung over her shoulder. Black platform sandals made her look even taller than he remembered.

She was chatting away to the desk-clerk—probably the same one who had rung him. He was a good-looking young man and was smiling at her. Luke told himself that it wasn't jealousy which jabbed at his heart, merely cynicism. She was still good at picking up members of the opposite sex, it seemed.

No doubt now, being a merry widow, she was making up for lost time. There would no longer be any need for subterfuge with her one-night stands—or deceit. She could have whatever man she fancied, whenever she fancied.

Luke's loins leapt at the thought, assuaging his earlier fear that he might not still want her.

The clerk must have spotted him coming down the stairs and said something to her, for she turned to look up at him.

His breath caught in his throat and he hesitated momentarily. For, although he knew it was the same woman—impossible to mistake those eyes—there was nothing of the sultry or seductive about the clear-skinned, clear-eyed face which tipped back to stare up at him. She was all natural beauty, fresh and innocent-looking, in a simple white blouse which buttoned right up to the neck. A sweetie, not a siren. A virgin, not a vamp.

Luke almost laughed at this last thought, his stupidity firing his fury and his feet forward. She was no virgin, this chameleon. No sweetie either. She was twenty-six years old, and a cool, calculating witch of a woman.

He revelled in the way her high, wide forehead began to crease into a frown as she continued to survey his measured descent. No doubt with his sunglasses firmly in place she couldn't be sure of his identity, but something was definitely teasing her brain. And her memory.

Meanwhile he soaked her in. Every gorgeous inch

of her. Damn, but she was beautiful. So beautiful that he already ached with longing to possess her just one more time. No, once would not be enough. He had to have her more than that. He had to have till he could not bear to do it one more time.

Maybe then he would be at peace.

Maybe then he would stop fantasising that he was in love with her.

He chose the perfect moment to remove his sunglasses, having schooled his face into a superbly bland expression, masking his feelings behind a façade so cool and so casual that she would surely have to doubt his own recognition of her.

The glasses swept aside, he strode across the tiled foyer floor, disarming her totally by smiling politely then reaching out his hand as he drew near. 'Miss Manning, I presume?'

Her obvious shock disintegrated into confusion, her stunned gaze going from his face to his outstretched hand and to his face again. Clearly she had no practice at facing a one-night stand who failed to recognise her. And clearly she was very disconcerted.

To give her credit, she swiftly pulled herself together, placing a brave but betrayingly shaky hand in his for a few brief moments before dredging up a polite smile of her own from somewhere.

'That's correct,' she said, her voice crisp and rather strained, with not a trace of the huskily sexy tones she'd used on him that night. 'And you're Mr St Clair?'

'The one and only,' he drawled.

'But…but the agency said you were an Australian photographer.'

'And so I am. The accent is just a relic of my living and working in LA for ten years.'

'Oh. Oh, I see…'

No, you don't, you deceiving witch. You can't see at all! But *he* could. Could see perfectly how relieved she was to find that he didn't recognise her. She'd gone almost as white as her hair for a moment, but now the colour was flooding back into her cheeks— those gorgeous cheeks and gorgeous cheekbones and gorgeous everything else!

'I come home to Sydney for a visit every now and then,' he went on, silkily putting her mind at ease some more. 'This time I decided to combine my holiday with a little work. Last time I came home I did far too much partying and spent most of the time totally hungover. You don't mind if I call you Rachel, do you? And you must learn to call me Luke. First names are much more relaxing than Miss and Mr, don't you think?'

'I suppose so.'

Her wariness was gradually dissolving, although not entirely gone yet. A certain tension remained. She wasn't comfortable with him or the situation, that much was evident.

'Ready to start work?' he asked abruptly, sliding his sunglasses back into place over his eyes. The opaque lenses and wrap-around style gave him the opportunity to study her and her reactions closely without her being too aware of it.

'What? Oh…oh, yes—yes, I guess so.'

There was no doubting that she was still highly agitated. He wasn't sure if he liked that or not. Ongoing agitation did not fit in with the image of her he'd carried around all these months, or of how he'd imagined she'd react to his supposedly not recognising her.

After the initial shock, he'd expected her to quickly take his reappearance in her life in her stride. Now that she was a widow, he was even hoping she'd be flirtatious with him.

Such was not the case. She was stiff and silent, her lovely green eyes clouded with worry.

'Where have you parked your car?' he asked, annoyed with himself for feeling guilt over what he was doing. Clearly the guilt was all on her part, which was as it should be. But he did wish she'd stop flicking him those anxious and startled glances, as though she still could not believe who Luke St Clair had turned out to be.

'In the street,' she said, nodding towards the revolving glass door. 'Outside.'

'Do you need anything out of it for the day?'

'No, not really. I have all my make-up and hair things in here.'

'In that case I suggest you drive your car up to the hotel entrance and I'll arrange to have it parked downstairs, in the hotel car park. You are staying here tonight, after all.'

The momentary terror which flashed into her face absolutely floored him. 'Well, I... Well, actually, I don't think... I mean,' she stumbled and bumbled. 'I...I might have to go home tonight,' she finished up, all flushed and flustered. 'I can always drive up again in the morning.'

Luke stared at her from behind his glasses. What in hell was going on here? Why was she so frightened of him? Or, more to the point, of staying at the same hotel with him?

Could it be that she still wanted him, as he still wanted her, but that she didn't *want* to want him? Could it be that she was afraid to put herself into a potentially intimate situation with him, lest she surrender to the temptation to do what she'd done once before?

But why would that frighten her? he puzzled, at the same trying to contain his excitement that this deduction might be right.

The obvious answer to his question brought a sickening jolt to his stomach. There had to be another man on the scene. If not a husband then a fiancé, or a boyfriend, or a lover. Maybe, once again, she was not free to dally with whomever she fancied.

Hell, he hadn't thought of that. Yet he should have. A woman like her would not be alone for long.

'And where is home, exactly?' he asked curtly.

'Caringbah.'

Caringbah was a Sydney suburb even more south than his mother's own Monterey.

'But that's a good two hours' drive,' he argued. 'Surely the boyfriend can do without you for one night?' he added, trying not to sound as blackly jealous as he was feeling.

'Boyfriend?' she repeated blankly, and Luke's heart soared.

There was no boyfriend. No boyfriend and no lover and no fiancé. He was sure of it!

'I was trying to think of the reason why you'd have to go home,' he said, thrown back to the original puzzle. Why *was* she afraid of him?

'My…my mother-in-law hasn't been well,' she explained, if reluctantly. 'I've been a little worried about leaving her for the night.'

'You live alone with your mother-in-law?'

Her hesitation to answer inflamed his curiosity further. 'Yes,' she said at last. 'Yes, I do. I…I'm a widow, you see,' she admitted tautly.

'Ahh…' He didn't really see, of course. And it was killing him. 'Well, perhaps you could give her a call later in the day and put your mind to rest. I'm sure she wouldn't want you driving all the way back home through Sydney in peak hour traffic, only to have to turn round and come back the next morning.'

'No—no, I suppose not.'

'That's settled, then. You can ring her after we've finished for the day. Now, off you go and get your car while I speak to the parking attendant.'

He watched her walk away, watched the way the breeze blew her long fair hair once she'd made it through the revolving door. Her right hand lifted to hold it back from her face, and when she glanced back over her shoulder at him he found himself caught up in her stunning beauty once more.

Yet it was such a different beauty this time—her lovely face free of make-up, her lush breasts no longer put on blatant display, her sexuality and sensuality much more subtle.

The effect on Luke was twice as strong.

He stood there, staring at her, every muscle in his body stiff with instant tension. She frowned back for a few seconds, then turned and strode off with long, elegant strides. Luke had to almost literally drag his eyes away from her. Damn, but he wanted her more than ever. Would *die* if he didn't spend this coming night with her.

Yet achieving that end this time would not be as easy as he'd hoped it would be. She meant to resist him, that was clear. Though the reason was not. He tried reassuring himself that she still found him physically attractive. She had once, and most women did.

So there had to be other factors involved—factors hidden from him but which hopefully might become clearer as the day wore on.

When she stepped out of her small white sedan a couple of minutes later, she too was wearing sunglasses, which irritated Luke. Now he couldn't see what she was thinking, or feeling. Still, she would have to take them off for the shoot. He vowed to slip in a few pointed questions whenever he had her at his visual mercy.

'Where's *your* gear?' she asked.

'In my car.'

'Which is?'

'Down where your car is heading. There's a door over here,' he went on, taking her nearest arm in a firm grip. 'This way...'

Her instant disengaging of his arm held a distressed fluster which startled then infuriated him.

'Sorry,' he bit out. 'I was only trying to help. I didn't realise you were one of those women who don't like to be touched.'

God, but did he have to sound so sarcastic, so bloody cynical?

'Sorry again,' he said quickly. 'That sounded rotten, and I didn't mean it to.' Which was so true. Hell, the last thing he wanted was to tip her off that he recognised her.

'No, *I'm* sorry,' she said with a shuddering sigh. 'I was being super-touchy. Look, the thing is I had this rather unfortunate experience with a male photographer a while back, and I've become a little gun-shy of being alone with them ever since.'

Luke was astonished by his immediate and fierce fury against the creep. 'What happened? My God, he didn't assault you, did he?'

'No, no, it didn't go that far,' she hastened to explain. 'But the man's attentions were...unwanted. I found the whole thing most distasteful.'

'You've nothing to fear from me, Rachel,' he assured her, and for the life of him he almost meant it! Good God, what was it about this woman that made him want to protect her at the same time as just wanting her? 'I've never had to force myself on a woman in my life,' he muttered, 'and I can't see myself starting now.'

A small rueful smile tugged at her lovely mouth. 'No,' she said softly. 'No, I can appreciate that.'

Luke slanted her a long glance, then took her arm again. This time she did not resist him.

It came to him then that she might not resist him tonight either, if he played his cards right. Her earlier fear had not been of him, but of that other fool, who'd been stupid enough to play rough with her. If Luke had learnt one thing from his other experience, it was that darling Rachel liked to take the lead in matters of sex and seduction. She liked doing the choosing and she preferred being on top, quite literally.

An electric current charged along Luke's veins as he struggled to suppress the hot memory of what she'd looked like that night—her back arched, her head thrown back, her lips parted.

But he failed miserably.

It took all of his control to lead her quietly downstairs to the underground car park and over to his rented white Futura. He would much rather have dragged her over to a dark corner and kissed her with all the mad desire already bubbling up inside him.

Patience, Luke, he kept telling himself. Patience. Tonight will come, and when it does...

He clenched his teeth hard in his jaw to stop the groan from escaping. Today was going to be hell. But a hell he had to endure. She simply was not going to be rushed.

Besides, he had more things to satisfy than his damned body. He still didn't have any answers to all those other questions which had plagued him this past eighteen months.

Yes, patience, he repeated to himself. That was the key. All things came to those who waited. Rachel had come, and so would all the other answers. All he had to do was wait.

CHAPTER FIVE

'WHAT swimsuit company are you doing these shots for?' she asked as he drove up the ramp of the underground car park and out into the sunshine.

Luke had been waiting for that question, and was glad that he'd worked out a good cover story.

'Actually, they're not for a swimsuit company. They're for the Central Coast Tourist Bureau, for a brochure they're producing. They only wanted scenic shots at first, but I convinced them that a gorgeous Australian blonde in a bikini would give their beaches some added appeal and impetus.'

Luke turned the car to the left and headed for the Skillion—a nearby headland which would make a good backdrop for some photos.

She slanted him a frowning glance. 'How come you chose me? I haven't been doing much work of late.'

'Yes, so the agency told me.' Luke thought he was being superbly casual, considering the state of his insides. 'You were recommended to me by an acquaintance. Ray Holland.'

Her mouth broke into a soft smile. 'Dear Ray. Now, there's a really nice man.'

'He says he did your wedding photographs.'

The smile faded. 'Yes, that's right,' she said stiffly, and fell silent.

Luke decided not to pursue the topic at this early stage, for fear of making her clam up entirely. He swung the car off Terrigal Drive onto the side road which led past the bay called the Haven and round to the base of the Skillion. Even at this early hour there were a couple walking hand in hand up the steep grassy incline which led up to the lookout and the abrupt drop beyond.

Luke noticed with a frown that a fence had been built since he'd last been up there some years back—no doubt as a guard against accidents. Anyone wanting to commit suicide would hardly have let a fairly low fence deter them. Still, the wooden and wire construction would not enhance any close-ups.

'If you're thinking of taking some shots of me up there,' Rachel said, glancing up at the unprotected clifftop, 'it'll be very windy.'

Luke frowned as he parked, nose frontwards, in a small cleared area to the left of the Skillion. He'd already dismissed the idea because of the fence, anyway.

'What about down there?' he suggested, pointing through the windscreen at the tiny rocky cove which lay straight ahead. 'I could still get the cliff in the background if I angled things right. What do you think?'

'I think that would be much better. Not as uncomfortable or as cold either. By the way, where am I supposed to change into the swimsuits?'

Luke almost swore. He hadn't thought of that. 'You'll have to do it in the back of the car,' he said. 'Sorry, I'm a bit out of practice at organising this type of shoot. Most of my photography these days is done inside.'

'And what type of photography is that?' she asked, her dry tone accompanied by a suspicious look.

Luke laughed. 'No, not that type. I specialise in portraiture.'

'And you make a good living from that?'

'I've done quite well out of it, actually.' Luke despised himself for suddenly wanting to brag. Where had his idea gone about her not knowing that he was well-off? Luke appreciated that his male ego could work against him at times, but the last thing he wanted was for Rachel to pay attention to him because she thought he was filthy rich.

He wished he knew what the circumstances of her marriage had been. How old her husband had actually been, and whether he had been wealthy to begin with. It would be naïve of him to discount her being a gold-digger, or even to assume that she *hadn't* come out of her marriage with the proverbial pot of gold.

She might not have come back to work out of financial difficulty at all. She might have merely wanted to put herself back into circulation. Hard to meet prospective lovers and husbands if one stayed at home with one's mother-in-law.

'Tell me, Luke, are you famous or something?' she asked. 'The agency implied you were very well known worldwide, but I thought they might be exaggerating. They have a tendency to do that sometimes.'

'I'm quite well known in California,' he admitted carefully, 'but I doubt too many people in Australia would even recognise my name.'

'I certainly didn't,' she said, and there was a wry note in the words.

'I wouldn't have expected you to. Now, why don't you slip into the back seat while I get the cameras and bikinis out of the boot?'

'Only bikinis?'

'You have some objection to that?'

'No. I just… I just…'

'Just what?'

'Nothing,' she muttered. 'I guess I've got out of the habit of freezing to death. This is my first outdoor assignment since coming back to modelling.'

'You can wear your jacket till I'm ready to shoot. Hopefully, when we get to the beaches, there'll be proper dressing-rooms for you to change in.'

'Which one do you want me to wear first?' she asked when he handed the costumes through the back window a couple of minutes later.

Luke had gone to a local boutique when he'd arrived the previous afternoon, and had bought several assorted bikinis in the size the agency had given him. All were colourful and depressingly minute, he recalled ruefully.

'Makes no difference,' he returned, truthfully

enough. Luke suspected that he was in trouble no matter which one she wore. 'Whatever one you fancy.'

'Stand with your back against the window,' she ordered. 'And no peeking!'

Luke had to work hard to keep a straight face as he did as he was told. Good God, there wasn't an inch of her that he hadn't seen—and at very close hand.

Still, the knowledge that she was taking off her clothes right behind him was tantalising in the extreme. He tried to keep his mind off the fact, aware of the discomfort that being turned on would cause him.

And he was marginally successful till the moment she climbed out of the car and that damned black jacket of hers flapped wide open for a few seconds.

Luke grimaced.

God, her body was even better! Her breasts looked fuller, and infinitely more lush, squashed as they were into the colourful half-cup bra. He decided that she must have put on a little weight, because her hips seemed curvier and her stomach rounder. The only things which looked exactly the same were her legs—those long, endless legs, whose firm honey-coloured thighs made him think of things that a man in tight jeans should never have thought of for more than a moment.

Luke suppressed a tortured groan and wrenched his eyes away, pretending to adjust the distance and light meters on the two cameras hanging around his neck.

Actually, Theo had already set them perfectly for

him, giving him easy instructions for the odd possible adjustment and at the same time telling him that even a fool couldn't make a mistake taking photographs with his two beauties.

Luke began to appreciate that he *was* a fool, to think he could look at this particular woman all day, dressed in next to nothing, and not become a quivering wreck. His plan to question her at the same time, cleverly extracting the information he wanted before setting about as callous and calculating a seduction as she had perpetrated on him, now seemed ludicrous. He would be lucky if he was bloody *sane* by the end of *this* day!

'Having trouble with the camera?' she asked, with a seemingly ingenuous innocence.

'Just a little.' Luke stopped fiddling with the Nikon and looked up again. Thank God the blazer was now firmly wrapped around her, and thank God he could keep his sunglasses on. His eyes had a habit of betraying him when he wanted a woman. They sort of blazed away, with pinpoints of light glittering wildly within their darkened depths.

Or so he'd been told.

In a way, he was sorry she'd had to take her sunglasses off, for those big, beautiful green eyes gazing unguardedly at him were almost as disturbing as her unclad body.

'Both these cameras belong to a friend of mine,' he explained rather sharply. 'All my equipment is still in America.' Except the equipment I *had* to bring with me, he thought with rueful savagery. Pity I couldn't have left some of that behind as well!

Damn, but he hated being a man sometimes. Women had by far the best deal sexually. They could hide how they felt, or fake it splendidly, and no one was any the wiser. Whereas men's responses were brutally on display for all the world to see.

Gritting his teeth, he willed his body to a modicum of comfort and strode over to find the best way down to the rocky cove. There were several pathways between the rocks, which didn't look all that dangerous till he began following one and his foot slipped on a patch of loose gravelly dirt.

'Watch your step,' he ordered, glancing back up at her as she moved to follow him down the path he'd chosen. 'It's a bit slippery in parts, and we wouldn't want you falling and hurting yourself.'

He might have taken her hand and helped her down, but he suspected that that was not a good idea—either for his immediate peace of mind or the future success of his mission. After what had happened earlier, back in the hotel, he didn't think it was a good idea to touch her at all…till the moment was right.

The photograph session down on the rocks went surprisingly well—Luke managing temporarily to put his desire aside by concentrating on making each shot the very best he could take. It was an automatic response to what had been his profession for many years. A pride thing, really. If he was going to take photographs, he was going to take damned good ones.

Unfortunately, to do so, he had to take his sunglasses off, for it really was impossible with them on. Sunglasses distorted one's sense of light and colour.

Fifteen minutes into the shoot, Luke realised that Rachel Manning was an exceptionally good model. A gem, in fact. Not only did the camera love her, she was also a true professional. She adopted the exact poses he was looking for with little prompting, her attitude and expression immediately echoing whatever image he wanted. Natural. Athletic. Girl-next-door. Bright and breezy. Dreamy.

It was the dreamy one that began his undoing. The way she arched her spine and dropped her head back, closing her eyes and smiling—so softly, and yet so... so...

'Now sexy,' he ordered, his voice thick and husky. 'Give me sexy.'

She shot him a startled glance before turning her eyes away and immediately giving him exactly what he'd stupidly asked for.

She lay back down on the smooth grey rock she'd been sitting on, her arms lifting up over her head to splay the long fair strands out with her fingers. Her back arched a little away from the rock and she bent her left knee slightly. It was then that she turned towards the camera, half opened her eyes and parted her lips in a pose so provocatively sensual that Luke's blood went from zero to boiling point in two seconds flat.

He swore under his breath and pressed his eye

harder against the viewfinder, which didn't improve things at all. His trembling finger moved and the camera clicked, not once but several times, before he got a hold of himself.

'That's great,' he complimented curtly. 'But that's enough for here. We'll move on to another spot. I'll just walk up the Skillion and get some postcard-style shots of the surrounding area before we do. You can pop yourself back into the car and warm up. Change costumes while you're waiting, if you like.'

Luke was scrambling back up the path when he heard her cry out. It was not a loud cry, but his heart leapt with alarm at the pained sound, and he whipped around to find her still sitting on the edge of the rock and frowning down at the small rock pool in which her feet were resting.

Thoughts of the deadly blue ringed octopus which could lurk in such pools had the blood draining from Luke's face. 'What is it?' he called out. 'You haven't been bitten, have you?'

Had his panic sounded in his voice? It must have, for her eyes widened on him as though she was thoroughly taken aback by his burst of fierce concern. As was Luke. He hadn't realised till that moment how much she meant to him—however perverse that meaning was.

'No,' she said, peering down into the pool. 'Some fool's been drinking down here and smashed a beer bottle against this rock. This pool's full of broken glass and I think I just stood on a bit. Don't worry, it's only a little piece by the feel of things. I'll just pull it out and wash my foot in the salt water. That should kill any germs.'

'No, don't touch it!' he said sharply. 'I'll come and look and make sure that's all it is.'

Luke hurried back down the path and over to where she was still looking at him with a bewildered expression on her lovely face. 'Truly, there's no need to fuss,' she said. 'I'm perfectly all right.'

'I'll be the judge of that,' Luke said, sitting down beside her on the rock and lifting her dripping feet gently up into his lap. 'Better to be safe than sorry,' he muttered.

She was right, however. It *was* a piece of broken beer bottle, speared right in the middle of the big toe of her left foot.

'Does it hurt much?' he asked her as he examined it to see if there was enough sticking out for him to pull it out with his fingers, turning her foot this way and that to catch the sunlight against the glass.

'N-no.'

Her stammering was so unlike her cool self that he snapped his eyes up, thinking that she might have gone into some kind of shock.

But it wasn't shock he saw in her face. It was tension. A blindingly electric sexual tension.

His fingers grew hotly aware of the frozen stillness in the foot he was holding, then of the sudden pounding of his own heart. The temptation to slide a hand up her calf was enormous.

'There's enough glass sticking out for me to pull it out without tweezers,' he said, finding some satisfaction in the fact that his voice remained cool and controlled.

'Do it, then,' she said thickly.

He did, and for a split-second there was nothing to show where it had been. But then the blood began to ooze from her skin, and before Luke could appreciate what he was doing he'd lifted her foot and bent his mouth at the same time, pressing his lips against the cut and sucking it clean.

The primitive intimacy of his instinctive action was slow to sink in, but when it did Luke's stomach contracted fiercely. He raised his head to look at her, and found that she was staring at him with wide green eyes, her lips parting softly under her fast, shallow breathing.

Seeing her arousal did terrible things to Luke. He'd spent eighteen months fantasising about having her in his sexual power. Now that he did, all hell broke loose.

That old dark fury welled up within him, and it was with deliberately wicked intent that he straightened and lifted her foot higher, then higher, till she was tipped back against the gentle incline of the rock. This time he took her whole toe into his mouth.

He sucked on it slowly, revelling in the way her eyes gradually went from round frightened orbs to narrow slits of desire, their green colour darkening to a smoky grey, her lips falling further apart under the ragged panting sounds that were coming from her lips.

Luke stared at those lips, remembering how they had felt when she'd done the same to his desire-filled flesh, and knowing that he would not rest till he thrilled to that experience again. But at *his* behest this time—not hers. He wanted her to be at *his* mercy, not the other way around.

Hearing distant laughter reminded him starkly of where they were, in full view of anyone and everyone walking up the Skillion. Hardly the place for a proper seduction.

The realisation that *she* was beyond hearing or seeing anything brought a swift jab of savage satisfaction. It was so different from his previous experience with her, where in the end she'd taken control of the lovemaking while he'd been totally off the planet—oblivious to everything but his own pleasure. Luke sensed that the boot was on the other foot at this moment, so to speak.

When he abruptly plucked her toe from his mouth she gasped, her stunned eyes showing him that she could hardly believe she'd allowed herself to get so carried away. Luke decided to salvage her pride temporarily, by pretending that he hadn't even noticed her sexual response to his ministrations and giving all his attention to her cut toe and not to her anguished face.

'That seems to have stopped the bleeding,' he said off-handedly. 'But we wouldn't want any dirt getting in there, so I'll carry you up to the car.'

'No!' she immediately blurted out, whereat he lifted a mock-innocent gaze.

'But why not? I assure you I can manage. I'm stronger than I look.'

'I never said you didn't look strong,' she bit out. 'But I prefer to go under my own steam, thank you. I…I'll hop.'

'Suit yourself.' When Luke felt the beginnings of a darkly smug smile tug at his mouth, he stood up quickly and turned away.

But his thoughts stayed with her. I've got you where I want you now, Miss Rachel Manning. You've just shown me that the cool, professional persona you've been projecting today is just a sham. Underneath you're still the same woman who picked me up that night. Your sexuality still simmers just beneath the surface, ready to be tapped by any man who has the right tools.

And that man is going to be me tonight, lady, Luke vowed as he made his way to the car. And for as many nights as it will take to rid you from my body and my mind! For I can't go on as I've been going on. I have to free myself of you…or make you mine forever.

Luke ground to a halt, disturbed by this last tacked-on thought. He recalled Theo's accusation that he had fallen in love and that he wanted to get married.

Luke whirled to glare at the woman who was the root cause of all his confusion, only to melt at the sight of her struggling to hop between the rocks. Furious with himself, and her, he covered the ground which separated them with angry strides, and before she could do more than squeal he swept her up into his arms.

'If there's one thing I can't stand,' he growled, 'it's a woman who won't ask a man for help when she needs it. You need me, Rachel. Why don't you just admit it?'

Their eyes locked—his blazing with frustration and hers bewildered. They searched his face, as though looking for something, till finally her chin tilted up proudly and her eyes cleared as she nodded slowly up and down.

'All right, Luke,' she said, her voice husky, yet quite composed. 'I'll admit it. I need you.'

A tremor raced through him, and he knew that once again the control had somehow slipped from his hands to hers.

Damn it all, he raged privately. Damn it!

The struggle to regroup his emotions was not easy. But he managed it, a cool smile masking any lingering exasperation.

'I'm glad to hear that, Rachel,' he said smoothly. 'A man likes to be needed. It makes him feel good. Now, let's get you up to the car and find a Bandaid,' he went on, adopting a very businesslike attitude. 'We have a long day ahead of us and a lot of work to be done.'

CHAPTER SIX

LUKE made it through the day.

Just.

His pride and ego came to the rescue—to a degree. Theo had magnanimously offered to develop all the films when he returned the cameras, so Luke's aversion to making a fool of himself—personally and photographically speaking—gave him the motivation to focus on what he was doing.

His aversion to making a fool of himself with women in general—and Rachel Manning in particular—also kept him safe during the moments when he wasn't taking photographs.

Not that he allowed too many of those. He swept her from Terrigal Beach straight to Wamberal, from there north to Forrester's Beach then on to Shelley's. A quick takeaway lunch at the Entrance was followed by further lengthy and quite gruelling sessions around the Entrance area and the surrounding lakes.

Conversation was kept to a minimum and was strictly professionally based. Luke had abandoned any idea of trying to worm out the personal and private details of Rachel's life and marriage while photographing her semi-naked.

He knew that it would be a waste of time and potentially hazardous to his razor-edge composure. He ruefully resolved to wait till dinner that night, when she would be fully dressed and hopefully under the influence of some relaxing glasses of wine.

Not that he expected her to tell him much, even then.

Rachel Manning was a cool customer all right—a mysterious and enigmatic creature who was really impossible to manipulate. Luke had the awful feeling that she was playing with him, like a cat with a mouse. He would catch her looking intently at him sometimes, as though trying to fathom what she would do with him in the end. Put him out of his misery? Or just leave him dangling...?

By the time the sun began to set and the air to cool Luke was utterly exhausted—physically, mentally and emotionally. He was also on his last roll of film.

'Let's call it a day,' he said abruptly.

'You don't want to try for any sunset shots?'

He shot her a sharp look. Who did she think she was kidding? She had to be exhausted too, yet she was wanting to prolong things further? 'No,' he bit out. 'I'm too tired. You must be too. Let's get back to the hotel. I could do with a long hot bath and a stiff drink.'

Her shrug seemed indifferent, but Luke gained the impression of a real reluctance for the evening to begin. He also thought he detected a glimmer of something like fear in her eyes.

His irritation as he strode back to the car knew no bounds. He wished she'd make up her damned mind what she wanted from him. He wished *he* could make up his mind what he wanted from *her*!

He also wished he could make up his mind what he believed about her. He'd labelled her an adulterous whore in his mind.

Now he wasn't so sure.

Which wasn't anything new. When had he ever been sure of her, or of anything she did? She was full of mysteries and contradictions, and the most aggravating changes of character.

The question was...who was the real Rachel Manning? What was she? Where had she come from and where was she going to?

Luke knew that he had to have some answers to those questions before he dared do anything sexual with her again—before he dared become any more emotionally involved.

And he *was* emotionally involved with her. That was one thing he was sure of. Exactly what that emotion was eluded him. Love, or hate. Lust, or simply fury. All he knew was that she was not going to play him for a fool again. He wanted answers and he wanted her. And he aimed to get everything he wanted this time—no matter what.

Hell, he would get her blind drunk if he had to!

All was fair in love and war. And this, Luke vowed darkly, was war! She wasn't going to get away scot-free this time. No, sirree. He'd waited eighteen interminable months for this opportunity, and he wasn't going to let it slip away from him.

*   *   *

By seven twenty-five that evening Luke was ready, refreshed and reasonably relaxed. Three Scotches in a row did rather have that effect on one.

He'd arranged to collect Madam Manning from her room at seven-thirty and take her down to dinner, having booked an intimate little corner table for two at the Norfolk Terrace Restaurant on the first floor.

At seven twenty-six he gave his appearance a last checkover, telling himself that he looked quite dashing in charcoal-grey trousers, black silk shirt and a pale grey sports jacket. A little gel made his dark brown hair look almost black in the night light, the slicked-back style suiting his strongly boned face and bringing attention to his best feature—his eyes.

They gleamed back at him in the mirror, his bitter resolve bringing a dangerously ruthless edge to the smile that found its way to his mouth.

'Let's go, handsome.' He lifted a sardonic eyebrow at himself in the mirror. 'And remember, this is the moment you've been waiting for. Don't stuff it up.'

Madam's room was on the same floor but at the opposite end of the long corridor. He hadn't wanted to be too obvious by asking for adjoining rooms.

Luke felt some resurgence of nerves during the longish walk down to her room, but remained in firm control of them. He found it irritating, however, to have to knock twice before she opened the door.

'Sorry to keep you waiting,' she said briskly. 'I was on the telephone. I'll just get my purse.'

She left the door open while she did so, showing

Luke a carbon copy of his own room. There might have been some minutely different details, but the blue and yellow colour-scheme was pretty much identical—the warm-wooded colonial furnishings very comfy, and pleasing to the eye.

It was classy accommodation with classy accoutrements. Luke was no stranger to five-star hotels all over the world, and this was as good as any he'd stayed in.

She walked back towards him, looking stunning and elegant in a silky green trouser-suit which had wide bottoms and a long flowing jacket with long sleeves and buttons right up to the neck. Despite the modesty of her clothes and the subtlety of her make-up, she looked incredibly sexy as she moved. Her loosely curled blonde hair swung about her face and shoulders. Her breasts—which might or might not have been braless—swayed sensuously beneath her top, riveting Luke's eyes.

He could have sworn her nipples peaked as he stared at them, but she didn't miss a beat as she swished out of the room, shutting the door behind her.

'Did you have that long hot bath you wanted?' she asked, her manner so cool that he might have imagined his staring had affected her in any way.

Except that Luke was gradually getting used to the fact that Miss Rachel Manning had two barometers. Her brain and her body. She could say one thing, he was beginning to appreciate, and feel quite another.

Luke determined to look past her words in future, to her more revealing body language. Yes, a quick

glance revealed that her nipples very definitely had
hardened. He could see them clearly outlined against
the thin silk. He wasn't sure if he was contemptuous
of her sexual vulnerability to such a small stimulus as
a look, or excited by it.

Both, probably.

'Sure did,' he drawled. 'And a good stiff drink as
well. And how did *you* fill in the last two hours?'

She slipped the key into her purse, her expression
blandly pleasant. 'Oh, I soaked in a tub as well, then
wickedly indulged in several cups of coffee while
watching my favourite game-shows on television.'

'You're a caffeine addict, are you?' he remarked as
they walked together down the corridor towards the
lifts.

'Decidedly. A game-show addict as well.'

'Would that we all had such harmless addictions,'
he murmured drily.

'Oh? And to what are you addicted, Luke St Clair?'

They had stopped at the twin lifts and she'd turned
to face him, her expression seemingly ingenuous and
curious. He eyed her closely in return while wondering
what game she'd decided to play with him tonight.
She appeared bent on a more leisurely seduction this
time, confident in the power of her physical attraction
and knowing full well that she only had to crook her
finger at most men and they would come running. It
would never have crossed her mind that he might
knock her back.

Luke almost wished he could, but masochism had never been one of his fetishes.

'Where would you like me to begin?' he said nonchalantly.

'At the beginning might be a good start. I'd like to know what you were like as a little boy. Where did you grow up? How did you get into photography?'

He was startled, and showed it. Damn, she was doing it again—taking further control and reversing more roles. *He* should have been the one asking *her* questions, not the other way round.

'Why do you want to know?' he asked, punching the 'down' button on the wall between the twin lift-wells.

Her shrug was superbly nonchalant. 'We have to talk about something over dinner, don't we? I've never known a man who didn't like talking about himself.'

'Ouch,' he said lightly, though underneath he was piqued by her answer. There he'd been, suddenly thinking she was interested in Luke St Clair the man, not just Luke St Clair the male body. More fool him. 'You don't seem to have a high opinion of the male gender,' he added blithely.

'No,' she returned wryly. 'I can't say I'm overly impressed in general.'

This judgemental reply sparked a sharp response from Luke. Who in hell did she think she was—a saint?

'I'm not in the business of impressing women,' he

said rather coldly. 'As far as I'm concerned they can take me or leave me.'

'I wasn't talking about you, Luke,' she denied. 'But from the sounds of things you're not all that impressed with the female gender in general either.'

His slow, sexually knowing smile was designed to melt even the iciest of women. 'You shouldn't take my cynicism personally, Rachel,' he said, in a low, silkily seductive voice. 'Believe when I say I'm *very* impressed with you.'

Their eyes clashed, and for the first time he didn't bother to hide the extent of his desire for her. It blazed, hot and strong, compelling her to keep staring deep into his eyes. Immediately that peculiar fear zoomed back into her face, but still she couldn't seem to drag her eyes away from his. Gradually, her fear changed to a flush of acute sexual awareness. Colour flooded her cheeks and her lips fell ever so slightly apart.

In that moment Luke knew that she would be his once again.

His sense of triumph was intense, and he might have kissed her then, if the lift doors hadn't opened to reveal another couple waiting to go down to dinner. Still feeling invincible, Luke put a masterful hand on her elbow and ushered her inside, thrilled to feel her arm quivering uncontrollably.

His thoughts were primitive and savage as they rode down to the first floor. He was secure in the knowledge that no matter what she said or did over dinner she would not refuse him afterwards.

Once out of the lift on the first floor, they soon found themselves alone again—Luke steering her right while the other couple turned left and headed for the La Mer restaurant, which was a more formal restaurant and not what Luke had wanted for this evening. A more relaxed atmosphere was preferable when seduction was on the menu for supper.

'You're hurting me,' she said shakily.

'Sorry,' he said, releasing his grip on her elbow to trail his fingers down her arm then link his hand with hers. 'I don't know my own strength sometimes. This better?'

He lifted their entwined hands and pressed the backs of her fingertips lightly to his lips. The heat which flooded her cheeks brought another wave of black triumph, as did the tremor which ricocheted through her. Luke felt it right down to her fingertips.

He held her flustered face for a long, long moment. 'We'd better go inside,' he said at last, with an intimate little smile, 'or they might think we're not turning up. Don't want them giving our table to someone else, do we? I don't know about you, but I'm suddenly awfully hungry...'

CHAPTER SEVEN

LUKE'S triumph was short-lived, as he should have expected. Rachel Manning was not the sort of female to relish being at a disadvantage for long—especially sexually.

Actually, he didn't begrudge her the sanctuary she found behind a rapid resumption of her usual composure. He rather admired the way she took hold of herself as he ushered her into the restaurant. The speed with which her heated cheeks cooled to a more dignified and very faint blush was testimony to a will of iron.

It gave Luke a glimpse of why he was so obsessed with this woman. She might be a lot of things, but never weak. Hell, no. She didn't know the meaning of the word.

'What a lovely view,' she said with superb style, after the waiter had departed with their drink order. 'We have the best table in the house.'

Which they did—right in the far corner, where the large plate glass windows met, providing them with a panoramic view on all sides. Although night had well and truly fallen, Terrigal was still a pretty sight, with the many streetlights showing the seaside town and the beach to advantage, their reflections sparkling like diamonds in the darkened water as it rolled in gentle waves onto the semicircle of golden sand.

Not that Luke was interested in views. His attention was all for the woman sitting opposite him.

Their eyes met momentarily, hers holding his quite coolly, revealing that she'd totally recovered from what had happened earlier.

Luke wasn't worried. He knew exactly what to do to whip her right back into that highly desirable state of flustered arousal. He would simply kiss her. No woman in all his wide range of experience had ever reacted to his kisses as she had done eighteen months before. He'd never forgotten those little whimpering noises, or the way she'd simply melted against him, like liquid velvet.

The waiter coming back with the bottle of white wine he'd ordered put a welcome halt to Luke's train of thought. He dragged his mind back from the mine-field of his memories to sample the crisply cold Chablis, gave his nod of approval and relaxed in his chair while the waiter filled both their glasses, then wiggled the bottle into the portable ice-bucket.

'Time to tell me the story of your life, I think,' she said abruptly, once the waiter had departed.

'You'll be bored to tears.'

'Believe me, I won't.'

Luke frowned at the edge in her voice, then decided just to go along with what she wanted. Besides, if he told her about his own life then she might tell him about hers.

'I have no idea where to start,' he said.

'Then just answer my questions. How old are you?'

'Thirty-two.'

'Are your parents both living?'

'My mother is. Dad died a few years back, of a heart attack. Mum lives in Monterey, in the same house I was born in.'

'I'll bet you're an only child.'

'Not at all. I have two older brothers—both married and both breeding like rabbits. Well, not exactly. Andy has two children, Mark three.'

'And you've never been married?'

'No.'

'Are you living with anyone?'

'No.'

'Got a girlfriend?'

He looked her straight in the eye. 'No.'

She arched one eyebrow, then stopped her questions to take a sip of her wine, sighing as she replaced the glass onto the crisp white tablecloth. Her hand, he thought, was trembling a little, but her eyes were as cool as ever as they lifted to him, and a wry smile was playing on her lips. 'I'll bet you were very popular at school. And good at everything.'

'Yes and no. I *was* popular, but not at all good at everything. Sport, yes—I was crazy about soccer—but not schoolwork. I had a type of attention deficiency syndrome, where my mind would wander off in all directions—never on the subject I was supposed to be studying. My report cards all said the same. ''Would do better if only he would concentrate.'' Still, I knew I was going to become a professional photographer from the age of thirteen, so my poor grades didn't really matter.'

'What made you decide to become a photographer so young?'

'Dad gave me a camera for my twelfth birthday, and I was immediately hooked. I found I had a talent for taking really flattering shots of people. I also found I could make money out of that talent.'

He smiled at the memory. 'I took glam photos of the best looking girls in school, then beefcakey shots of the hunkiest guys, and made a fortune selling copies around the playground. I even put out a calendar each year, using the pick of the bunch. Got into a bit of trouble when the tax department showed up in my classroom one day and demanded to see my books.'

Luke laughed. 'Luckily, the money I'd made up till then was in a tin under my bed. They went away in the end, after I'd convinced them photography was just my hobby, and I used all the money I'd made to buy equipment.'

'Clever,' she murmured.

'Streetwise more than clever, Rachel. I'm no genius, but I've made a success of my life. So far,' he added a touch bitterly.

She frowned and stared down at the table. Luke found her silence irritating and swept up his wine glass. 'So, what shall we drink to?' he said. 'My success, or yours?'

She glanced up, her rueful little laugh startling him.

'Can I share the joke?'

'Not really. The joke's definitely on me—but it is funny, in a way.'

'Funny ha-ha, or funny peculiar?' he drawled, knowing full well why she found the situation ironic, but since he wasn't supposed to know he had to play dumb.

'I doubt either of those adjectives fit,' she said drily, and took a decent sip of wine. 'It's certainly not amusing, and "peculiar" seems such a pathetically inadequate word.'

'To describe what, Rachel?'

She lifted the glass towards him in a toast-like gesture. 'You... Me... Us...'

'But there is no us...yet.'

'No, but there will be, won't there? In a fashion, that is,' she added, dropping her eyes while she sipped her wine.

Luke straightened in the chair. 'Precisely what do you mean by...in a fashion...?'

Her shrug seemed superbly nonchalant, but he fancied that it hid a lot of tension.

'You know exactly what I mean, Luke. You intend seducing me later. But come tomorrow morning that will be it, won't it? Unless, of course, you're tempted to finish up early and have another romantic interlude during the afternoon. Either way, by the end of the day you'll get in your car, I'll get in mine, and we'll go our separate ways.'

Luke's fingers tightened around his wine glass. 'Is that so?' he said curtly, not bothering to deny a thing. It certainly fitted one of the possible scenarios he had fantasised as happening with her.

'Yes, that's so,' she said with a soft sigh.

Her air of weary resignation infuriated him. 'You sound like you have no say in the matter,' he bit out, angry with her for assuming he was that kind of man, and angry with her for admitting that she would give herself to him on a silver platter like that.

Her eyes moved slowly to his, and Luke flinched at the pain in their depths. 'I don't,' came her simple but strained admission.

Luke didn't know what to say. Or think. Something was going on here that he was not privy to. But once again the secrets were all on her side, and he was not going to be let in on them. He wondered if she was some kind of nymphomaniac who, once turned on, could not stop herself from surrendering to the object of her desire. Maybe her sexual needs were so strong on occasion that she became an almost unwilling victim of her own body.

It would explain how she had acted at the exhibition that night. Luke began to see her love life as a series of one-night stands with men who meant nothing to her but a means to an end.

'Care to explain that remark?' he said tautly.

'Does it require an explanation? Do you really care? Good God, you're going to get what you want, so why make a fuss? Look, I told you this morning that I needed you. You knew what I meant then, just as you know now. But if you insist on my spelling it out then I will.

'You're an extremely handsome, very sexy man, Luke, and I'm madly attracted to you. I haven't been with a man for quite some time, and I find myself wanting to make love to you so badly that to sit here and act normally is almost impossible.'

Luke blinked his shock at her, for her words did not match her manner, which remained so cool and controlled that he wondered if she was joking.

How long was 'quite some time'? he wondered dazedly. A fortnight? A month? Not eighteen months, that was for sure!

He felt his blood beginning to boil, and his temper along with it. 'Then why not just do it?' he snapped. 'Get up, take my hand and take me back to your room right now. Why torture yourself any longer? Don't be a coward, Rachel. *Do it*!'

She threw him a look which riveted him to his chair, stunning him with its fury and its passion. And then she laughed again—a mad, demonic chuckle which chilled his soul.

'You really know how to get under a woman's skin, don't you, Luke?' she muttered, draining the rest of her wine with one swallow. 'I'll bet you've had plenty of practice. But you're quite right,' she added, astonishing him by actually standing up and picking up her purse. 'This is all such hypocrisy. Let's go,' she said,

and began to move off, her long legs carrying her
quickly from the restaurant.

Luke caught up with her at the lifts, his face flaming
from having to endure the embarrassment of inventing
an excuse to the startled waiter, not to mention the
many curious eyes which had stared at him as he'd
raced after her.

'It's just as well no one knows me around here,' he
flung at her.

'Or me,' she retorted, her cheeks pinkening as well.
'You think I'd be doing this if anyone around here
knew me?'

'Frankly, I don't know what to think,' he bit out
truthfully.

'Then don't,' she snapped. 'Just do what you usually do. Take what's on offer, and don't ask any questions.'

He glared at her through narrowed eyes, fearing at
that moment what he might do to her. Maybe she saw
the troubled turbulence in his gaze, or maybe she had
a sudden crisis of conscience. All he knew was that
her face unexpectedly began to crumple, her hands
flying up to try to hide her distress.

'Oh, God,' she cried. 'God…'

There were no actual tears, just a moaning sound
which tore into Luke's guts. Her shoulders began to
shake while she struggled for control. Unable to help
himself, he gathered her into a comforting embrace,
holding her tight against him as they waited for a lift.

'I'm sorry,' she choked out between shudders. 'So sorry…'

'Hush,' he soothed. 'Hush.'

'S-sorry,' she repeated raggedly.

'Me too,' he rasped, moved beyond words as she continued to tremble violently against him.

The lift doors opened and it was blessedly empty. Luke bundled her in, one arm staying wrapped around her while he punched the floor number.

'Here, give me this,' he said, removing the purse which was clenched defensively between them and was digging into Luke's ribs. He tucked it under his left arm then reached up to stroke her head, smoothing down the glossy blonde hair and pressing her face against his chest. She turned her head with a shuddering sigh to lay her cheek against him, the trusting gesture sending a sweet, curling sensation all through him.

Her rag-doll limpness evoked the same possessive protectiveness and tenderness in him which he'd felt for her during their first encounter. Where before it had thrown him, Luke now accepted it as perfectly reasonable. How else was he supposed to feel about the woman he loved?

He almost laughed at his own stupidity in having denied it for so long, at having listened to his own desperate reasonings.

You don't know anything about her, he'd tried telling himself many times over. You only spent one short evening with her. Love at first sight is just so much romantic rubbish. She's a slut, a whore, a…a…rotten damned adulteress! You can't possibly be in love with her!

But he was.

It wasn't logical, or reasonable, or even sensible. Clearly, she was one highly mixed-up woman. But, despite all that, he still loved her.

'Rachel,' he whispered, wanting to hear her name on his lips.

She lifted her strained face and he bent to press light lips on her forehead, then on her nose, followed by each cheek, and ending up at her softly parted lips. Her sharply sucked-in breath told him all he needed to know at that moment.

He kissed her, and it was exactly as he remembered. The sensuality of her mouth. The little sounds she made deep in her throat. The total surrendering of her body to his. She was clinging to him when the lift doors opened, and it took a moment for either of them to realise that there were people waiting to get in.

Luke summoned up a suave smile from somewhere, and swept a limp Rachel past the staring couple. She'd managed to find her feet a little better by the time they made it to her room, but remained shaken and silent while he opened the door with the key in her purse and ushered her inside. She stared at him while he tossed the key and the purse onto the bedside table then began taking off his jacket.

He smiled reassuringly at her, rather liking her silence and her hesitation. He draped his jacket over a nearby chair and began to attack his shirt.

'Luke,' she suddenly burst out.

His hand froze on the second button of his shirt, instinct warning him that he was not going to like what she was about to say.

'What?' came his curt query.

'I…I…I hope you've got some protection with you…'

His relief was mixed with some irony. So she wanted him to use something tonight, did she? No more mad risks? No more being totally carried away?

'That goes without saying,' he said brusquely. 'I'm not in the habit of taking insane chances.'

She blushed fiercely, her eyes unhappy as they dropped to the floor. Luke could see that things were in danger of deteriorating, so he did what any sensible desire-ravaged man would have done. He stopped undressing and stalked over to drag her into his arms again, his mouth descending with a hunger and force which brooked no more nonsense or delay.

It came as little surprise that she seemed to relish his mad display of passion, moaning beneath the savage sweeps of his tongue then actually matching his passion by wrapping her arms tightly around his waist.

He responded by sliding his own hands down over her buttocks and pulling her hard against him, all his stomach muscles contracting at the feel of his erection pressed into the mound above her sex. He only just managed to keep a lid on his wildly flaring arousal.

Till she made a rotating movement with her hips.

'God, Rachel,' he gasped as he burst away from her, raking both his hands through his hair while he battled to control his throbbing flesh. 'You shouldn't do things like that. Not at this point.'

'I suppose not,' she agreed huskily. 'But you do have an unfortunate effect on me.'

'Unfortunate?' he repeated, his nostrils flaring when her hands lifted to the top button of her jacket. 'How do you mean...unfortunate?'

A strange smile played on her lips while her hands moved tantalisingly down her front, undoing each button as she went. 'You make me do things I know I shouldn't. You make me...weak...and wicked,' she added, parting her jacket and pushing it back off her shoulders.

Luke's breath caught in his throat. For she was naked underneath, had been all along.

The silky top slid down her arms and fluttered away onto the carpet. Luke sucked in another sharp breath when her hands went to her waist and she began to slip the silk trousers down over her hips, taking her underwear with her.

She had to bend over to complete the action, and those glorious hard-tipped breasts swung away from her body, twin orbs of lush perfection. Various erotic tableaux teased his brain, sending torturous messages from his brain to his body. His loins filled with a dull, heavy ache the like of which he'd never known before.

He had to have her, and he had to have her quickly.

'For pity's sake, Rachel,' he practically implored when she straightened, even the simple action of her tossing her hair back from her shoulders bringing a flash of unbearable discomfort.

There was no pity for him, however, in her glazed green eyes. 'Now you,' she ordered huskily.

'Me?'

'Yes. I want to undress you.'

His groan finally communicated his hell to her.

But, if her smile was anything to go by, the knowledge evoked a perverse pleasure in her, not pity. 'Poor Luke,' she murmured, stepping forward to reach up on tiptoe and kiss him lightly on the lips, her naked nipples brushing his chest. 'I won't take too long,' she said huskily, busy fingers nimbly flicking open the remaining buttons on his shirt.

But then she slowed, taking her time in peeling the shirt back from his tensely squared shoulders and feasting her eyes over his bared chest.

'God, but you're beautiful,' she said thickly, and spread both her hands over the curls in the centre of his chest. 'Beautiful,' she repeated, and began rubbing her satin-soft palms out over the broad flat muscles which housed his male nipples, trailing repeatedly over them till they tightened into round hard pebbles of heightened sensitivity.

'Don't blame me if this doesn't work out as well as you hope,' he warned darkly, struggling desperately for control as she went about her ruthless journey of discovery.

She didn't answer. She merely smiled and bent to lick where her fingers had been.

Luke bit his bottom lip and let her do it for a while, loving yet hating the way his stomach somersaulted at every sweep of her tongue. But when she actually took one of the taut nubs between her teeth, and tugged it none too gently, he grabbed her shoulders and wrenched her head away.

'That's enough of that,' he growled, putting her from him quite firmly then stripping off the rest of his clothes himself. While he was at it he rummaged through his pockets to find his wallet, extracting some protection before he was beyond caring.

He could not believe it when she took the condom from his wildly unsteady hands, knelt down and did the job for him. Her expertise shattered any secret hope he might have harboured about how often she'd done this type of thing. Hell, her idea of not having had a man for a long time was probably three whole days!

God, if only she'd take her hands off him. If only she'd stop caressing him. He couldn't take much more of such intimate foreplay. Not this first time.

No, don't do that, for pity's sake, he screamed silently, even as he let her. Oh, sweet Jesus…

'Rachel,' he choked out at last. 'You simply must stop.'

She ignored him.

'Didn't you hear what I said?' he groaned, dragging her upright and shaking her.

Her bewildered blinking told him how far she'd retreated from reality. She was breathing heavily, but then so was he. Luke stared at her mouth, that pouting, panting mouth, which only moments before had brought him right to the edge.

He was still on the edge, damn it.

'Make love to me, Luke,' she had the hide to say at that point, and she sidled against him once more.

Luke's blood pressure reached new heights, as did his frustration. 'You haven't given me much of a chance.'

'I know,' she rasped, lifting her right leg and sliding her thigh provocatively up and down the outside of his. 'I wanted to be ready for you. I'm ready now, Luke. Do it to me now.'

He needed little encouragement, and surged inside her, groaning with pleasure and dismay when he felt himself begin to come almost immediately. Hell, he knew he wasn't going to be able to hang on. She was so hot and wet and wild, writhing and rotating on him till nothing was going to stop his desire exploding. He gritted his teeth and tried to will it away, but nothing could stop him. Nothing.

He cried out his agony and ecstasy, holding her tightly as he shuddered violently into her. Just as his male ego began to tip him into despair she did the most incredible thing. She came too, her flesh answering his in the most intensely mutual release he had ever experienced. Their bodies throbbed as one, pulsing deep within each other, bringing a physical and emotional satisfaction to Luke which quite blew him away.

They fell onto the bed together, their bodies still fused, both still climaxing uncontrollably. Luke rolled her on top of him, where he grasped her buttocks and kept rocking her against him, seeking to prolong the sensations, not wanting them ever to end. Finally they both became still, with Rachel collapsed across him. She moaned one last moan against his chest, her arms flopping wide on the bed in an attitude of total exhaustion and satiation.

Luke felt as if he'd just run a marathon, his heart still pounding. All that could be heard in the room was his ragged breathing. But gradually his blood calmed down, and the room became very quiet. He was beginning to think he just might live to make love again in the near future when a jarring sound broke the silence.

Wide green eyes jolted immediately open, to stare at the telephone by the bed. Luke scowled his impatience at the interruption, then frowned at Rachel's obvious alarm.

Who on earth, he wondered, was ringing her room at this hour? And why did she look so damned worried all of a sudden?

CHAPTER EIGHT

'AREN'T you going to answer it?' Luke said after a few more rings. 'This is your room, after all.'

'Well…er…um…' She glanced down at where their bodies were still intimately joined.

Luke came pretty close to blushing. 'Right,' he muttered, easing away from her and swinging his legs over the side of the bed, thankfully on the opposite side of the bed to the telephone. 'You can answer it now,' he added as he stood up and stalked off towards the bathroom.

He shouldn't have done it, he supposed. Hurried to do what he had to do, then sneakily opened the bathroom door just far enough so that he could listen to what she was saying.

But he had, telling himself that he simply had to find out all he could about the woman he loved—especially since she wasn't about to offer any information. He needed knowledge if he was to get past this hard protective shell she'd built around herself.

'So what did the doctor think?' she was saying, when he first tuned in to her side of the conversation. 'Are you sure, Sarah? I could quite easily come home for tonight and drive back in the morning. I'm sure I can talk the photographer into letting me start a bit later or delaying the shoot another day. If not, he'll just have to find himself another model. The money's not that important, compared to my son's health.'

Luke gripped the doorknob. A *son*? She already had a son!

Black jealousy speared through him, mixed with torment over her dismissive attitude towards him. And there he'd been thinking he must mean something special to her for her body to respond to him so swiftly and totally.

The realisation that he'd just been callously used once again filled him with dismay and disgust. It added to her guilt, somehow, that she'd only cheated on her husband eighteen months before, but had done so after having had his baby. God, but she was despicable!

'No, Sarah, I've made up my mind,' she swept on firmly. 'I'm coming home right away. I know there's nothing much I can do but sit with him, but I won't be able to sleep tonight anyway for worrying. If I leave straight away I should be there in well under two hours. The traffic will be light at this hour. See you then, Sarah… Yes, I will… Bye.'

She hung up and turned, still nude, to find him standing at the foot of the bed, equally buck naked, glaring his frustration at her. 'Yes, I will, what?' he demanded sharply.

'Yes, I…I will drive carefully,' she returned, her momentary stammer the only evidence that the situation was in any way rattling her. 'That was my mother-in-law,' she explained hurriedly. 'I told you she'd been sick. Well, she's taken a turn for the worse. I have to go home. I can drive back up here tomorrow, if you insist.'

'Don't bother lying to me, Rachel,' he snapped. 'I heard everything.'

He rather enjoyed seeing her go pale. He would enjoy seeing the bitch go a damned sight paler before he let her go this time.

'You never mentioned that you had a child,' he added coldly.

Now heat raced back into her pale cheeks. 'You were listening!' she accused him, and he almost laughed at her indignation. The pot was calling the kettle black!

'It seemed the only way to find out anything about you,' he said testily. 'You do have this passion for secrecy. And secrets. So, I ask you again, why didn't you tell me you had a son?' Even as he said the words, the most ghastly suspicion began to form in the back of his mind.

'Why should I?' she tossed back, momentarily throwing him with her offhand manner. 'My son is none of your business. If you must know, having a baby is not always good for business. Now, if you'll excuse me,' she said, scooping up her scattered clothes from the floor, 'I have to get dressed and get going.'

'And you have to come back tomorrow and finish this job,' he demanded, all the while desperately trying to push that irrational suspicion to the back of his mind. For it just couldn't be true. It was too fanciful for words. Even *she* wouldn't be *that* wicked.

But, damn it all, he didn't like the word 'baby'. Initially he'd imagined her child to be a small boy, of maybe two or three. A baby suggested less than a year old. Dear God, what if he was only nine months old? What if…?

'I don't *have* to do anything,' she threw at him as she straightened, clutching the clothes in front of her nakedness. 'I quit. Find yourself another blonde. I'm sure you won't have any trouble. You know what they say, Luke. Variety is the spice of life.'

His hands balled into fists by his sides, and for a few seconds Luke warred with a thousand primitive emotions—not the least of which was the desire for murder.

He watched, seething, as she turned her back on him and disappeared into the bathroom.

By the time she came out of the bathroom a couple of minutes later, fully dressed, he too had dragged on his clothes and was sitting on the side of the bed. He watched while she packed the rest of her things, torn between wanting to ask her the critical question and remaining silent.

Better you don't know, came the voice of common sense. Let her go, man. She's bad news.

But ignorance was not bliss in the end. He could not bear not to know.

'How old is your son, Rachel?' he asked abruptly.

Her shock at his question was so acute that Luke was almost sick on the spot. Dear God, no, he groaned to himself.

'Why…why do you want to know?' she asked shakily, her face as white as a sheet.

Luke jumped to his feet and swore. Then swore again. Violently. Obscenely. He wanted to weep, but it just wasn't the done thing. Men didn't blubber. They swore. So he swore a third time and glared his hatred at her. Hatred would sustain him, he hoped.

She stared back at him with eyes like saucers, her mouth gaping. He saw her shock change to outrage, her lips snapping shut and her eyes flashing fury at him. 'You bastard,' she hissed. 'You knew who I was all along!'

His top lip curled with contempt at her indignation. 'Yes, of course. That's why I hired you. I knew I was on to a sure thing. Now, answer my question, damn you! How old is your son? And don't bother to lie. I can find out easily enough now that I know of his existence.'

'Eleven months,' she snapped, her own attitude just as contemptuous of him. 'Too old to be yours, lover. So you don't have to worry. You can continue on your merry way without the millstone of an unwanted child around your oh, so handsome neck! My baby is my husband's child. Patrick Reginald Cleary, the third.'

Luke wasn't sure if he was relieved or revolted. So she'd already been a couple of months pregnant that night—a son and heir already growing inside her. If it *was* her husband's child, that was!

Still, it explained why she hadn't been worried about not using protection. Being pregnant had freed her to fulfil all her sexual fantasies without being caught out.

'You rotten bitch,' he said in a low quaking voice. 'You filthy rotten bitch. Get out of here before I kill you.'

Her stricken look produced no pity in him. He could find no excuse for her behaviour in his heart. On top of that, he could find no excuse for himself, for feeling perversely disappointed that the child wasn't his. This was not a woman worth loving! She wasn't worth spitting on!

'Get out!' he snarled through gritted teeth.

She gave him one last anguished look, grabbed her things and fled, leaving the door open behind her. Luke stormed over and slammed it, then paced furiously about the room, raking his hands repeatedly through his hair.

'I do not believe this,' he muttered to himself. 'None of it makes sense. It doesn't feel right.'

Luke ground to an abrupt halt, black eyes flinging wide.

That's because it *isn't* right, man, came the astoundingly certain answer.

Luke gasped, then grimaced. Oh, my God, what if she'd lied about the baby's age? What if he wasn't eleven months old? What if she'd called his bluff about finding out the child's age and simply added two months? Clearly she hadn't thought he was all that interested in the baby as such, anyway. She saw him as the swinging bachelor-type of photographer—going from woman to woman, model to model, one-night stand to one-night stand.

Luke's insides began to churn, his gut feeling telling him that he'd just come to the right conclusion. The child *was* his! It was the only logical answer to her reactions to him—the only thing that made any sense at all. My God, it explained so much. About tonight and about eighteen months ago.

'I have no time for cowards tonight,' was what she'd said back then.

Which had been oh, so true, he thought bitterly. She'd wanted a child and her husband had obviously not been able to give her one—her much older and possibly ill husband. So she'd gone out and got herself one, the same way women had been getting themselves babies and heirs since time immemorial—by seducing some poor unsuspecting devil—namely himself!

But she'd run into snags with him from the first, hadn't she? To begin with he'd surprised her, by taking over the lovemaking and insisting on using protection. That had been why she'd had to seduce him a second time. *Really* seduce him, so that he'd been so turned on he was beyond caring about the risk. After which she'd coolly done a flit without leaving a clue as to her identity.

Of course, she had to have planned all that in advance—booking the hotel room in a false name, paying by cash and not credit card. Every single move had been planned—from her provocative clothing right down to her selection of a suitable candidate.

Luke wondered sourly what it had been about him which had made her choose him. His looks, perhaps, or just his having been alone? Had it merely been chance which had drawn him into her web of deceit, or had there been a perverse destiny behind it all?

She'd never expected to run into him again. Hell, why should she have? She'd thought he was an American tourist. But when their paths had crossed again, and she'd been given the let-off by his seemingly not recognising her, she'd run into a second snag.

She'd found that she actually still fancied him, sexually speaking.

Luke had been with enough woman to know that she'd really fancied him the first time too. More, perhaps, than she'd ever anticipated—so much so that she simply could not resist having another sampling of his services.

Which brought him full circle to what he'd thought about her in the first place. She was a rotten bitch—a cold, calculating slut who at this very moment was on her way out of his life a second time. Only this time she was taking his son with her!

Over my dead body, he vowed darkly.

Luke acted quickly and decisively, racing down to his room, collecting his car keys and setting off after her. He figured that he'd easily catch up with her on the expressway to Sydney. That small Nissan of hers couldn't do what his Ford could do, and she'd be easy enough to spot at this hour of the night, with few cars on the road. The dark would also mean he'd be able to follow her without being observed in her rear-vision mirror.

He spotted her car shortly after Mount White, keeping well back till the expressway ended, after which he had to move closer or risk being left behind at red lights. As it was, he did lose her at one intersection for a few minutes, but luckily he knew the roads south of the city quite well, and knew where he would catch up.

The digital clock on the dashboard showed just on eleven when she finally turned from the main road, not far from the Cronulla shopping centre. Luke dropped back a bit as he too turned left, pulling over to the kerb and switching off his headlights when he saw her brakelights come on and stay on. He watched as she turned into a driveway a hundred metres or so up the street, the car disappearing down the far side of a house.

When he was sure that she'd had enough time to go inside, he climbed out of the car and walked along to stand and stare at the house which he believed held his son.

It was an old brick-veneer cottage, with a red-tiled roof, a ramshackle carport attached and lawns which needed mowing.

Luke frowned. If this was where Rachel was living, then she *hadn't* come out of her marriage flushed with money. His assumption that she'd wanted to provide an heir for the Cleary family fortune had clearly been amiss. Unless unforeseen circumstance had somehow dissipated any wealth. People *had* been known to make bad investments—to lose all their money in one fell swoop.

Luke gave himself a mental shake. There was no use trying to second-guess Rachel or her motivations. No use confronting her either. She would simply lie to him again. He would have to be far more devious than that in finding out the truth of the matter.

Luke noted the number on the postbox, then walked up to the nearest corner, where he memorised the street name. On his way back down past the house he stopped for a few moments to stare some more.

What if you're wrong, Luke? a niggling voice whispered. What if he's not your son? What if…?

'I'm not wrong,' he growled aloud. 'I just know it!' And, whirling on his heels, he strode back down the street towards his car.

CHAPTER NINE

LUKE didn't drive back up to Terrigal. He went home, from where he rang the hotel, told them there had been a family emergency back in Sydney and asked them to pack his things in his bag—which was in the bottom of the wardrobe in his room—and send it down by courier. He also asked them to check Miss Manning's room, in case she'd left anything behind, and do likewise. They were to bill everything to his credit card, of which they already had an imprint.

He had just hung up the telephone in the front hallway when his mother emerged from her bedroom, looking bleary-eyed and bewildered.

'I thought I heard your voice, Luke. What are you doing home? I thought you said you were staying up on the coast tonight.'

'I was. But things didn't quite work out as I'd hoped.'

Grace couldn't say that she was sorry. Luke had given her some story about doing some photographs for Theo around the Central Coast beaches, but she'd suspected all along that he'd gone away with a woman—probably that married one he was mixed up with.

Frankly, Grace was both surprised and disappointed

in Luke for having anything to do with a married woman in the first place. It wasn't like him at all. For all his being a nineties man in a lot of ways, he'd always held fairly old-fashioned views in matters of morals and marriage.

Unless, of course, he hadn't known she was married till after he'd become emotionally and physically involved. Now, that was a likely explanation...

Dear me, but the poor love looked all done-in, and quite shattered. Still, it was all for the best if he'd broken up with *that* type.

'Want a cup of tea, love?' she asked gently.

'That'd be great, Mum.'

Grace smiled ruefully as she made her way out to the kitchen. At least she was still good for something, if only making cups of tea.

'And a toasted sandwich wouldn't go astray, either,' Luke added as he followed her. 'I...er...didn't get round to having any dinner.'

Grace glanced over her shoulder at him, her mouth opening to ask him why on earth not, but another look at Luke's bleak face closed it again. Not tonight, she decided wisely. He wasn't in a fit state for the third degree tonight. Maybe tomorrow.

'In that case sit down and I'll get you one,' she said briskly, and began filling the electric jug.

She heard him scrape out a kitchen chair behind her and slump down into it. 'Thanks, Mum,' he said, a grim weariness in his actions and his words.

Grace resolved not to ask him about his miserable mood, or the reason behind it. Luke would be returning to America in ten days or so, which would no doubt be the end of the affair for once and for all. At least, she hoped so...

Luke woke to depression and indecisiveness, but he ruthlessly pushed both aside. There was nothing to be gained by wallowing in self-pity and doubt. Nothing to be gained by wondering and worrying. Hamlet had waffled for too long, and look where that had got him.

Luke's job this morning was to glean the truth, after which his course of action would become clear. One step at a time, he vowed. Find out if the boy is yours first.

Strange, but he didn't feel quite as sure of that this morning as he had last night.

Luke lay in bed for ages, tracing over everything Rachel had ever said and done, including that mini-breakdown in front of the lifts. What had her repeated apologies meant? What had she been saying sorry for? Surely not just her behaviour in the restaurant? True, she'd acted pretty badly, but was it more logical that she had been saying sorry for having used him to father a child, without his knowledge or consent?

Damn, but it was all so confusing and confounding!

Luke threw back the bedclothes and bounced out of bed before he went bonkers. Time to find out for sure, Luke. Time to get some answers.

* * *

He sat low behind the wheel of his mother's battered old blue sedan, biting his fingernails while he watched and waited for his opportunity.

Not a soul had stirred all morning, and it was nearly eleven. He'd hoped to catch a glimpse of the child, perhaps—though on reflection a baby under one year old wouldn't play in the yard. He probably couldn't even walk yet! His life would largely be indoors, unless either Rachel or the mother-in-law took him out in a pram or a stroller or whatever.

Another half-hour passed, and Luke was about to make the decision to go up to the front door and just knock when that same front door opened and Rachel emerged, wearing jeans and a long-sleeved blue top. She turned to speak to a white-haired lady in the doorway, her own long blonde hair caught up in a ponytail. Suddenly she whirled and hurried down the front steps with what looked like a purse in her right hand.

Luke slid further down in the seat till he could only just see her, but, as he'd hoped, she didn't give the old blue car across the road a second glance as she walked quickly down the front path and through the slightly rickety front gate.

Luke came back upright once she'd taken off up the street, letting out a shuddering sigh when she turned right at the corner and headed in the direction of the shopping centre, which he knew was a good ten-minute walk away. Even if she was able to buy whatever she wanted in five minutes flat, he still had a conservative twenty-five-minute leeway to find out all he needed to know.

His heart thudding heavily behind his ribs, he climbed out of the car, thankful that he'd taken the trouble to dress well. He didn't want the old lady being suspicious of him in any way. He had to charm his way right into that house and into her confidence in five minutes flat.

Luke's first shock came when Rachel's mother-in-law answered the door. For, although she did have white hair, she was not even remotely an *old* lady. She looked no older than his own mother, who was in her mid-sixties. How old, then, had Patrick Cleary been? Maybe not as old as Luke had assumed.

'Mrs Cleary?' Luke asked, smoothing any shock from his face and finding his most winning smile.

'Yes,' the lady returned hesitantly.

'Goodness, you look too young to be Rachel's mum-in-law,' he said, actually meaning the words even as he recognised the remark as an obviously flattering line which men used on women all the time.

He felt quite guilty when it worked, her pale cheeks pinkening with pleasure.

'I'm Luke St Clair, Mrs Cleary,' he went on while she was still slightly flushed and flustered. 'I'm the photographer Rachel was working with yesterday. Is she home? I need to talk to her about rescheduling the rest of the shoot. I really don't want to use another model. As I'm sure you understand, not too many models have that special quality and style which Rachel has.'

'Oh, dear, you just missed her. But she won't be

long. She's just popped down to the chemist to pick up some more medicine for Derek's gums. The poor baby's having teething troubles—but I suppose she told you that.'

'Derek?' Luke repeated, taken aback a second time. 'I thought her son was called Patrick?'

'Really? How odd. Maybe you misunderstood. Patrick was his father's name. Actually, his father *did* want him to be called Patrick, after himself and his grandfather, but Rachel—sensible girl that she is—put her foot down and said that that type of thing went out with the Dark Ages. I have to admit I agree with her. I didn't want to call my Patrick Patrick when he was born, but my husband insisted, and women in those days went along with what their husbands wanted more than they do nowadays.'

She gave a wan little smile, which Luke wasn't sure how to interpret, although he'd somehow gained the impression that Mrs Cleary's relationship with her husband had not been all she'd wanted it to be. Still, he could see that she was a softie—one of those refined, delicate old-world women, who didn't have the spirit or the strength to stand up for themselves. Confrontation was not their style at all.

'Goodness, how I am rattling on,' she dithered. 'And you still out on the doorstep, Mr St Clair. You must think me very rude. Do come in.'

'Call me Luke,' he insisted as he followed her down a neat narrow hallway then into an equally neat but cluttered lounge-room. There was much too much furniture and knick-knacks for the size of the room, and, although some were pieces of obvious quality, a lot of them were worn and just a little shabby.

'Then you must call me Sarah,' the old lady tittered back, and Luke's conscience pricked again. It didn't feel right, worming his way into this sweet old darling's confidence. But it had to be done!

'I'll just pop out to the kitchen and make some tea,' she said. 'Do make yourself at home.'

Luke let out a long-held breath once he was alone. He hadn't realised till that moment just how tense he was.

Some wedding photographs on the wall immediately drew Luke's attention, and he slowly picked his way between the furniture to get closer, his frown deepening as it became clear that the man standing beside Rachel was far from elderly. Grey hair he might have had back then, but it must have been premature, for the handsome smiling face beaming out at Luke from inside that silver frame belonged to a man no older than his mid-thirties—if that!

It rather blasted away one of his preconceptions about Rachel, as had this house last night. She had not married some old man for money, which meant that she must have married for love.

Luke tore his tortured gaze away from the wedding pictures, his eyes narrowing and swinging around the room in search of what he knew had to be there somewhere.

And then he saw it—a baby photograph, sitting on

top of a beautifully carved bookcase which was half hidden behind a couple of overstuffed chintzy armchairs.

He swallowed, and squeezed between the arms to pick up the silver-framed picture. The baby in the ten-by-eight coloured print looked about six months old, and was stark naked, sitting in a bath. He was an extremely beautiful child, with soft blond curls covering his head and the brightest blue eyes Luke had ever seen.

Luke's chest tightened. His own eyes were such a dark brown people thought them black. Dark brown eyes were dominant in his family, on both sides. Even though Rachel had green eyes, Luke himself would have had to carry a recessive blue gene to have a blue-eyed child.

He didn't think that he carried that gene. His two brothers definitely didn't, all their five children having brown eyes. It had often been a matter of family discussion, their dark brown eyes.

A sudden thought struck Luke, and he hurried back to peer at the wedding photos. Damn it all but it looked as if Rachel's husband had had brown eyes as well. Not as dark brown as his, however.

One of Luke's other suspicions about Rachel returned with a vengeance. The baby might not be his, but he might not be her husband's either. It would explain why she'd been so adamant about not calling the baby Patrick. Doing so would have been a constant reminder of her guilt.

Luke decided not to waste any further time. He would find out the child's exact age, then get the hell out of here. Taking the baby's photograph with him as a talking point, he easily found the kitchen in the small house, where Sarah Cleary was busy making up a teatray.

She looked up with a ready smile, making Luke feel rotten again. 'Oh, so you've found Derek's picture. Such a beautiful child, don't you think? There again, he has an exceptionally beautiful mother.'

Luke found a dark irony in the woman's generosity in giving most of the credit for the child's looks to the mother. Little did she know that it was possible her own son had contributed a big zero to the boy's beauty. No doubt there was some handsome blue-eyed hunk somewhere around Australia—or maybe the world—who was equally ignorant of the contribution he'd made to the Cleary family.

'Rachel said he turns one next month,' Luke said innocently, and held his breath for the answer.

'Yes, that's right,' Sarah tripped back, and Luke's heart hit rock bottom. 'October the fourteenth.'

Self-disgust was hard on the heels of his disappointment.

Good God, don't tell me I was still hoping, despite the blue eyes. What kind of fool am I?

The kind who just doesn't know when to quit, came back the rueful answer.

He was searching his mind for some excuse to go and have a look at the child, whom he assumed must be asleep, when the house was rent by the sound of a child's cries. They were high-pitched and quite loud, more like a temper tantrum than the sounds of a distressed baby.

His eyes flew to Sarah, who didn't look all that concerned. 'It seems Master Derek has awakened from his morning nap. I know he sounds like he's distressed, but he's not. He's just bored. He can't bear being in bed once he's awake. Would you mind pouring yourself some tea while I get him up, Luke?'

'Er…not at all.' Luke glanced at his watch and saw that only fifteen minutes had gone by since he had entered the house. With a bit of luck he would still be away before Madame Lash returned from the shops.

'I'll be a minute or two,' Sarah warned him. 'I'll have to change his nappy before he makes an appearance in public.'

The crocodile tears were becoming louder and more demanding. What a little tyrant, Luke thought, yet found himself smiling when the sounds stopped abruptly the moment Sarah opened his bedroom door.

Luke poured himself a cup of tea and was sitting, dunking in a biscuit, when Sarah came back, carrying a dry-eyed Derek who looked considerably older and even more good-looking than in his photograph. Never had Luke seen such beautiful big brown…

'Brown,' he choked out, after almost choking on the biscuit.

'What's that, dear?' Sarah said as she slid the baby boy into the highchair at the end of the table. The job completed, child and grandmother both turned curious looks on him.

'His eyes,' Luke repeated dazedly. 'They're brown. But they're blue here in this photograph.' He picked up the frame to stare at those bright blue eyes once more.

Sarah's laugh was soft and gentle. 'Didn't you know? All babies are born with blue eyes. Some take several months before they change to their final colour. Derek's eyes are exactly the same colour as his father's eyes. Really, it's the only part of his father that he's inherited.'

Luke felt that sick feeling once more. She was right. Derek's eyes were not nearly as dark as his own—more like the mid-brown of Patrick Cleary's.

His sigh carried a resigned finality. He'd come full circle, hadn't he? With all his preconceptions about Derek's conception now well and truly routed. Rachel had been guilty of one night of infidelity, that was all. One mad night when, for whatever reasons best known to herself, she'd simply needed a man.

And she'd chosen him.

Dear God, why me? he groaned silently.

He now wished he had not come—wished that he'd listened to that other voice which had told him to leave well enough alone.

But he *had* come, and would have to stay and face Rachel, who would no doubt be furious with him. Ahh, well…

'Is he a difficult baby?' Luke asked, more to make

conversation than out of any real interest. The child was not his. His instinct had failed him for the first time in his life.

Sarah handed the baby a fruit stick to chew on and sat down to pour herself some tea.

'He's been a right pain,' Sarah admitted. 'But he's getting better. Of course, Rachel fusses over him far too much—but that's understandable, considering his precarious start to life.'

'Oh? He was a sickly baby, was he?'

'Well, not exactly. Just premature. Two whole months. He spent the first six weeks of his life in a humidicrib.'

Luke was glad that Sarah chose that moment to stand up and tie a bib around the baby's neck, for Luke knew that his face must have shown his feelings. There was no rage. Just shock, followed by a wave of intense elation which threatened to undermine every ounce of control he was desperately trying to muster. Dear God, he almost burst into tears!

Luke's eyes still watered as they turned to stare at his son. It was totally involuntary, the love that welled up in his heart for the boy, the all-consuming feeling of pride and paternal joy. His eyes locked with the child's, and maybe he communicated his emotion to his offspring, for the child seemed transfixed with his father, his big brown eyes rounding further.

'Derek,' he said softly, and a happy gurgle erupted from those baby lips, his arms flapping in a gesture of uninhibited delight.

Sarah smiled at her guest as she sat back down. 'He likes you, Luke. Which is a first. He doesn't usually like men. Of course,' she added with a sad little sigh, 'he hasn't had much contact with them. I suppose Rachel told you Derek's father died when he was only a couple of weeks old?'

'Er…actually no, she didn't. But I knew she was a widow when I hired her. What did your son die from, Sarah?'

'Leukaemia. He was diagnosed about a year after he and Rachel were married. After some intensive chemotherapy he went into remission for a year or so, but then it flared up again, worse than ever, and we all knew it was only a matter of time. Patrick only lasted as long as he did because Rachel was expecting his baby. He'd always wanted a son, you see. Quite obsessively. I can't tell you how relieved I was when Rachel's ultrasound showed she was having a boy.'

'It must have been a difficult time for all of you,' he murmured.

'It was, but Rachel was marvellous. That girl has such strength, you've no idea. I would have fallen apart if it hadn't been for her. She means the world to me—as, of course, does little Derek here. We've both got him to thank for pulling us through the bad spots. Being responsible for another human being does make you snap out of self-pity, and it gives you a purpose in life.'

Luke was trying to find some answer to that when

the front door banged, and three seconds later Rachel
swept into the kitchen, speaking as she went.

'I bought some gel for Derek's gums and some infant dose Pana—' Her voice broke off when she spotted Luke sitting there, all the blood draining from her
face.

CHAPTER TEN

ODDLY enough, Luke's reaction to her distress was not anger or resentment, but pity. No sensible-thinking man could have looked upon that lovely pale face with its haunted green eyes and imagined for one moment that she was wicked or, God forbid, some kind of conscienceless whore. Whatever had driven her to do what she had done eighteen months ago, it had not been selfish desire or nympho-maniacal need.

It had been desperation.

Of that he was certain. Desperation to give her dying husband the son he'd always wanted.

'Luke,' was all she could manage to say, the word as strained as her expression.

'Hello, Rachel,' he returned, trying to put her at ease. 'I dropped by to see when you might be free to finish the shoot. Sarah here said you wouldn't be long, then kindly invited me in for tea.'

'Yes, and you should see how Derek has taken to him, Rachel,' Sarah chimed on, oblivious to the underlying tension in the room. 'Why, he was laughing and smiling a moment ago. I was telling Luke, that's not like him at all. Most men make him go all quiet and shy. See—he's smiling at Luke right now.'

'Yes, yes, I see,' Rachel said stiffly, although some

colour had come back into her face. Obviously she'd begun clinging to the hope that nothing had been said or done to give the game away.

Luke decided that he wasn't going to allow her to play that game any more. But he was not so cruel or insensitive as to say anything in front of Sarah.

'Rachel, I really do need to have a private word with you,' Luke said firmly, which brought another panic-stricken glance from those dark-ringed green eyes. She really did look awfully tired this morning, but still incredibly beautiful.

'Why don't you take Luke into the lounge-room, Rachel?' Sarah offered. 'I'll take Derek out into the yard for a play in his sandpit. And don't worry. I'll put some sunscreen and a hat on him.' This with a rueful smile at Luke, as if to say, See what I mean? Such a fusspot of a mother!

'All right,' Rachel said, lifting her son out of the highchair, her face going all soft and glowing as she gave him a peck on the cheek. 'You be a good boy for your nan—and no tantrums, mind. When she says it's time to come inside then it's time to come in. Only fifteen minutes at this time of day, Sarah. Luke and I should be finished by then.'

Luke returned her challenging glance with a bland face, not wanting to tip his hand in advance.

'This way,' she said coolly once Sarah and Derek had departed for the great outdoors. 'First door on the left.'

Luke felt his chest tightening as she waved him

ahead of her out of the kitchen. He walked rather stiffly down the narrow hallway and into the cluttered lounge once more, wishing at that moment that he was anywhere else but where he was. Even a visit to the dentist would have been preferable to what he was about to say.

He sat down in one of the overstuffed armchairs and watched while she closed the door behind her, then crossed her arms as she whirled to face him across the room.

'Don't think I'm impressed with the way you've wormed yourself into Sarah's affections just to get to me,' she snapped. 'You're a sneaky, conscienceless, manipulative devil, Luke St Clair, and I want nothing more to do with you.'

Luke scooped in a deep, steadying breath and let it out slowly as he reclined fully in the chair. There was no point in losing his temper—nothing to be gained by trading insults. But, damn it all, his heart was pounding away inside his chest and he was having a hard battle controlling his blood pressure. He planted both his hands firmly over the ends of the armrests, tipped his head back and locked eyes with her.

'I wish it were as simple as that, Rachel,' he began. 'I wish all that had brought me here was a desire to sample your delectable wares one more time. But that is not the case…'

'Really!' she snorted. 'Pardon me if I find that hard to believe. I've met your type before.'

'I doubt that, Rachel,' he replied coldly. 'I'm not a

type. I'm an individual, with a mind of my own, a passion for the truth, and a stubbornness of spirit which only a mother can admire.'

'Charming. Now get to the point!'

'Very well.' The cords in Luke's neck stood out as he struggled for composure. 'I know Derek was born two months premature. I know your husband was ill with leukaemia for some time before he actually died. I suspect Derek is my child. What have you to say to that?'

Nothing.

That was what she had to say to that. She merely stared at him with pained eyes, then started shaking her head as though she could not believe that this was happening. Her arms unfolded and fell limply to her sides, her shoulders sagging in defeat.

'No,' she finally whispered. 'No…'

Turning, she clenched her hands into fists against the door, and was about to bang them on the wood when she stopped herself, spinning back to face him with a determined and tortured face. 'No,' she denied in a low, shaking voice, but with a firmness that had Luke leaping to his feet.

'What do you mean…*no*?' he demanded. 'You had unprotected sex with me seven months before Derek was born. Since he was born two months premature, even I can add seven and two and make nine. Even if you slept with dozens of other men around the same time, how can you be sure he's not mine?'

'There weren't dozens of other men,' she admitted

at last in a strangled voice. 'The only person who could have been the father of my baby other than my husband was you. And you're quite right. I couldn't be sure, so I had DNA tests done after Derek was born. I know whose baby my son is, Luke, and you don't have to worry any more. He's not yours. He's a Cleary.'

Luke sank slowly down into the armchair, his eyes dropping blankly to the floor. He felt as if someone had just punched him in the stomach. Derek wasn't his. Rachel wasn't the mother of his baby. Everything he'd been secretly hoping and planning...poof! Out of the window.

'I can appreciate how relieved you must be,' Rachel said, the caustic note in her voice sending his eyes flashing up to find hers.

But she wasn't looking at him any more. She'd turned to stare at her wedding pictures on the wall, the action hurting Luke so much that it propelled him from self-pity into a simmering fury.

'So why did you do it?' he snarled. 'Just tell me that. Hell, I think I at least deserve an explanation.'

She turned slowly to set bitter eyes upon him. 'Do you, just? And why is that? You came with me that night without a second thought, Luke. And I'll bet you didn't give me a second thought the next morning either.'

'Then you'd be wrong, lover,' he snapped, jumping to his feet. 'I gave you plenty of thought while I worried my guts out for the next three months that I might have caught bloody AIDS!'

'Oh!' she cried, her remorseful expression seemingly real. 'So you did worry about that. I...I wondered afterwards. I *am* sorry for putting you through that, Luke. Truly.'

'Then why did you do it?' he demanded to know, his heart still aching from her disclosure. 'Tell me. I want...no, *need* to know. Hell, Rachel, would it hurt to tell me the whole truth? I can see now you're not some kind of slut, who'd make a habit of doing that sort of thing. But you were deliberately trying to get pregnant with me that night, weren't you? It wasn't some kind of crazy fling you were having, was it?'

'No,' came the husky admission. 'No, you're quite right. I was trying to get pregnant.' Tears filled her eyes and began falling silently down her cheeks. 'You'd never understand how it was, Luke. No man could ever understand...'

Her tears moved him deeply, but he wasn't about to back away. Only by knowing the whole truth could he begin to come to terms with the disappointment of Derek not being his.

'Try me, Rachel,' he choked out. 'I'm a good listener.'

Which was a lie, Luke realised, the moment the claim came out of his mouth. He'd never been a good listener. All his life he'd trodden a selfish path, where only *his* wishes mattered, only *his* desires and dreams.

When had he ever stopped to really listen to anyone else's dreams or problems?

Bloody never.

Even now he wasn't wanting to listen for *her* sake, but to salve his own male ego.

This brutally honest self-realisation had him taking a good look at himself from Rachel's point of view. Hell, if she had a bad opinion of him then he only had himself to blame.

But all that was going to change, he vowed. As of right now.

'Even if I tell you everything,' she said, blinking away her tears, 'you'll never appreciate the situation at the time. No man could.'

'Rachel,' he said firmly. 'In another ten minutes Sarah will come back inside with Derek. Just give me the facts. I won't think the worst of you. Just tell me how it was, and what led you to taking such desperate measures.'

'And then you'll go?' she cried, her voice pleading.

'We'll see, Rachel.' Already his mind was shifting to other hopes, other dreams. Attainable ones.

He must have betrayed something of his secret desires, for her face hardened then. 'Don't go misunderstanding what happened last night, Luke,' she said sharply. 'It was a mistake, and one which I won't repeat. I know I gave the impression I was a sure thing where you're concerned, but that's not true any more. Believe me when I tell you I won't go to bed with you again. Never, ever. So you'd be wasting your time hanging around here.'

He believed that *she* believed what she was saying. So he let her believe it for the time being.

'Just tell me what happened, Rachel?'

His firm stance brought a wearily resigned sigh. 'All right, but I'm beyond dressing it up to make you feel sympathetic. I'm beyond caring what you think of me, anyway. I did it, and given the same circumstances I'd probably do it again. Not that that makes it right...'

Luke sat down while she stood there silently for a few seconds, her mind obviously off in the past. He waited impatiently for her to continue, and was about to say something when she launched into the explanation.

'I never knew my father,' she said, and Luke's head snapped back in the chair. Good God, she was going back a long way. But he remained silent, knowing that any further interruptions would only delay things.

'He died when I was only two. My mother was a wonderful woman, but inclined to be overprotective—especially when I grew up to be better than average-looking. She was afraid, you see, that I would become easy prey to the rich, handsome, conscienceless men of this world, who sought to use any pretty but naïve young woman who crossed their path. When I became a model I began to see what she meant. I *was* pursued by such men, and I fell prey to their empty charm a couple of times before I woke up to their lies. And my own silly self.'

Luke frowned at this, and might have said something if she hadn't immediately swept on with her
story.

'By the time I met my future husband, at the ripe
old age of twenty-two, I'd become somewhat wary of
all super-good-looking men—rich or not. Patrick
wasn't overly handsome or overly rich or overly anything. He was, however, a fascinating man, with a brilliant mind, who was already at the top of his scientific
field at only thirty-four.

'We met at a benefit to raise money for research
into congenital defects in children—his field. I fell in
love with him, and when he asked me to quit modelling, marry him and have his children, I said yes like
a shot. My mother was delighted—she'd begun to seriously worry about the direction of my life—and
wished me every happiness as Mrs Patrick Cleary.'

Rachel's unhappy sigh led Luke to the astonishing
thought that she had not found such great happiness
as Mrs Patrick Cleary. Had this been due to his sick-
ness, he wondered, or something else? Hadn't her brilliant husband turned out to be the Prince Charming
she'd imagined him to be?

Not too many men, Luke reckoned, were saints. He
would imagine that a man who had chosen scientific
research as a career might be a very self-absorbed individual, a workaholic-type with little time put aside
for the little wife at home.

But it was hardly the right time to suggest as much.

'A few weeks after our wedding,' Rachel said quietly, 'my mum died suddenly of a stroke. It…it was a big shock to me. She was only forty-nine. I found it difficult to come to terms with her death. If it hadn't been for Sarah's sweet sympathy and kindness, I might have actually had a breakdown.

'She was a big comfort, too, when several months went by and I didn't fall pregnant. Patrick was most upset by this, and impossible to reason with. He was anxious to have children, and especially a son to carry on the family name. I told him that conceiving sometimes took time, but he insisted I went for every test in the book.

'When the news came back that I was fine, he finally consented to have tests done himself. He found out that his sperm count *was* a little low, but… worse…he was suffering from leukaemia—the same disease which had claimed his own father thirty years before.

'We were all devastated by the news. Patrick knew he had a long stint of chemotherapy ahead of him and, unbeknown to me, he had some of his sperm frozen and stored in the sperm bank of a large Sydney hospital. He had no intention, it seemed, of giving up his idea of having a son and heir.

'Meanwhile, he wasn't well enough for a normal sex life—although we did manage to make love every so often. Still, not enough to make conception a likelihood. He did go into a type of remission for a few short months, and we did resume marital relations on a regular basis, but still…no baby.

'When Patrick became ill again, and was diagnosed as terminal, he came up with the idea of my being artificially inseminated with his sperm every month. He had me take my temperature every morning before rising, and charted everything. Then, when my temperature dropped and it seemed ovulation was imminent, I would take the train up to Sydney, visit the hospital for the necessary procedure, spend the rest of that day and night resting in a hotel room, then return home the next day.

'I did this for five consecutive months, and every time...nothing. I began to dread getting my period and seeing the despair in Patrick's eyes. I would have done anything to stop him looking like that. The doctors said that if I could get pregnant he might find the will to last another couple of years, but I have to admit that I wanted a child myself. My life had become so lonely and so wretched, without focus or meaning. I needed something of my own to love and hold. It had been so long since Patrick had even touched me, let alone held me.'

Rachel faced him then, for the first time since she'd started talking. 'So I did what I did, God forgive me, thinking I was doing something noble. But from the moment you touched me, Luke, and held me and kissed me, I became caught up in something so different from what I'd originally intended. I won't lie and say I didn't enjoy every single moment I spent with you that night. I did. But believe me when I say I've suffered for my sin, Luke. I'm only sorry that I unwittingly made you suffer as well. I apologise deeply for that. I really do.'

'And you're absolutely sure of the child's parentage?' he asked thickly. 'There's no doubt?'

Rachel stiffened and drew herself up tall, as if in indignation that he would ask that question a second time. 'No doubt at all,' came her staunch reply. 'I'd been artificially inseminated with Patrick's sperm that same afternoon. I can only assume that my making love with you set off more normal processes within my body, which resulted in it being more conducive to conception.'

Luke couldn't help the grimace of distaste which flitted across his face.

'Yes, it's all very tacky, isn't it?' she snapped. 'Just like last night was tacky. I don't want to be tacky with you any more, Luke,' she said, her voice shaking with emotion. 'Enough is enough. Now I want you to go.' Again she crossed her arms, her expression and her stance carrying the message that this encounter was at an end.

He stood up slowly, that she was far too upset at that moment to accept anything from him at all. But he had no intention of leaving her alone. Either her or the boy. Derek might not be his child, but he could have been…oh, so easily.

As perverse as it might have seemed, it was enough for Luke. For some strange reason he didn't feel any different about the child for knowing he was not the biological father. His heart filled as he imagined what it would have been like to be such a child's *real* father—to love him and look after him. Luke liked the feeling it gave him. It felt right.

'I fully agree with you, Rachel,' he said quietly. 'I don't want there to be anything tacky between us any more either. *Au revoir*,' he said, and, nodding towards her stunned face, he swept past her, out into the hallway and out of the house.

Luke wasn't too sure what he was going to do, or how he was going to achieve his objectives. All he knew was that he was going to win that woman—that beautiful, brave, wonderful woman. Indeed, a woman worth loving!

CHAPTER ELEVEN

'FORGIVE me for asking,' his mother said to him over dinner that evening. 'But are you involved with a married woman?'

Luke's first reaction was a mixture of surprise and resentment at such a question. But seeing the real worry in his mother's eyes softened his attitude, and he decided—after a moment's hesitation—to tell her about Rachel and Derek. She would have to know eventually, anyway, because they were going to become part of his life. Luke wasn't sure how he was going to make that miracle come true, but make it come true, he would. Or die trying.

'So that's the story,' he finished over coffee. 'Now, before you open your mouth and put your foot in it, Mum,' he warned her, 'I want to add that I'm going to marry Rachel. Derek might not be mine, but it makes no difference. He's a grand little kid and needs a father. That father is going to be me!'

'But...but the mother doesn't want to have any more to do with you!'

Trust his own mother to come straight to the crux of his problem! 'Yes, do I realise that,' he tossed back, recklessly dismissing the niggling qualms which lurked deep within over Rachel's antagonism. 'But I aim to start overcoming that small hurdle in the near future.'

Somehow...

'How?' his mother asked, and Luke's pessimistic gut-feeling raised its ugly head again, filling him with exasperation.

'Must you be so negative? Look, I can't say I know, rightly. *Yet*. I'll sleep on it.' He carried his coffee-cup and saucer over to the sink. 'After I've helped my favourite girl with the washing-up, that is. This male chauvinist pig is going to have to turn over a new leaf if he's going to settle down to married bliss and family responsibilities.'

Grace rolled her eyes, stood up and carried her own half-full cup over to pour down the sink. 'You can't *make* her love you, Luke,' she said. 'Or marry you.'

'You think not?' he returned darkly. 'I have the advantage of certain admissions she once made to me. If all else fails, I will have to resort to desperation tactics.'

Grace stared at her son. She hoped he didn't mean what she thought he meant. Men who believed sex and seduction were the way to a woman's heart were fools! Lord, she hoped he wasn't planning on making her pregnant again. That would be a disaster!

'Mind if I make a suggestion, Luke?'

'Not as long as it's constructive.'

'You mentioned that you thought their house looked a bit shabby, and the yard unkempt. You might do something about that to start with.'

Luke frowned. 'You mean pay someone to fix it up?'

'Heavens, no. From the sound of things your Rachel would bitterly resent that. She sounds like a very proud lady. I was thinking more of you doing some work around the place yourself. You were pretty good with a mower and a paintbrush when you were a lad. The old mower in the garage still works. And there's a fairly new whipper-snipper Mark and Andy bought me last year, plus more paint than you can climb over. Those brothers of yours are always using *my* garage to store *their* leftovers. Serve them right if some of it goes missing.'

Luke's face broke into a wide smile, and Grace's heart turned over as he hugged her close. 'What a fantastic idea, Mum! I never would have thought of it. Thanks a million. I'll get started on ''Project Cool Hand Luke'' first thing in the morning. But let's hope I'm more successful than the original Cool Hand Luke. He died at the end of the movie. 'Night, Mum. Sleep tight.'

Grace went to bed, trying to feel optimistic about Luke's future with this woman, but it wasn't easy. She hoped it hadn't been just sexual frustration which had made this Rachel respond to Luke during that first torrid encounter and then again this week. She hoped that somehow, some way, his basic decency and good character had shone through his distracting sex appeal and had captured a little of her heart as well as her body.

Grace's thoughts finally turned to the boy who could quite easily have been her own grandchild. What a shame, she thought, that the baby hadn't turned out to be Luke's. Patrick Cleary was dead now, so it wouldn't have mattered to him, and, as she'd always believed, Luke would have made a very good father.

He would still make a good father to the boy, Grace believed, if only the mother would give him a chance.

Let her give him a chance, Lord, Grace prayed as she drifted off to sleep. He really is a good man.

The house was empty when Luke turned up the following morning, and Luke panicked for a moment till he went round to the backyard and saw lots of toys still in the sandpit. Peering through the kitchen window, he also spied a few breakfast dishes in the sink. He couldn't imagine someone like Sarah being persuaded to abandon the house without doing the washing-up. She was of his mother's vintage, and such a wickedness would not be allowed.

Rachel, however, was another matter. Luke could well imagine her deserting the washing-up if she had other priorities for her time. Various X-rated thoughts zoomed into his head, and with a groan of frustration Luke spun away from the window. This would never do. He hadn't come back to bed her again, but to win her love.

Still, as he'd implied to his mother, he would use whatever weapons were at his disposal if failure was on the cards. For how could he simply walk away, when he knew that this was the woman he'd waited for all his life?

Two hours later the front and backyards had been transformed—the lawns mowed, the edges done, the garden beds weeded. But there was still no sight of the occupants.

Luke ran through the various possibilities in his head. They might have gone shopping, or to the doctor, or simply gone out for a drive. A glance at his watch showed eleven-thirty. One would think they wouldn't stay out too long with an eleven-month-old child. Derek would need a sleep soon, surely.

Hunger pangs reminded Luke that it had been a few hours since breakfast. He drank some water out of the hose, and was contemplating going back home for lunch when he heard a car throttling down out at the front. His heart was in his mouth as he hurried around the side of the house, relief flooding through him on seeing Rachel's car turn into the driveway and stop at the gates. He could see Sarah in the passenger seat and baby Derek perched up in a baby car-seat in the back.

Luke strode quickly down the pathway to open the gates, but Rachel was out of the car and there before him. The look she gave him was lethal.

'What in hell are you doing here?' she snapped under her breath as he drew near. 'And who in hell do you think you are, mowing my lawns without permission?'

'Morning, Rachel,' he returned coolly, totally ignoring her angry tirade. 'Been shopping, have you?' he said and waved at Sarah, who was smiling at him from the passenger seat, then at Derek, who was looking cranky. 'Now, don't make a scene in front of the family,' he whispered as he helped her open the gates.

'This isn't going to work, Luke,' she muttered. 'I want you to go away and stay away.'

He gave her a steely look. 'Don't be so bloody stupid. I care about you, Rachel, and I'm not going anywhere, so you might as well get used to me hanging around.'

'But...but you can't!'

'Can't what? Can't care about you? Why not? You're a lovely woman, with a lot more going for you than your looks, though you do seem to have a problem with your temper.'

'But you...you said you were going back to America,' she wailed.

'My plans have changed.'

'Oh, God...'

'There's no need to pray, Rachel. I have no intention of hurting you.'

'But you will. Don't you see?' she groaned. 'Every time I look at you it will hurt me.'

Sarah, unwinding the window and putting her head out, stopped that conversation dead in its tracks. 'Derek's beginning to grizzle, Rachel,' she called out.

'Coming,' Rachel said. 'We'll finish this later.'

'Over dinner tonight?'

Her eyes flashed fury at him.

'I'm not going to go away, Rachel.'

'Damn you, Luke. Why can't you be like all the others?' she threw at him, before whirling and striding back to the car, slamming the door as she climbed in and driving past him to park under the carport.

All the others?

Luke frowned his disgruntled puzzlement as he just stood there.

What others? Other lovers she'd had? Ones who'd loved and left her?

Damn it all. He hated to think of her with other men. It was hard enough coming to terms with her husband!

Derek's irritable cries snapped Luke out of his brooding reverie, although he was in no mood to be all sweetness and light as he strode over and yanked open the back door. He used brisk, somewhat brusque movements to unbuckle the child from his baby carseat and whisk him out.

'Now, you stop that grizzling this instant, you little tyrant!' he ordered as he perched Derek firmly on his hip.

Derek's whingeing dried up immediately, a wide smile breaking over his cherubic face. His big glistening brown eyes twinkled cheekily as he reached up and started playing with a lock of Luke's hair which had fallen across his forehead. He even began making 'ga-ga' noises which sounded rather close to 'da-da'.

Luke couldn't help it. He was instantly entranced, a slave from that moment onward.

'See, Rachel?' Sarah said. 'That's just what Derek needs occasionally. A firm male hand. Look, he's being as good as gold for Luke.'

'In that case Luke can mind the little devil for the rest of the afternoon,' she retorted as she gathered up several bags of groceries from the car and set off towards the house. 'I suppose you'd better invite the Good Samaritan in for lunch, Sarah,' she called back over her shoulder in waspish tones. 'No doubt he'll expect some payment for all his work,' she finished drily.

Sarah sent Luke an apologetic shrug. 'It's been a trying morning,' she whispered. 'I'd better go and open the back door for Rachel before she drops all the shopping. *Again*,' she added meaningfully before hurrying off.

Derek immediately blotted his copybook by bursting into loud cries the moment his grandmother disappeared.

'I can see where you get your sweet temperament,' he told the bawling infant as he walked him round the yard, trying to get him to stop crying. But to no avail.

Sarah popped her head out of the back door. 'Better bring him inside, Luke. The poor love's tired and hungry and needs his nappy changed.'

The poor love created merry hell till Rachel took him off to bed. Luke had by then finished the last of the two huge sandwiches Sarah had made him, and he put down his mug of coffee with a relieved sigh at the sudden blessed silence. 'My God, is he always as bad as that?' he asked.

'Heavens, no. He's just overtired from our shopping expedition. He should have been in bed at ten for his morning nap. Any other child would have just dropped off in his stroller, but not Derek. He finds looking around in the mall far too interesting to go to sleep. Same thing in the car. Most babies drift off during a drive, but never Derek. He likes looking around too much.'

'Mum says I was like that,' Luke remarked. 'I was a bad sleeper too. Never lasted longer than four hours at a time. Apparently my bedroom was filled with different coloured lamps, and the whole ceiling was covered in colourful mobiles because it was the only way Mum could get some rest. I used to lie there for hours just watching the shapes move and the light play on the various surfaces.'

'Maybe that's why you became a photographer?' Sarah suggested.

'You could be right. I never connected the two things before. How clever of you, Sarah. Speaking of photography, I'd like to take some shots of Derek later. I have a few frames left in a roll I have in a camera in the car, and I might as well use them up before I get the roll developed.'

'Oh, that would be wonderful. We really haven't got all that many photos of him. As I'm sure you've gathered, money's a bit tight. Patrick's illness used up all his savings, and then some more. After he died we found out he'd taken a second mortgage on the house. Naturally he hadn't earned any salary for ages. He lost his position with the international drug company he'd been doing research for soon after he was diagnosed with cancer. They treated him shamefully. Quite shamefully.'

'Do you own this place?'

'Oh, no. There's no money left at all. We rent. For a while after Patrick died we both got by, by pooling our social security cheques. But Rachel realised that wasn't going to be enough when Derek got older so she decided to go back to work. She's been doing quite well too, getting more and more work all the time.'

'She's a very good model.'

'And very beautiful,' Sarah added, managing to put a questioning note into the words and worry into her glance at Luke.

He smiled a reassuring smile. 'I can see I'm not going to be able to put anything over on you, Sarah. Yes, my interest in Rachel is more than professional, but my intentions are honourable. The only trouble around here will be convincing Rachel of that.'

'She…she did love Patrick very much,' Sarah said hesitantly. 'She's been through a lot.'

'Yes,' was all he said.

Sarah sighed. 'But life goes on, doesn't it? I mean…she's only a young woman, and it's silly to think there won't be another man for her one day.

If...if that man turns out to be you, Luke, then I for one couldn't be happier.'

Luke reached across the table to squeeze Sarah's hand. 'Thank you. I appreciate that. Do you think you might talk her into going out to dinner with me tonight?'

'You mean she's refused?' Sarah's surprise was both flattering and encouraging.

'Uh-huh.'

'Don't take it personally, Luke. She probably just doesn't want to ask me to mind Derek again. Which is so silly, really. I love minding him, and he's usually quite good at night. The other night was an exception. Now that we have that stuff for his gums, it'll be plain sailing.'

'I'll play with him when he wakes up later and tire him right out,' Luke suggested enthusiastically.

Sarah laughed. 'What a good idea! And you can take those photographs while you're at it.'

'What photographs?' Rachel asked as she walked back into the room, casting a suspicious glare at Luke.

'Of Derek,' Sarah answered. 'Luke's going to take a few snapshots and give them to us. Isn't that nice of him?'

'Yes,' came the taut reply. 'Very nice.'

'I assured him I don't mind minding Derek while you two young ones go out to dinner tonight.'

Rachel's smile was brittle. 'That's sweet of you, Sarah, but I really can't accept.'

'Nonsense. I insist.'

'And so do I,' Luke piped up. 'I think it's the least you can do to repay me for all the work I've done around here today. I haven't finished either. I thought I'd slap some paint on the carport. The posts are beginning to weather badly.'

Rachel looked from one to the other, then sighed and smiled sweetly. 'I can see I've been successfully outmanoeuvred. All right. Dinner tonight it is. Luke, can I see you outside for a minute? I'd like to see exactly what colour paint you're going to use. The landlord might not appreciate a pink carport.'

Any air of sweet acquiescence disappeared the second she was alone with him. 'Now, you listen here, Luke St Clair,' she spat, poking him in the chest with a very angry finger. 'I told you once and now I'm telling you again. I will not have you conning poor Sarah just to get to me. Neither will I have you blatantly using my son for the same reasons. I know exactly what you want, and it isn't just an innocent dinner-date!'

'True.'

'Ahh, so you finally admit it!' She folded her arms and glared up at him, looking incredibly beautiful with her cheeks all flushed and her green eyes flashing with anger.

'That depends. Exactly what am I supposed to be admitting to?'

'That the only reason you're…hanging around, as you so delicately put it earlier…is because you think I'm a sure thing where you're concerned.'

'Which you are,' he muttered, surprising her and himself by suddenly grabbing her shoulders and yanking her hard against him.

But, dear heaven, there was only so much pushing a man could take. Having gone this far, Luke didn't give her enough time to do more than gasp with shock before his mouth covered hers and his tongue was driving deep between her startled lips.

She didn't disappoint him.

God, no. She wouldn't be so bloody merciful!

It was the same as it had always been, once she was in his arms and being thoroughly kissed, every muscle in her body freezing for a few tantalising seconds before melting against him in one deliciously submissive wave of surrender. The feeling of power it sent crashing through Luke's veins was so intoxicating that he wondered momentarily if this *was* all he wanted of her. Hell, she made him feel more of a man than any woman he'd ever known.

Yet she was in no way a weak woman.

Till she was in his arms.

Then she *was* weak.

He broke from her mouth and she gazed up at him with anguished green eyes. 'You bastard,' she cried, even while she still clung to him. 'Why can't you leave me alone?'

'Because you don't want me to,' he returned thickly, then kissed her again—kissed her till she was jelly-kneed and trembling. Luke himself wasn't feeling too calm either, the state of his body routing all his earlier good intentions.

'We must stop,' she moaned, after the kissing had gone on for even more minutes, by which time Luke was in danger of spontaneous combustion.

It crossed his mind to push her round to the side of the house right now, or into the back of her car, and just do it, like two hormone-crazed teenagers. But it was stark daylight, and Sarah might come looking for them at any second.

Thinking of Sarah brought Luke back to earth with a jolt. Hell, what was he doing, letting the heat of the moment reduce his feelings for Rachel to nothing but lust? Clearly she expected a little more of him, and it was up to him to prove otherwise to her.

Dammit, he wasn't handling this encounter at all well!

'You're right,' he said abruptly, after tearing his mouth away from hers again. 'This isn't at all what I want.' His arms dropped back to his sides and he took a backward step, putting some distance between himself and the heat of her softly lush curves.

Her face remained flushed, but her mouth took on a cynical twist as her gaze swept down to where his tight jeans hid nothing of his stark arousal.

'Oh, I don't doubt that,' she said caustically. 'Men like you want it all, yet in reality you want nothing of value!'

'You're wrong, Rachel. Wrong about me and wrong about what I want.'

'Am I?' she jeered. 'Well, we'll see tonight, won't we, who's right and who's wrong? I'm sure you won't surprise me.'

Luke dragged in then let out a shuddering sigh. 'Look, we could keep trading insults all afternoon, but it won't prove anything. I'll let my actions speak for me tonight.'

'Like your actions spoke for you a few moments ago?' she scorned. 'Well, they do say actions speak louder than words.'

Luke's teeth clenched down hard in his jaw. Geez, but she would try the patience of a saint. It was no wonder he'd ended up kissing her. It was the only way to shut that smart mouth of hers.

'If you're so sure of my shallow character and intentions,' he pointed out testily, 'then why are you going out with me tonight at all?'

'Why, indeed?' she said in a self-mocking tone. 'Maybe I'm a masochist. Or maybe I just like to live dangerously.'

'Or maybe you like me a whole lot more than you care to admit!'

Her reaction to his ground out remark was a familiar one.

Fear.

It totally exasperated Luke.

'For pity's sake, Rachel, why do you have to look like that?' he groaned. 'How many times do I have to tell that I won't hurt you?'

'And how many times do I have to tell *you* that you

will—by just being *you*!' she countered, any fear quickly changing to a heart-wrenching sadness. 'As for pity…why don't you take pity on me and just go away? Can't you see that's what I really want? What do I have to do to make you go away and stay away?'

'A while back you said actions spoke louder than words, Rachel. Well, you're right!' Quite ruthlessly, he scooped an arm around her waist and drew her hard against him, cupping her chin with his other hand while he took her mouth in a brief but hungry kiss.

It was enough for her lips to quiver and her eyes to dilate wildly. 'When you stop responding to my kisses the way you do,' he rasped, 'then and only then will I go away and stay away. Now I want *you* to go away. Temporarily. I think I need a break from your hating me so much.'

She looked up at him with hurt eyes, but he felt no mercy at that point in time. He suspected that he would have little mercy for her tonight either, if things turned bad. Her fierce desire for him was the only weapon he had left, and if needs be he would use it.

She knew it too. Which was perhaps why she was looking at him the way she was. With real hatred this time.

'Men like you should be drowned at birth,' she snapped, and, whirling, sailed off towards the back door.

But the message her bejeaned bottom sent back to Luke as it swayed seductively from side to side was totally at odds with what she'd just said. Luke smiled a devilish smile, then set about painting the carport, whistling as he worked.

CHAPTER TWELVE

'So how did it go?' Grace asked Luke the moment he walked in the door. She'd been on tenterhooks all day, wondering and worrying about him.

He waved his hand in a so-so gesture. 'I'll know more after tonight. I'm taking her out to dinner.'

'Where?'

'Just a small seafood restaurant. Nowhere extra fancy. She wouldn't like that. She'd only think I was trying to impress her. Or seduce her.'

The bitter tone in that last remark bothered Grace, till she put two and two together and came up with a very obvious four. 'She thinks you only want an affair, doesn't she?'

'Something like that.'

Looking at Luke, Grace could appreciate that. Did he have any idea how handsome and sexy a man he was? She was his mother, and she could see it. How much more would a young attractive woman?

'What did she think of your mowing her lawns?'

'She thought it was all a ploy to get her into bed. She even thinks the same about my being nice to the boy.'

'You'll just have to hang in there, Luke, and prove

her wrong. Time should do that. Meanwhile, try to keep your hands off.'

'Would it were that simple,' he muttered. 'Mum, could you iron me a shirt while I have a shower? I have to hurry.'

'But it's only five past five. When do you have to pick her up?'

'Seven. But I've a bit of shopping I'd like to do first. And I have to drop by at Theo's on the way. I left some rolls of film with him to be developed, and he's doing them for me straight away.'

'Are they the photos you took of Rachel in bikinis?'

'Yes, but it's not them that the hurry's for. I took a few snaps of Derek this afternoon, playing in his sand-pit, which I thought might turn out rather well, and I wanted to give them to Rachel tonight.'

'Oh, I'd love to see them too. Have Theo run off an extra copy of them for me, will you? Actually, I wouldn't mind having a peek at the ones of Rachel too.'

'Sticky-beak. No worry. He's doing two of every-thing as a matter of course. Now, how about ironing that shirt? I'd do it, but you do it so much better.'

'Flatterer. Which one?'

'The black silk.'

Grace gave him a sharp look. 'Don't you think an-other shirt would be a wiser choice? Why not your cream one? Or that lovely blue lawn one with the stitched down pocket?'

'The black silk,' he repeated stubbornly.

Grace heaved a resigned sigh. 'You're still trying to get to her through sex, Luke, and it's not the right way.'

'Agreed. But it might end up being the only way. And if it is, I'm going to take it.'

Grace shook her head, her heart full of real fear for Luke's future. But she knew there was no arguing with him. He would simply clean up, then iron his own damned shirt.

She cluck-clucked her tongue in utter exasperation as she walked out to the laundry and drew the afore-mentioned garment out of the clothes basket, glaring at it as she spread it out on the ironing-board. He looked as handsome as the devil in that shirt, and wickedly sexy.

Poor Rachel, she thought.

And poor Luke.

The man simply had no idea. Women with babies didn't want just sex. Not without security in tow. And Luke in that shirt represented only the former.

But he would have to learn the bitter lessons of life for himself, wouldn't he? Maybe next time he'd listen to his mother!

'Wow, wow, and triple wow!' was Theo's greeting to Luke when he dropped by to pick up the photos. 'Now I understand. I'd fall in love with her myself if you hadn't got there first.'

'Thanks, Theo,' Luke returned, with a wry smile as

he took the large brown envelopes. 'I take it your little beauties performed well?'

'You'd take great pictures with a box Brownie, Luke. If you weren't such a good mate I'd be filthy jealous. I take it you're off to see the gorgeous blonde in the bikini?' he said, casting a rueful eye over Luke's appearance.

'Yes, and I'm running late.' Luke had taken simply ages in the baby shop, selecting mobiles for Derek's room.

'Off you go, then. Far be it from me to stand in the way of true love. Oh, by the way, who's the kid? The one with eyes you could drown in.'

'That's Derek. He belongs to the gorgeous blonde in the bikini.'

'Really? Would I be out of line asking if you're the father?'

Luke's chest contracted. He wished.

'No, I'm not,' he said brusquely.

'Then, who is?'

'Her husband.'

'Oh, hell.'

'Not quite. She's a widow.'

Theo still wrinkled his nose at the situation. 'Not good, man. I wouldn't raise another man's kid. Not even if the mother *was* a golden goddess. Give it ten years or so, man, and the kid'll be telling you to get lost, and not to tell him what to do 'cause you're not his *real* father.'

'But I *will* be his real father, Theo. I'm going to

adopt him. Now, I must go. We'll go out for drinks some time shortly, right?'

'Only if I can be best man at the wedding.'

'You're on!'

Theo's words stayed with Luke during the drive down to Rachel's place. He could see the sense in his friend's warning, but somehow it didn't seem to apply to his relationship with Derek. When Luke looked at that kid, and held him and played with him, he felt a bonding which transcended biological fatherhood. It was an emotional thing which could not be analysed. He loved the child as surely as he loved the mother.

He even loved the grandmother too, in a way. They were a grand trio, and he wanted quite desperately to make life good for them again, to buy them all a beautiful big house, to lavish some luxuries on them to make up for the hard times they'd had before and since Patrick Cleary's death.

Luke thought of the mobiles he'd bought Derek and smiled. He'd love the dancing elephant one. Kids always liked elephants. The butterfly one was cute too. Then there was the racing car one, and last but not least the fairies. God, he hoped buying a boy a fairy mobile wouldn't be looked askance upon by Sarah or Rachel. It had been the most colourful—the fairies having luminescent wings which glowed in the dark.

When Luke stopped at the next set of red lights, he snatched up the brown envelope lying on the passenger seat, ripped open the flap and slid out the thick bundle of coloured prints.

Derek's were on top, and Luke could see what Theo had meant. His eyes were incredibly expressive—big, liquid brown pools. There again, the photographs were excellent too.

'Must have had a good photographer,' Luke said to himself, smiling.

Damn, but he was a cute kid!

Luke finally moved on to look at the shots of Rachel, and they quite blew him away. She was beautiful enough in the flesh, but on film she was something else. Again, it was in the eyes, he realised. They seemed to follow you, their expressions vivid, bringing to vibrant life a wide range of emotions, not to mention her sexuality and sensuality. No man could have looked at them and not wanted her. It was as simple as that.

He wanted her. Not for a day, or a night, but for always. He would marry her tomorrow if she would have him.

The horn blowing behind him reminded Luke that the lights had turned green. Throwing down the bundle of photos onto the seat, he accelerated off, the thought coming that maybe if he told Rachel he loved her straight off the bat, if he asked her to marry him, then she would know how serious he was.

OK, so she might not love him back. Yet. But she did desire him, and it wasn't such a big step, surely, from desire to love. He could also start letting her know how damned well-off he was—anything to sway her opinion of him as a heartless womaniser to a serious suitor of depth and standing.

It wasn't till he was standing on the front porch and ringing Rachel's doorbell that Luke remembered the black silk shirt and his mother's disapproval of it. He was frowning as Rachel opened the door, at which point his own appearance immediately ran a poor second to hers.

Dear Lord, but she was exquisite—breathtakingly so in that classically cut cream suit, her hair up and pearls at her ears and throat. A second, closer inspection revealed that the suit was far from new and the pearls only cheap imitations, but neither observation detracted from her beauty, or his admiration of her. In fact, he admired her all the more—for she had an inner beauty as well, born of an inner pride and strength of character.

'Hello, Rachel,' he said simply. 'You look lovely.'

'You're late,' she reprimanded him tautly.

'Only fifteen minutes.'

'I…I thought you weren't coming.'

Luke saw that her knuckles were white within the clenched fists at her sides. It was as telling as the tension in her voice.

'And I thought you wanted me to go away and stay away,' he returned drily.

She gave him a look which had a disturbingly strained edge to it.

Luke decided that some defusing was called for. 'I had some shopping to do,' he explained. 'For Derek.'

'For Derek?' Her tension moved up a notch, if any-thing.

'Yes. Some mobiles for his room. Would we have time to put one up, do you think?'

'You…you bought Derek some mobiles?'

'Yes. There's this elephant one which I'm dying to put up. I was telling Sarah earlier today how I was a difficult baby too, and how Mum found that mobiles hanging from my ceiling used to amuse me for hours when I wouldn't sleep. I think they might help with Derek. Can I come in and do the honours? Don't tell me the little devil is asleep at this early hour.'

Luke was startled when Rachel abruptly burst into tears. 'Oh, God,' she sobbed, covering her face with her hands. 'God…'

Luke didn't know what to do. 'Rachel…darling…' He came inside, closing the door behind him and propped the large parcel from the baby shop against the door before taking her in his arms. 'What did I say? What's the matter? It's not Derek, is it? He's all right, isn't he?'

Sarah came hurrying down the hall. 'What is it?' she asked anxiously. 'What's wrong?'

Luke's bewilderment must have shown on his face and in his voice. 'I don't know. I…I think my buying Derek some mobiles upset her.'

Rachel began crying all the harder, sobbing into his shirtfront. Luke threw Sarah a desperate look.

'Rachel, dear,' Sarah soothed, prying her away from Luke's rapidly soaking shirt and leading her distressed daughter-in-law back down the hall. 'You're going to make yourself sick, crying like this. Now, why don't you have a little lie-down and—?'

'Make him go away,' she choked out, throwing a wild-eyed and tortured glance over her shoulder at Luke. 'I want him to go away. I can't stand the sight of him any longer. I can't, I tell you.'

Luke felt himself go cold all over.

'Rachel!' Sarah exclaimed, utterly shocked.

'I've told him and told him, but he just won't listen!' Rachel ranted hysterically. 'I don't want him in my life any more, but I don't have the strength to send him away! You have to do it for me, Sarah, before I do something dreadful. It's all become too much. The guilt and the pain. I can't bear any more guilt...or any more pain. Please, Sarah,' she cried. 'Make him go away.' And she collapsed against the older woman, sobbing piteously.

'Rachel...dear...I...I don't know what you're talking about. Do...do you know what she's talking about, Luke?'

'Yes,' he said bitterly.

'Perhaps if you told me I could—'

'No, don't!' Rachel wailed, her ravaged face jerking up to plead with him far more eloquently than any words. 'Please, Luke,' she begged hoarsely. 'Just go...'

Luke stared at her, and he saw the truth clearly for the first time.

She would never get over what she had done eighteen months ago. Never!

Technically she was an adulteress who had enjoyed her adultery, and she despised herself for it. Sarah had told him how much Rachel had loved Patrick, so the guilt had to have been enormous at the time—and long afterwards. As much as Rachel might still desire him, Luke, he would always be the symbol of her guilt and her shame. She had momentarily given in to the temptation of having what she'd thought was another one-night stand with him the other night, and then, when he'd followed her, she'd toyed with the idea of having a temporary affair with him.

But a lasting relationship had never been on the cards.

By buying her son such a personal present he'd crossed the line she'd made for him in her mind, and now there was nowhere for Luke to go except out of her life forever. He took one hard look at her dangerously distraught self, saw what his presence was doing to the woman he loved, and made the most difficult decision he had ever made in his life.

'It's all right, Rachel,' he said quietly, unaware that the pain in his face was more than a match for hers. 'I'll do what you want. I'll go. And you don't have to worry. I won't be back. Goodbye, Sarah. It's been a pleasure knowing you.'

He bent and picked up the package of mobiles, then handed it towards a white-faced Rachel. 'There's no reason why Derek can't enjoy these, is there? I mean...he doesn't ever have to know who they're from?'

When Rachel choked out another strangled sob, Luke shoved the mobiles into her arms, then spun away so that he didn't have to look upon her any more. He bit out a curt goodbye as he strode stiffly down the hall to let himself out, not looking back once.

Seeing the packet of photos on the passenger seat almost broke his iron composure, and only by sheer will power did Luke start that damned car and drive off. He kept a tight rein on his feelings all the way home, putting himself into a traffic-induced trance, thinking of nothing but getting from point A to point B.

Impossible, though, to maintain his stoic façade once he came face to face with his mother, with her puzzled questions and gently concerned face. He could feel himself dissolving inside as he explained rather curtly that it was over between himself and Rachel.

'But... But...'

'No buts, Mum. Just over. She doesn't want to see me any more. To use her exact words—she can't stand the sight of me!'

Luke knew he had to get out of his mother's presence before he embarrassed himself totally. Hell, any moment now he'd be blubbering like an idiot!

Steeling his ominously quivering chin, he tossed the envelope full of photographs on the kitchen table and stalked off towards his bedroom. 'Burn them once you've satisfied your curiosity,' he snarled over his shoulder. 'I couldn't bear to set eyes on *her* again either.'

CHAPTER THIRTEEN

GRACE shuddered at the slamming of Luke's bedroom door. She wasn't fooled by his display of temper, knowing full well that it was just a cover for a deep, deep hurt. If he'd been twelve, instead of thirty-two, she might have gone after him, taken him in her arms and tried to comfort him. Instead, all she could realistically do was give him some space.

Her eyes went to the envelope lying on the table, her curiosity very definitely piqued now. Grace sat down and poured the photos out of the open flap onto the table. She picked up the first two, her eyes going from one to the other.

What she saw was an extraordinarily beautiful girl, whose sex appeal rivalled Luke's. It fairly leapt out at one. But she had more than that, Grace appreciated. There was a strength of character in that lovely face which bespoke that she'd been through a lot, this Rachel. She was no little blonde dolly-bird. She was a woman in every sense of the word.

Grace studied each photograph in turn, noting with maternal pride that it wasn't just the model who was spectacular. The photographs themselves were breathtaking—especially the panoramic shots of the beaches and coastline. It would be a wicked shame to burn such art!

She began dividing the photographs into the ones which included Rachel and the ones which didn't. The former she would gladly burn. She was down to the last half-dozen prints before she came across the first one of the boy.

Grace blinked her shock, then quickly glanced at the others. Slowly, and with shaking hands, she spread the portraits of the laughing child out in front of her and just stared at them. Stared and stared and stared.

After a good ten minutes of staring, she rose and went in search of the family albums she kept in the bottom of the hall cupboard. And it was while she was kneeling there, extracting the oldest and largest of the albums, that she heard sounds coming from Luke's nearby bedroom which tore great holes in her mother's heart.

Her son was crying. Her thirty-two-year-old adult son was weeping as she was sure he hadn't wept in twenty years. Grace could remember well the last time he'd broken down this way. His pet dog—a big old Labrador that his father had bought when he was born and which had been Luke's constant companion since—had just been run over and killed.

Tears welled up in her own eyes as she recalled her son's heartbreak that day, as well as the hardness which had gradually replaced the tears. He'd vowed two things that day: never to have another dog, and never to waste his time crying over something, because it never did any good. His dog was dead and was going to stay dead—tears or no tears.

Grace knew that only total despair would have made Luke weep as he was weeping at this very moment. His hoarsely muffled sobs were just breaking her heart. Anger consumed her at this Rachel. Who did she think she was to play with her Luke's life like that? To ruthlessly use him as she had—not once, but twice—then toss him away?

The urge to burst into her son's room and tell him what she suspected about the boy's parentage was acute, but then she began to wonder if Luke already knew the awful truth—if that was the reason he was so distraught. She didn't know what to do then.

Grace decided to do what she usually did when faced with a stiff decision. She would put on the television and have a glass of sherry. Maybe even *two* glasses of sherry. Then, when she'd calmed down and Luke had calmed down, she might know what to do for the best.

Nearly forty minutes later, Grace was sitting in her favourite chair in the front room, mindlessly watching a movie on television and sipping the dregs of her second sherry, when the front doorbell rang. A frowning glance at the clock on the wall showed a quarter past nine. A little late for callers.

Shrugging, she levered herself out of the deep armchair, placed her glass down on a side-table and padded out to answer the front door.

Seeing Rachel in the photograph hadn't quite prepared Grace for seeing her in the flesh. The girl was so fair and so tall! And so incredibly lovely. Even red-rimmed eyes and a general air of distress didn't destroy her quite extraordinary beauty.

'Mrs St Clair?' she asked straight away, her voice soft and shaky.

'That's correct,' Grace returned stiffly, not feeling too kindly disposed towards her visitor.

'Is…is Luke here?'

Grace's chin lifted. 'He is,' she returned coldly. 'You're Rachel, aren't you?'

'Yes. Yes, I'm Rachel,' she admitted rather bleakly, as though she wasn't too proud of herself.

And rightly so too, Grace thought sourly. Beautiful is as beautiful does!

'I must see him, Mrs St Clair,' Rachel pleaded. 'Please… It…it's very important.'

It was difficult not to be touched by the girl's distress. But Grace wasn't prepared to make it easy on her. 'Well, I don't know,' she said. 'I'm not sure Luke will want to see you. He's very upset.'

'Oh, but I must see him! You don't understand. I have something very, very important to tell him.'

'I think I understand only too well, Rachel. I've seen the photographs Luke took of your boy. He bears an amazing resemblance to his father at the same age.'

Shocked green eyes confirmed what Grace had been thinking for the past hour. 'Oh, God,' Rachel groaned. 'He…he hasn't guessed too, has he? You didn't tell him what you…you…?'

'No,' Grace denied. 'He hasn't guessed as far as I know.'

'Then, please, Mrs St Clair, let me be the one to tell him. It has to come from me—don't you see?'

Grace could see the sense of that. 'I suppose so. But let me warn you, I won't have my son being used by you again. He's a good man, and he deserves better than the way you've treated him.'

'Yes, I know,' the girl said wretchedly. 'My behaviour has been inexcusable. All I can do is try to make things right now. Please…let me go to him…'

'You haven't changed your mind about this because you've found out Luke's a very rich, very successful man, have you?'

Again, her shocked green eyes told their own story. Lord, but the girl did have expressive eyes. 'No, no, I can see you haven't,' Grace muttered. 'Come along, then. I'll take you to him.'

Luke was sprawled across his bed, face-down, feeling nothing but a deep emotional exhaustion. Women claimed to feel better after they'd wept. From Luke's experience, men only felt more wretched. Weeping weakened a man's resolves and undermined his inner strength. He hadn't succumbed to it in twenty years, and it would be another damned twenty years before he succumbed again.

He was lying there thinking black thoughts when the front doorbell rang and his mother went to answer it. One of her cronies, he supposed, then turned his mind to other things. He would go back to America. Put some distance between himself and Rachel. It was the only way he could guarantee that he wouldn't give in to the temptation to see her again. It would be hell, but he would endure.

His mother's timid tapping on his bedroom door irritated him. Why couldn't she just leave him alone? Surely she could see that he wanted to be alone?

Well, not really. He wanted to be with Rachel. What he wouldn't give for her to walk into this room right this minute, throw her arms around him and tell him that she loved him…

Geez, what was he—a masochist? That wasn't going to happen. Not ever!

'What?' he snapped, when the tap-tap came again.

'You have a visitor, Luke,' his mother said.

Luke's heart jumped into his mouth. He sat bolt-upright and swung his legs over the side of the bed, staring wildly as the door opened. No, it couldn't be. It simply couldn't be.

Yet there she was, standing alone in the open doorway, staring back at him, his mother nowhere in sight.

Once he accepted that Rachel was real, and not some cruel figment of his imagination, a torrent of emotions raged through him—not the least of which was fury.

'What in hell are you doing here?' he snarled. 'Haven't you turned the screw enough yet? Or have you decided you want some more screwing for yourself? Is that it, Rachel? Is sex worth a little more guilt and shame? Hell, woman, don't just stand there, if that's the case. Get in here and get your gear off!'

She stunned him by walking in and actually shutting the door, though her expression was full of pain, not passion. 'You have every right to be angry with me, Luke. So I'll try not to be hurt by what you're saying. In a way, it's very telling of you to be so mad at me. I'll take some comfort from that.'

'Then don't! I think you're a right royal bitch, and if I ever see you again after tonight, it'll be too soon!'

'You don't mean that, Luke. I know you don't mean it.'

'And how in hell do you know that, pray tell?' he scorned, even while he recognised the truth of it. Man, he had to be the biggest fool of all time! She'd already shot him right between the eyes—metaphorically speaking—and he was lining up to be shot again.

'Sarah told me so. She also told me that you loved me, that you genuinely cared for Derek too, and that you probably wanted to marry me and make a family.'

'No kidding? And you couldn't see any of that for yourself? You needed an independent party to tell you what had to be bloody obvious to anyone with half a brain?'

Her face twisted into an anguished expression. 'Yes. Yes, I needed an independent party to tell me, because I've long ceased to be able to think straight where you're concerned, Luke. I stopped thinking straight about you the moment I saw you...eighteen months ago...at that exhibition.'

Luke felt his mouth go instantly dry. He stared at her, not daring to hope, but hoping all the same. He swallowed convulsively, and, when that didn't work, noisily cleared his throat. 'Don't go saying anything that isn't true, Rachel,' he choked out. 'If you do, I won't be responsible for what I might do.'

'I'm done with anything but the truth, Luke. It has to be the whole truth and nothing but the truth from now on.'

Tears shimmered in her eyes, and he was afraid. Afraid of what she was going to say, and afraid of how he might react.

'Go on,' he said tautly.

'I came to that exhibition in a state of utter desperation. I could no longer bear my existence at home—the way Patrick looked every month when my period came, plus my own awful loneliness. Sarah didn't live with us then, and Patrick had never been the husband I thought he would be. There was no real partnership between us—no sharing or companionship. He had his work and I...I had nothing.

'Oh, I'd been quite happy to give up my modelling to become a full-time wife and mother, because I was in love with Patrick, but when I didn't conceive straight away, his attitude changed towards me.

'Gradually I began to see that he'd married me not so much for love but because I was the perfect genetic specimen to be the mother of his children. I was, in reality, a type of experiment—an incubator for the child who was to inherit the best of both of us. Brains *and* beauty.

'Of course, I didn't see all this at first—the penny not dropping till well after I'd become pregnant with Derek. But I was confused and hurt at how my marriage was turning out. I blamed my discontent on my failure to conceive and I placed all my energies on succeeding with that, ignoring the fact that I no longer loved my husband as I should have.

'In a way, I was relieved when he couldn't make love to me any more. I had long ceased to find any real pleasure in it, only guilt. Not that I liked being artificially inseminated either. But I imagined that if I gave Patrick the child he wanted he would be happy again, and *I* would be happy again too.

'My failure to conceive month after month began affecting my emotional and mental state. I was very depressed and decidedly unstable the night I decided to dress up like some kind of whore and seduce the first brown-eyed man I came across. Nothing mattered but conceiving a baby.'

Luke's heart twisted at her words. Was that all he'd been to her? A brown-eyed man? Hell...

'It never crossed my mind that I might be totally bewitched by that brown-eyed man,' she went on, green eyes glistening. 'That from the moment he took me in his arms, I'd belong to that brown-eyed man— not for just that night but for the rest of my life...'

Luke rose slowly to his feet, his heart beginning to thud heavily in his chest.

'I don't know if I fell in love with you that night, Luke,' she confessed. 'All I know is that afterwards I couldn't forget you. You haunted my thoughts every day and my dreams every night. Oh, the tears I cried over you. When you walked down that staircase the other morning, I nearly died. I didn't know what to do. When it seemed you didn't recognise me I *was* relieved at first, but then I was overwhelmed with the same feelings I'd felt that first night. God, how I wanted you!'

A tremor raced through Luke at the passion in her voice. But was she admitting to love? Or just lust? And when was she going to get back to the guilt which had crippled her, and their burgeoning relationship?

'God knows how I got through that day,' she said with an expressive shudder. 'What happened that night…I have no excuse for. I was mad with wanting you, Luke. I tried telling myself it was only sex, that afterwards I'd feel differently. But if anything I wanted you more than ever. I ran from you at the first excuse I could find, and when you came after me in the end I was forced to accept my true feelings for you.'

'Which are?' he asked, and held his breath.

'I love you, Luke. Love you,' she repeated croakily, then burst into tears again.

He groaned, then held his arms out to her. She ran into them and he clasped her to him, pressing his lips into her hair while he battled for control over his own heaving emotions. He kept a tight hold on her and himself till her sobs had subsided to shudders. When only the occasional quavering sigh whispered from her lungs, he held her out at arm's length.

'Then why, Rachel?' he asked, still not fully understanding. 'Why did you send me away? Why did you act as you did?'

'Promise me you won't hate me,' she cried softly. 'Promise me you'll try to understand.'

'I promise,' he said sincerely, knowing that nothing could ever make him hate her.

'Derek's yours, Luke,' came the shocking admission. 'I lied about the DNA test. Oh, yes, I got one done all right—after Patrick died. The hospital still had some of his frozen sperm samples. The child wasn't his, Luke. He had to be yours.'

Luke couldn't help it. Shock sent his arms dropping away from her as he took a staggered step backwards. 'But why did you lie?' he rasped. '*Why*?'

Tears welled up in her eyes again. 'At first I couldn't bring myself to believe you really loved me. And then I couldn't face hurting Sarah—taking away the one thing in her life which she had left to love. She has no one else, you see. No husband. No other children. No brothers or sisters. No one. Only me and Derek.

'I convinced myself you'd go away after you'd had some more sex. But then, when I was waiting for you to pick me up for dinner tonight and I became agitated about your being late, Sarah kept telling me not to worry—that Blind Freddie could see you cared about me, and Derek as well.

'I scoffed at her suggestions, but then you came, and you'd bought Derek those mobiles, and I saw that you might really love us. I just knew I couldn't go on seeing you and deceiving you. I didn't know what to do but send you away. But after you'd gone I just went crazy. I…I think I might have done something stupid, but Sarah made me pull myself together and insisted upon an explanation. She wouldn't take no for an answer for once, and in the end I told her everything.

'She…she was so brave about it, Luke. And so kind. She wasn't angry with me at all. She told me that she understood Patrick had not been a good husband, that he had been as difficult and as selfish a man as his own father. She also told me she loved Derek for himself, not his genes. She then insisted I find you and tell you the truth. It seems you told her this afternoon you were staying with your mother, who lived at Monterey, so I looked up her address in the phonebook and…and here I am.'

She sent him a despairing look. 'Can you ever forgive me, Luke?'

'Derek's my son,' was all he could say.

'Yes, my darling,' she murmured, and came to wind her arms around his waist, resting her head against his chest. '*Your* son. *Our* son.'

He wrapped his arms around her and closed his ̶Never in all his life had he been this happy, or

this sad. Eleven months wasted. All that love…
wasted.

Don't look back, Luke, came the wise words of advice from deep inside. It's stupid and self-destructive.
Looking forward is much, much better. If you think
you've had a rotten time, think of her. God but she's
had it hard. Time to make it easy for her. Time to
prove your love.

He eased out of her embrace, smiling into her worried eyes while he started poking some stray strands
of blonde hair behind her ears. 'I think that before I
fully forgive you,' he began, 'I should extract a couple
of promises.'

'Anything.'

'First thing tomorrow you will come with me while
we look for a decent house to live in.'

Her face broke into the loveliest of smiles.

'Somewhere near here, so that my mother can visit
her grandson. Something large enough to include a
studio and a darkroom for myself and my photographic assistant-cum-model to work in. And somewhere that has a nice little self-contained flat attached
for Sarah to live in. She is forthwith Derek's god-
mother and adopted grandmother.'

Rachel nodded, clearly all choked up with emotion
and approval.

'Secondly, you will marry me as quickly as the
proper paperwork can be done.'

She bit her bottom lip and nodded again.

'Meanwhile you are to do nothing to stop me conceiving a little brother or sister for Derek—starting with later tonight. Is that clear?'

'Perfectly clear,' she whispered, with an erotic little quiver.

Luke could not help himself. He had to kiss her at that point, although he rationed himself to only a couple of seconds. Any longer and he knew they'd both be in trouble.

'Do you realise I haven't told you yet that I love you?' he murmured against her oh, so willing mouth.

'Yes, you have, my darling,' she murmured back. 'You told me when you mowed my lawns and painted my carport. You told me when you bought our son those beautiful mobiles. You've been telling me all along, and I just refused to listen. But you can tell me again if you like,' she finished, and brushed her lips tantalisingly against his.

Damn, but she was a minx in that department!

'I love you, Rachel. I loved you from the first moment I saw you.'

'It must have been the same with me, Luke. I only hope your mother warms to the idea. I don't think she likes me very much.'

'She'll warm up to you soon enough, when she knows Derek's her grandson.'

'She already knows.'

'She *what*?'

'She guessed, Luke, after looking at Derek's photographs. She says they're the dead spit of you at the same age.'

'Ahh. Well, in that case, no problem. Mum's very large on family.'

'And very large on her favourite son.'

'What makes you say that?'

'Believe me, I know. But anyone who loves you that much is all right by me. Let's go and talk to her, Luke. She must be worried.'

'And then we'll drive down and talk to Sarah,' Luke suggested. 'She must be worried too. After which I'm going to wake up my son and talk to him. He doesn't like sleeping much anyway.'

'Luke St Clair—you're not going to be one of those fathers who spoil their children rotten, are you?'

'You'd better believe it, sweetheart. And I'm going to be one of those husbands who spoils his wife rotten too.'

'Oh, well, in that case, I have no objections. Spoil away!'

They opened the door of the bedroom, laughing together.

Grace heard the happy sounds from where she was sitting at the kitchen table and sighed a huge sigh of relief. Dashing the tears from her eyes, she slipped the photographs of her grandson into the family album, looking up just in time to see a smiling Luke bring Rachel into the room, his arm around her shoulders and his eyes full of love as he glanced over at her.

'Mum,' he began, 'say hello to your newest daughter-in-law.'

Grace's own smile came from the heart. 'How

lovely,' she said, and rose to her feet, walking over to give Rachel a kiss on the cheek. 'Welcome to the family, my dear. I hope you'll both be very happy.'

Grace was moved by the look Rachel sent her son. So full of relief and love. She accepts me, it seemed to say. Everything is going to be all right.

And it was.

*   *   *   *   *

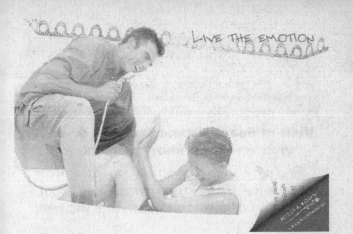

LIVE THE EMOTION

Modern
romance™

...international affairs
– seduction and
passion guaranteed

Medical
romance™

...pulse-raising
romance – heart-
racing medical drama

Tender
romance™

...sparkling, emotional,
feel-good romance

Sensual
romance™

...teasing, tempting,
provocatively playful

Historical
romance™

...rich, vivid and
passionate

Blaze™

...scorching hot
sexy reads

30 new titles every month.

Live the emotion

MILLS & BOON®

MB5 P6